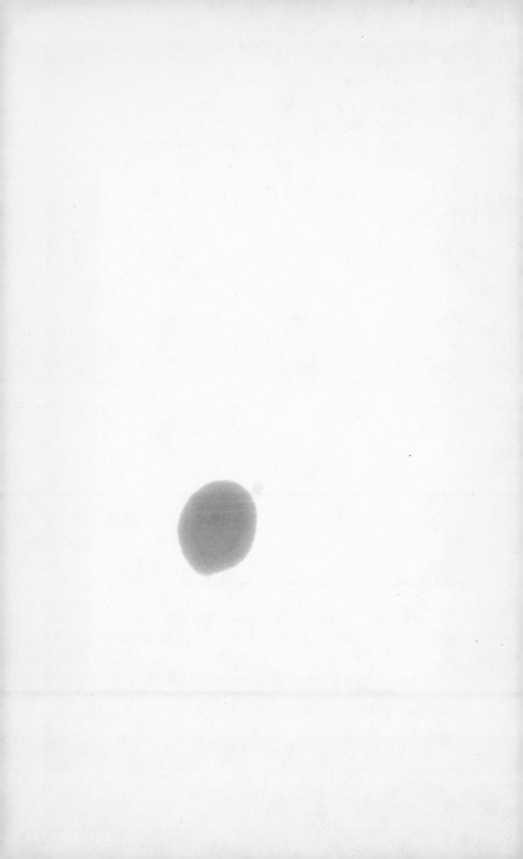

ESSAYS ON
THE HISTORY OF PHYSIOLOGY
IN RUSSIA

by

Kh. S. Koshtoyants

Editor of English Translation
DONALD B. LINDSLEY

Translated from the Russian by
DAVID P. BODER
KRISTAN HANES
NATALIE O'BRIEN

Published by
AMERICAN INSTITUTE OF BIOLOGICAL SCIENCES
and Co-Sponsored by
AMERICAN PSYCHOLOGICAL ASSOCIATION
WASHINGTON, D. C.

Library of Congress Catalog Card Number 64-22694

Copyright 1964

AMERICAN INSTITUTE OF BIOLOGICAL SCIENCES
2000 P Street NW, Washington, D.C. 20036

This book was set in cold type. The remaining volumes in this series
will be typeset and printed in Baltimore, Maryland by the
Garamond/Pridemark Press.

ACADEMY OF SCIENCES OF THE UNION SSR

Scientific—Popular Series

Kʜ. S. Kosʜᴛoʏᴀɴᴛs

Member, Academy of Sciences, Armenian SSR
Corresponding Member, Academy of Sciences, USSR
Professor of Physiology, Moscow State University

ESSAYS ON
THE HISTORY OF PHYSIOLOGY
IN RUSSIA

PUBLISHING HOUSE OF THE ACADEMY OF SCIENCES OF USSR

Moscow 1946 Leningrad

Under the general editorship of the
Commission of the Academy of Sciences, USSR

An edition of the Scientific-Popular Literature

Chairman of the Commission, President of the Academy of Sciences, USSR
ACADEMICIAN S. I. VAVILOV

Vice-Chairman, Corresponding Member Academy of Sciences, USSR
P. F. YUDIN

Leningrad
October 14, 1934

From a letter of I. P. Pavlov to the Leningrad Society of Physiologists imeni I. M. Sechenov. Reproduction in Koshtoyants is in Pavlov's handwriting.

Yes, I am glad that together with Ivan Mikhaylovich and a host of my dear collaborators we have gained for mighty physiological investigation not just a fragment, but the whole integrated animal organism. And this is entirely our own incontestable Russian contribution to world science, to general human thought.

IVAN PAVLOV

ILLUSTRATIONS

EDITOR'S PREFACE

These essays by Koshtoyants review broadly the history of the development of physiology as a science in Russia, beginning in the early 18th century and continuing to modern times. They are more than a history for they deal with the personal characteristics and strivings of great scientists who forged teaching and research disciplines in anatomy, physiology and psychology. Two hundred years have witnessed great changes, not only in the disciplines, which have been divided, subdivided and reoriented, but also in the freedom of science to attack problems once shrouded in darkness, due to religious dogma, political oppression, and adverse philosophic thought.

Koshtoyants focusses upon two central figures, Sechenov and Pavlov, giants in the history of physiology in Russia and throughout the world. But he has chosen well his materials so that many scientists of distinction are woven into the matrix. One gets the impression that the development of science in Russia was a closely knit, nationalistic affair, often fraught with friction and academic politics.

It is a fascinating history; personal, warm and scientifically stimulating. From it emerges the background of many individual creative efforts leading to scientific contributions which constitute a proud heritage little known in the scientific world outside Russia, owing no doubt to the long-standing language barrier.

Donald B. Lindsley

FOREWORD

This is the first of a series of translations of Russian monographs on brain and behavior, concentrating upon the historical background of investigations in neurophysiology and conditioned behavior as well as upon certain contemporary advances in these fields.

The translation program was initiated by H. W. Magoun and D. B. Lindsley and has been continued by the latter. It has been supported by U. S. Public Health Service grant NB-02347. Grateful acknowledgement is made to the publisher, the American Institute of Biological Sciences, and to Tom Wheaton Coward, Manager of Publications, for spearheading the final preparations for publication.

Thanks to the persistent and devoted effort of the translators, some valuable materials will have been made available for the first time in the English language.

Donald B. Lindsley
Professor of Psychology and Physiology
University of California, Los Angeles
March, 1964

CONTENTS

I dedicate this work to the
memory of my mother.
The author

PREFACE

In the preface to the Russian translation of his work, Features in Architecture of Physiological Function, one of the greatest contemporary physiologists, the Cambridge Professor Joseph Barcroft, made the following statement. "Great is the debt of world physiology to Russian science. These are the feelings which I experience writing these lines in the hope that the Soviet biologists may find a grain of value within the covers of this book. I am well aware that my modest work is incapable of reducing this debt in any appreciable measure, but I should like to think that it shall serve in some way as a 'token payment,' as an acknowledgment of this indebtedness" (1937). These words of Great Britain's great physiologist express his acknowledgment of the role of the Russian physiological school, and his opinion is shared by other physiologists throughout the world.

In a work designed to illuminate the remarkable development of physiology in Russia, the most illustrious, the most glorious, and the most significant name of Ivan Mikhaylovich Sechenov should be mentioned first of all. Sechenov is considered "the father of Russian physiology"— as Pavlov used to call him—and the pride of Russian physiology. Sechenov is the scientist who delineated the basic ideological and methodical procedures which have assured Russian physiology an outstanding place in world culture during recent decades.

Sechenov and Pavlov—these are two names which, together with the names of other celebrated sons of Russia, reverberated around the world in the somber November days of 1941 in the speech of Comrade Stalin, when the German Fascist hordes threatened the heart and brain of our country, the glorious city of Moscow. They reverberated as a symbol of the greatness of our science, exceptionally influencing world culture, sounding like a call to the defense of the highest achievements of science, art, and literature of our country, which were developed through the centuries in the general process of the struggle of the vanguard of our country against reaction, stagnation, and backwardness, and have given a stormy impetus to the Soviet period in the history of our country.

In the person of its founder, I. M. Sechenov, the Russian physiological school has grown on the ideological soil which in the '40's and '50's of the nineteenth century was cultivated by the great philosophers of enlightenment—A. I. Gertsen and N. G. Chernyshevskiy. As is now known, they were continuing the glorious work already started at the end of the eighteenth century by A. N. Radishchev.

The tradition of consistent, militant materialism, extending into the most difficult field of science, into the realm of problems of consciousness, problems of correlation of "soul" and body, must be considered the outstanding tradition of the Russian physiological school. Sechenov adopted this glorious tradition from the school of Russian philosopher-materialists and passed it on to his followers.

It would be impossible to review the basic tendencies of the history of Soviet physiology and its striking ideological purposefulness without mentioning its development, as well as the ideological education and activity of its foremost representatives, on the general background of social thinking in our country, and without mentioning the fight for advance in science at various periods in the history of Russia. Without Radishchev, Belinskiy, Gertsen, Chernyshevskiy, and Pisarev, who raised and solved the problem of unity of physical and psychic processes, it would be difficult to describe the development of the basic ideology in Russian physiology, as well as its progress in the area of research techniques and subject matter independent of world-wide development of science and techniques.

We took upon ourselves the task of providing a historically logical relationship between the ideas and events which led Sechenov to the fundamental propositions contained in Reflexes of the Brain and which led his successor, Pavlov, to the study of conditioned reflexes. This historical-logical (rather than chronological) principle of exposition of the Russian physiological school's paths of development also explains why the Pavlovian conditioned reflex theory is presented in these Essays right after the historical review of Sechenov's psycho-physiological concepts, although the former emerged chronologically much later.

As was true of the whole body of natural sciences during the second half of the nineteenth century, the glorious Sechenov period in the development of physiology in our country was organically linked with the facts, methods, and conclusions obtained by the great natural scientists of the seventeenth, eighteenth and first half of the nineteenth centuries.

Thus, the pre-Sechenov period in the development of physiology in our country has a special interest. We devote considerable space to it in these Essays, since history indicates that a number of the faculty in physiology in the Academy of Sciences explored physiological problems intensively and that, both before Sechenov and during the early period of his activities, the scientists of our country contributed significantly to world physiology and created their own direction for scientific investigations.

This early period of development in Russian physiology abounds with significant names and events full of the kind of fascination that overwhelms one upon acquaintance with the lucid images of the past. Many of these names have been forgotten and others have not been properly appreciated, but many of the events still inspire us to this day. Together, these names and events resurrect the beautiful traditions of the best representatives of science in our country and, in the light of indisputable historical facts, demonstrate the strength and authority of our country's physiology since the early periods of its history. The readers (including critical scientists) will hardly reproach the author for his attempt to present, with considerable detail and a somewhat lyrical style, the personalities of such physiologists of the past as Peter Posnikov, Daniil Vellanskiy, Aleksey Filomafitskiy, and Nikolay Yakubovich. Indeed, considerable space has been devoted to them, but they deserve it by their inspiring activities and ways of life.

The space devoted to Sechenov is also somewhat out of proportion, but this was done for a different reason. After the publication of my monograph on Sechenov, I had the opportunity to explore a whole array of new material, including some valuable letters of Sechenov's which illuminate many problems of the history of physiology in our country. It is this original, previously unpublished material which increases the volume of the Sechenov section in this book. But Sechenov is the history of Russian physiology itself.

After presentation of the enormous creative developments of Russian philosophical and physiological thought, which led to formulation of the views of Sechenov and Pavlov with regard to the unity of physical and psychic processes and the physiological basis of complex manifestations of higher nervous activity, we turn in these essays to a presentation of the history of the development of the main physiological schools of Russia. Not all aspects of physiological investigation in our country have been treated in these Essays. They do not deal with the history of development of physiological chemistry, pharmacology, and pathological physiology, although their significance in the development of physiology is immense, and the investigations of such outstanding physicians as A. A. Bogomolets, N. N. Burdenko, and others represent valuable contributions to Soviet physiology. The history of these branches of biology and medicine deserves special investigation, and some attempts to that effect are beginning to appear in our literature.

One should bear in mind the immense volume of labor connected with the field of history of science. For almost 20 years, since the publication of my first essay on the history of physiology (1928), I have collected material dealing with this subject, of which I am making use in the present Essays. And, although I am perfectly aware of its incompleteness, I hope to awaken interest in a whole array of fascinating but little-explored problems in the history of Russian physiology and thus lend impetus to a more profound treatment of the subject.

In working on these Essays, I also had in mind my colleagues who are teaching physiology at universities and other institutions of higher learning in our country. It would give me great satisfaction if these Essays were to be of value to students and candidates for higher degrees by providing the long-needed, strictly scientific approach to the history of science.

Even more than in my work on the "Sechenov" monograph, I had to make use of materials from various periods and divergent fields of the natural sciences and the humanities. I was in constant need of bibliographical and reference materials which were invariably supplied me by the Library of Moscow State University. It appeared advisable in this work to diverge somewhat from the general practice of quotation from sources. The names of a number of journals and proceedings are given in the body of the text, since, in many cases, they are indicative of the period, the people, and the ideas under discussion.

In the fall of 1943, I was honored with an invitation from Moscow University to present a paper on the significance of the Russian physiological school in world science. The occasion was a special conference at the university dedicated to the evaluation of the role of Russian science in world culture. Some of the principal postulations of this report were later taken as basis for the present Essays.

I am unable to conceal that I have worked on these Essays during a period of great apprehension. Full of deep love for their country and of proud patriotism, the people of the Soviet Union have striven devotedly towards victory. The country has demanded the greatest creative effort from the scientists, and it has been necessary to work and work more. During this period the attention of scientists has been attracted to the problems of the history of the natural sciences, the importance of which was emphasized by Comrade I. V. Stalin in a conversation with Academician V. L. Komarov. It is my desire that the work presented here may serve, in some small measure, as part of the great contribution of the Soviet people in their struggle against the dark forces of Fascism towards victory and the glory of science and culture in our wonderful land.

Kh. Koshtoyants

Department of Animal Physiology
at Moscow State University
imeni M. V. Lomonosov and Commission
on the History of the Biological Sciences
in Russia under the Department of
Biological Sciences of the Academy
of Sciences, USSR

CHAPTER I

The early period of development of physiology in Russia. Peter Posnikov. The first academician-physiologists. The role of the Petersburg Academy of Sciences in the development of physiology in the eighteenth century.

The history of physiology in Russia, like the history of other natural sciences, dates back to the brilliant epoch of Russian history which is connected with Peter The Great and with the beginning of the activities of the Petersburg Academy of Sciences. Numerous documents have preserved the image of Peter The Great, both as an outstanding statesman and as a man who deeply appreciated the great significance of science, especially the exact sciences.

Peter's acquaintance with the Dutch anatomist Ruysch gave him an insight into the anatomical and physiological orientation of medicine, and many documents testify to his immense interest in this branch of science. Due to Peter's endeavors, a science museum was established and a collection of Ruysch's anatomical preparations was assembled, which formed the basis for the early biological investigation in the Russian Academy of Sciences.

Peter's military activities and his concern for the army and the people in general confronted him with the need for establishing in Russia a group of its own physicians well trained in contemporary science. This led to the founding of medical schools and the selection of gifted people capable both of treating patients and of doing creative work in the field of medicine. Thus, through the veil of two and one-half centuries, emerges the brilliant image of one of Peter's coworkers, the Russian doctor of philosophy and medicine Peter Vasil'yevich Posnikov, who also appears as the first Russian physiologist.

Peter Posnikov (born about 1676) was the grandson of Timofei Posnikov, a clerk in the Apothecary Office of the government. This office was in possession of an excellent library of original and translated medical books and, in 1678, it established a special position for a person to translate books from which "Russians could acquire the necessary perfection in the professions of physician and apothecary."[1] One foreigner, a

---

[1] This and the further quotations are taken from Professor D. Tsvetayev's book Russian Physicians of the Moscow Period and the First Russian Doctor [Mediki v Moskovskoy Rossii i pervyy russkiy doktor], Warsaw, 1896.

contemporary of Tsarina Sofiya, became acquainted with the Moscow apothecary shops of this time and wrote about the Old Kremlin Apothecary "I can say, indeed, that I never saw such an excellent apothecary shop."

Peter Posnikov acquired his early education in the same Moscow Slavic-Greek-Latin Academy attended many years later by the genius of Russian science, Mikhail Lomonosov. Posnikov had ample opportunity to obtain a medical preparation through the Apothecary Commission, but this was not sufficient for the gifted young man and for a country undergoing great reforms. On orders of Peter The Great, Posnikov left in 1692 for the famous University of Padua. In the archive material dealing with Posnikov we read: "Upon personal orders of the great Emperor and Grandduke Peter Alekseyevich, plenipotentiary of all Russia, leave is permitted for Peter Vasil'yevich, the son of Posnikov, to journey from Moscow to Venice to perfect himself in the sciences at the Academy of Padua. For his travels through various countries and for his residence at the mentioned Padua Academy [2] this letter of identification is given to Peter from the Imperial Ambassadorial Commission."

For five years Peter Posnikov studied at the University of Padua, which was already famous because the great founder of physiological science, the Englishman William Harvey, was educated within its walls at the beginning of the century. Posnikov revealed himself as a brilliant scientist, philosopher, and physician. The text of the diploma for doctor of philosophy and medicine given to Posnikov by the University Council recognized him as "a man of wisdom and of outstanding honesty, worthy of ascending the chair of a teacher...and to do public and private teaching in all philosophical and medical sciences, to recognize, counsel and make public his findings...and to dedicate himself to philosophical and medical creativity over the whole surface of the earth...." [3] In conclusion it states: "With great praise and many honors this elegant gentleman, Peter Posnikov, has achieved (with God's help) the highest rank as a teacher of philosophy and medicine." [4]

This diploma was dated May 2, 1695. Thus, May 1945 marks the 250th anniversary of the day when, for the first time, the scientific degree of Doctor was conferred on a Russian physician, Peter Posnikov.

The young Russian scientist who was awarded such high praise and recognition by the University of Padua, which still preserves his autograph (Petrus Posnicovius Basilis filius Moscoviensis, 14 Aug. 1694), refused to rest on his laurels. He visited universities in other countries because

---

[2] This footnote contains a correction of the spelling of the word Padua.

[3] As stated in Posnikov's diploma, the ritual of conferring the scientific degree of doctor stipulated: "Adorn his finger with a golden ring and cover his head with the cap of a teacher."

[4] The text of the diploma is quoted from D. Tsvetayev. According to the latter, the Latin original of the diploma, in the Apothecary Commission, was lost in later years.

of his great interest in scientific work, especially in the field of physiology. He journeyed to Naples to undertake vivisection so that he could explore important problems in physiology and medicine. But this brilliant activity of the young Russian investigator, who might have become the originator of Russian experimental physiology and medicine, was interrupted by unusual circumstances.

In that period every educated Russian was of enormous value in the sweeping reforms of Peter The Great, whose broad undertakings constantly involved international relations with foreign powers. In this field, Posnikov, who knew a number of languages, naturally became indispensable. Driven by his scientific interests, he left for Naples, but, having already been assigned upon graduation from the University of Padua to the ambassadorial service, he received orders to put himself at the disposal of the Embassy. The Secretary of the Embassy, Vosnitsyn, insistently demanded the departure of Posnikov from Naples. One of Voznitsyn's letters acquaints us with the first page of the history of experimental physiology in our country, connected with Peter Vasil'yevich Posnikov's name.

Voznitsyn wrote: "You are risking the Emperor's anger since you were ordered to be with me on the Turkish Commission, and we are helpless without you. This involves discussions with the Turkish and Greek ambassadors and, for that reason, you have been assigned to us since you can speak to them in Greek, Italian, French and Latin, for they know all these languages....You, however, went to Naples to waste your time and, as it says in your letter, 'to kill live dogs and to revive the dead ones.' Of such business, we have no need...."[5]

Thus wrote Voznitsyn, remonstrating with Posnikov, threatening him with the Emperor's anger, and calling him to important state duties which, in fact, were to absorb completely all the energy and knowledge of this outstanding representative of Russian culture.

Upon returning home for a short period, he joined the Apothecary Commission, where he could devote himself to medical and scientific endeavors. However, he was soon to be assigned to greater diplomatic duties and was again torn away from his favorite work. This break with his prime interests was very difficult for Posnikov, the more so since, by nature of his activities, he had to travel constantly to various European countries. Posnikov's letters attest to his longing for his favorite work and to his deep dissatisfaction with the activities that were imposed upon him. Recognizing, however, that a man's first duty lies in devotion to the interests of the state, he wrote: "I despise all this distant and difficult travel and, God willing, mean to despise it, but this work is the will of our great Russian hero and is done in the interest of our greatness." He writes further: "I do not want any villages, I do not desire rewards, only to serve with honor and usefulness.... I do not seek superfluous monetary

---

[5] Documents on the Diplomatic Relations of Russia with Foreign Powers, vol. IX, pp. 87-88, 98. Quoted from Tsvetayev, pp. 30-31.

acquisitions, and thanks to the Lord I greatly disdain them; I am directing my intentions toward an honest and useful service to His Majesty and to the public interests and needs."[6] Beautiful traditions emanate from these lines written by the first Russian medical scientist, who placed service to great state reforms in Russia above his personal scientific interests, for the realization of which conditions were not yet ripe.

A quarter of a century passed between the writing of these lines and the inauguration of the Russian Academy of Sciences, in which Peter Posnikov would have occupied by right and merit an academic chair, that of physiology and anatomy, together with the others chosen. Although the period defined the nature of Posnikov's public service differently, and although no scientific works of his remain in the field of experimental medicine and physiology, the six words of his letter which have reached us—"to kill live dogs and revive dead ones"—are sufficient to acknowledge Peter Posnikov as the first Russian physiologist.

It is possible that the name of Posnikov is linked with one of the most remarkable moments in the development of anatomy, physiology, and medicine in our country, i.e., the establishment of connections between Russia and the great anatomist and physician of the seventeenth century, the Dutchman Ruysch. During the years 1697 to 1701, Posnikov journeyed to Amsterdam on orders of Peter The Great for the purchase of medicines, instruments, and books. It would be inconceivable to assume that the gifted doctor from the University of Padua, long famous for its anatomical school, would not have visited Ruysch while in Amsterdam. Such a supposition is, of course, entirely excluded. It may well be that the documents which could answer our questions lie somewhere, and the answers could be of great significance with respect to the contact between Ruysch and Peter The Great, which was made during Posnikov's stay in Amsterdam. Could it not have been Posnikov who first acquainted the Emperor with the work of the famous Amsterdam anatomist?

In 1698, about a year after Posnikov's first visit to Amsterdam, Peter I apparently came to Amsterdam too and met the famous anatomist Ruysch, not as a royal traveler but as a man interested in science. He attended Ruysch's lectures and watched him at work. He was astounded by Ruysch's anatomical preparations and persistently tried to learn the secret of Ruysch's embalming method and to purchase the entire collection to send to Russia. Ruysch apparently communicated the secret of his method of embalming to Peter. Such a secret could have been understood only by a man who had considerable knowledge of anatomy and physiology. Peter The Great was such a man; he not only visited the anatomical theater but also made the rounds of the patients in the hospital with Ruysch. After his departure from Holland, Peter kept in touch with the famous scientist and, in spite of the difficult years of war at the beginning of the eighteenth century, he managed to find the time to send specimens of various animals to Ruysch in Holland and, in return, he received rare items for his own collection.

_____

[6] Ibid. Tsvetayev, pp. 38-39.

On his second trip to Amsterdam, in 1717, Peter purchased from his teacher and friend the entire collection assembled by Ruysch during 40 years of scientific work and had it shipped to Russia. Eight years later this collection was transferred to the Academy of Sciences, newly created on Peter's initiative, and the work of classification and description of the collection was entrusted to the department of anatomy and physiology.

On Peter's instructions, the negotiations with Ruysch were handled by his personal physician, Areskin (d. 1718), and by the future president of the Academy of Sciences, a Moscow-born doctor, L.A. Blyumentrost (1692-1755). Upon arrival at Amsterdam, Blyumentrost worked under Ruysch and learned the delicate technique of embalming and of injection of blood vessels, developed by the famous anatomist. The negotiations were lengthy and proceeded with some friction, as can be seen from a letter of Ruysch's to Russia which is kept at the Academy of Sciences. In it, Ruysch writes in part:

"As to the price, I was greatly in error in appraising my collection, and acted injudiciously in requesting only 30,000 gulden. Had I asked for 60,000 gulden (the price at which everyone appraises my collection), they would have given me at least 40,000. But now, since it has been done, honor will not permit me to go back on my word. Moreover, Mr. Areskin demands that I reveal to him the secret, known only to me, of preparation and preservation of anatomical material, and the methods of rubbing dead bodies with ointment; no matter how much I have inquired and investigated, nobody else actually knows how to do it. Dr. Blyumentrost, who arrived here from Paris where he had lived at the home of the anatomist, Duverney, says that the knowledge of this famous man in this field is of but little importance, since all his preparations are of little durability. I am not ashamed to say that if somebody had only my knowledge of the subject instead of all his wealth he would, in my opinion, be sufficiently rich to live out his life comfortably. Thus, if Mr. Areskin should withdraw this particular request, I should be agreeable concerning all the others. In spite of my advanced age, I am not willing to part with this secret for less than 50,000 gulden.

"Do not think I have achieved all this without great labor; I used to get up every morning at four o'clock, spent all my income on this work and was often in despair as to the eventual outcome. In this work, I used more than 1,000 cadavers, not only fresh ones but others which were already eaten through by worms, exposing myself to dangerous illness. Let Mr. Areskin buy from others all he wants to, but he shall regret it in the future if he obtains from others any method other than mine, to which I have devoted almost my entire life, without enjoying any of the gaieties of this world, and on which even now I am working day and night. The late Roman Emperor Leopold, blessed be his memory, offered me the sum of 20,000 gulden for the secret of preserving dead bodies, and we had nearly come to terms but negotiations were suspended by his death. On the other hand I desire that His Imperial Majesty, Peter I, be in possession of my collections rather than any other Emperor, since between me and His Majesty there is a long-standing and devoted friendship, because when I had the honor of seeing His Majesty in my own home, he graciously stretched out his hand to me and said, 'Thou art still an old teacher of mine!' "[7]

In this exceptionally interesting letter we find a remarkable self-portrait of the scientist which may be compared with the self-portrait of his contemporary and countryman, Rembrandt. These lines of the one, just like the masterful colors of the other, reveal to us with the same brilliance the image of his personality. The letter further describes Peter I as "the disciple" of the best anatomist in Europe in the seventeenth and eighteenth centuries and, finally, it reminds us of the dramatic history of Ruysch's secret. Peter I's physician Areskin was assigned for training in the embalming of cadavers under Ruysch in Amsterdam.

But Areskin's visit to Ruysch did not materialize and, according to Blyumentrost, Ruysch agreed to transmit his secret to Areskin in a sealed envelope. Apparently Ruysch revealed his secret to Peter both verbally and in writing. This secret was kept unrevealed until it fell into the hands of the well-known academic "figure" Schumacher (who occupied the official post of librarian), who revealed it to a German, Doctor Rieger. After leaving Russia, the latter took the liberty of making public—without any right to do so—the secret of embalming discovered by the great Dutch anatomist and to do so in no place other than in the latter's own country, at The Hague, in 1743.

All these events took place almost on the eve of the opening of the Academy of Sciences in Russia. They provided the foundation for a duly important place in the Academy for biology and, in particular, for anatomy and physiology. Indeed, a chair in these subjects was among the first to be established in the St. Petersburg Academy of Sciences. When the Academy opened in 1725, the future great mathematician, Daniel Bernoulli (1700-1782), was invited to this post. In the first schedule of lectures at the Petersburg Academy of Sciences, which began on January 26, 1726, it was announced that "Daniel Bernoulli, professor of physiology, will teach the mathematical approach to the theory of medicine and the application of this approach to physiology (from 7:00 to 8:00 a.m. on Mondays, Wednesdays, Thursday and Saturdays)." From the report for the year 1727 we learn that "Bernoulli teaches that physiology is indispensable, first of all, for understanding the movements of animals and their relation to the laws of mechanics and hydrostatics."

After he had graduated in medicine at the University of Basel in 1721, Daniel Bernoulli defended and published a dissertation on the subject, "De respiratione." In his introduction, the young scientist states that he

---

[7] Quoted from the interesting essay by Professor V.N. Ternovskiy under the original title: "F. Ruysch in the anatomical laboratory of Kazan' University" (Kazan' Medical Journal, 1927, no. 8). This article reports on Ruysch's preparations that are preserved at Kazan' University and on the remarkable history of the relations between the famous anatomist and Peter I.

had in mind to attempt a mathematical analysis of problems in physiology. From this it follows that his occupation of the chair of physiology was not just accidental. During the two years of his tenure, he delivered a series of papers and lectures and published numerous works which were of real significance in the development of physiology as it related to physics and mechanics. The reports of the Academy of Sciences, from which we present a few excerpts, testify to this eloquently. In a report dated August 27, 1727, we read: "Daniel Bernoulli, professor of physiology, has written and read to the assembly of the Academy dissertations which dealt with the following subjects. (1) The solution of the known physiological problem of expulsion of moisture in the bodies of animals; (2) Some new notes on the structure of the blood vessels of the eye, with the clarification of a most interesting optical phenomenon mentioned in the literary reports (Lit. Acta, P. 68, 1683); [(3) Omitted; (4) Omitted;] (5) Theorems dealing with the circulatory arches, as well as the waves of muscular movement; (6) A new theory on muscular movement dealing with various phenomena as well as the mechanisms of muscular coordination; (7) Proof that the assumptions of the most famous scientists of our century concerning the movement of liquids through tubes do not correspond to logic and experiments; (8) These propositions were of course proved by geometrical evidence and by many experiments performed before the scientists of the Academy; (9) Such theories are useful in physiology, particularly in the study of circulation of the blood on which, if it is disturbed, depend all illnesses." From the reports of the same year one learns that Daniel Bernoulli "is writing a system of physiology," and, in the report for the following two years, it is indicated that he worked on a compendium of medical physiology presented on the basis of mathematical principles.

In the first volume of the Commentaries of the Petersburg Academy of Sciences for 1726, Bernoulli published a paper on mechanics and another on muscular movement. This first physiological paper to be published in Russia appeared in 1726 in Latin and bore the title "Tentamen novae de motu musculorum theoria." The same paper was published in Russian two years later in the Abstracts of the Commentaries of the Academy of Sciences (pp. 57-62, 1728) under the title "On muscular movement." In the same issue of the Commentaries for 1726, Bernoulli published a paper on the optic nerve.[8]

After two years in the chair of physiology, Daniel Bernoulli turned completely to the field of mathematics. The mathematical genius Leonard

---

[8] It must be noted that infomation about Bernoulli's works, as the first works in physiology in the Academy of Sciences, was not included in the special publication, Works in Physiology in the Publications of the Academy of Sciences, prepared by the library of the Academy of Sciences of the USSR (published in 1935 for the XV International Physiological Congress). For some reason, the list of works begins with the year 1735, with the works of Bernoulli's pupil Weitbrecht, and, thus the early period, an extremely important one, was left out. It must be pointed out also that of the later periods in this publication a number of very important physiological investigations published in the works of our Academy of Sciences were not listed. It is sufficient to mention that a number of valuable works of such great nineteenth century physiologists as Tsion, Tarkhanov, and even Sechenov were not listed.

Euler (1707-1783), was invited to replace him as Professor (Academician) of Physiology. Euler was familiar with physiological problems; among his works we find a treatise on the circulation of blood in vessels under the title "Principia pro motu sanguinis per arterias determinando." But Euler, too, occupied the chair of physiology only a short time and, in 1731, relinquished his place to I. Weitbrecht (1702-1747), who was on the faculty of anatomy and physiology of the Petersburg Academy of Sciences for sixteen years, until his death in 1747.

Weitbrecht arrived in Russia at the age of 23 and remained there for the rest of his life, dedicating himself to scientific work. In the Petersburg Academy of Sciences he acquired a good scientific preparation. We find him among the first students to attend the lectures at the Petersburg Academy of Sciences and, in particular, those delivered by Daniel Bernoulli.

In 1729 he published his first scientific contribution of a medical nature in Russian in the Supplements to the St. Petersburg News under the interesting title "On hydrophobia, i.e., water sickness from the bite of a mad dog." During the following four years, Weitbrecht published in the same Supplement his short medical notes ("About old age," "On sympathy and antipathy"), and, beginning with 1735, he published in Latin in the Commentaries of the Petersburg Academy a series of papers devoted to problems of anatomy and physiology of the muscles and circulation, in which the influence of Daniel Bernoulli's lectures and work was noticeable. Bernoulli gave great consideration to the muscle apparatus as the basis for the mechanics of animal movements and to the circulation system ("the moving around of the blood"), in which he was especially interested in the application of the laws of liquids' movements in vessels, including capillaries, to the mechanics of the movements of blood in the blood vessels.

In 1742 Weitbrecht published in Latin his Syndesmology, which contains a number of original and, for their time, important conclusions. It was based on more than 100 autopsies performed by Weitbrecht in the first half of the eighteenth century. The book was highly praised by his contemporaries, and after his death it was translated and published in France in 1752 and in Germany in 1779 (32 years after the author's death). The book made such an impression that its significance was recognized even by Weitbrecht's personal enemies among members of the Academy. Thus, Academician Yunker presented an enthusiastic report on it to Bestuzhev-Ryumin (1742), in spite of the fact that at one of the meetings of the Academy an actual fight took place between him and Weitbrecht, the reason being that the academician-physiologist, having excellent command of Latin, made fun of the Latin verses of Academician Yunker. Weitbrecht had quite a few enemies among the "governors" of the Academy, who could not forgive his stinging remark "The administration office is but the tail, and the professorial conference is the head of the Academy." M.V. Lomonosov and other Academicians considered Schumacher's intrigues to be responsible for the untimely death of Weitbrecht at the age of 45. V. Richter, author of the earliest work on the history of medicine in Russia (History of Medicine in Russia, Vol. III, Moscow, 1820), wrote that Weitbrecht's book was a classic, and that he was the first to prove the significance, of the walls of the small arterial blood vessels in the dynamics of circulation, basing this on the assumption that cardiac contractions alone are insufficient in strength for the circulation of blood in the blood vessels.

Weitbrecht's great scientific merit lies in his systematization and description of the valuable collection of anatomical preparations obtained from Ruysch. Having started this work in 1727, he composed an "anatomical compendium" (in Latin) as an introduction to the catalogue of the Ruysch museum.

The work done by the physiologists of the Academy of Sciences indicates that at that period, as well as in the next century, no sharp line was yet drawn between anatomy and physiology, and that the former dominated the latter. This work indicates also that, even before the official opening of the Academy of Sciences, a basis for its scientific work was laid by the efforts of Peter I and his collaborators.

While dwelling on this early period of the development of physiology in our country, we must take note as well of the great significance in this field of the scientific genius M.V. Lomonosov. In the history of physiology, after Harvey's discovery of circulation, one of the most important milestones was the chemical confirmation of the phenomena of oxidation, linked in scientific history with the name of Lavoisier. It not only became the basis of the law of conservation of matter - one of the great new scientific conclusions - but it also was the basis for the chemical interpretation of the nature of the respiration phenomenon. Thus, the chemical theory of oxidation was a main stage in the development of physiology. Lavoisier's first communication relating to the chemical theory of oxidation was published in 1773, but it now has been established (as was first pointed out by Menshutkin in 1912)[9] and acknowledged by some foreign chemists that 17 years earlier the modern chemical theory of oxidation was formulated by Lomonosov in his work "Reflections on the Cause of Heat" (1756), on the basis of experiments he performed which revealed the sources of the British chemist Robert Boyle's errors and the unsoundness of Stahl's phlogiston theory.

In 1776 the Petersburg Academy of Sciences, which had already done a great deal to encourage world science in various fields, announced an award for the solution of problems in the field of physiology (and of mathematics). The work presented for this contest by the Frenchman P. Thouvenel (1745-1815) on the subject of blood production was printed by the Petersburg Academy in 1777 as a separate issue in the French language under the title "Mémoire chimique et médicinal sur le mécanisme et les produits de la sanguification."[10] Thouvenel had published a number of

---

[9] See, for instance, the article by the president of the British Chemical Society, U.P. Whinny, "On the significance of the contributions of Russian chemists to world chemistry" (Russian translation of the Academician V. Khlopin, 1924, NTI VSNKh).

[10] The correspondence of the Academy of Sciences refers in error to Thouvenel's work as an investigation "On circulation of the blood," while in fact the work deals with production of blood.

other medical-chemical articles, in particular memoirs on the mucous tissues, published in 1770. There are reasons for considering Thouvenel, who had received the support of the Petersburg Academy of Sciences, an outstanding chemist and physician for his time. As late as 1847 the famous chemist Berzelius, in one of his letters, mentioned the memoirs of Thouvenel, published in the 1870's.[11]

In the competition for the award in physiology offered by our Academy 1784, another French scientist, Grimaud, submitted his memoirs on nutrition and digestion, for which he received the award only after a second presentation in 1788. These memoirs were published in Petersburg in 1789 under the title "Mémoire sur la nutrition."

The great authority of the young Russian Academy of Sciences is clearly shown in the history of its relationships with the famous biologist and physiologist of the eighteenth century, Spallanzani. In 1773 Spallanzani sent his classical work on the physiology of circulation from Pavia to the Petersburg Academy of Sciences, and, four years later, in 1777, he sent the French translation of his memoirs, "On animal and plant physics" ("Dissertationi di fisica animale et vegetabile"). In an accompanying letter, Spallanzani expressed a desire to become a member of the Petersburg Academy of Sciences. Due to the absence of a vacancy, he was not elected a member and was notified to that effect in April 1780. This, however, did not terminate the connection of the great physiologist with our Academy; two years later, in March of 1782, he notified the Academy that he was sending some new material dealing with his research.

In 1797 the Petersburg Academy published in its proceedings (Nova acta Academiae Scientarium Petropolitanae, Vol. IX) the memoirs sent from abroad by A. Ipey, which dealt with the then active problem of respiration. As we shall indicate below, a dissertation on the subject of respiration had already been defended at the Moscow University by F. Barsuk-Moiseyev in 1794.

As is well known, in the fifth to the seventh decade of the eighteenth century, just preceding the classic investigations of L. Galvani and A. Volta, interest in electrical phenomena in animals had come to the foreground. Outstanding physicists, natural scientists, and physicians of that period developed a special interest in the electrical fish. M. Adamson in 1751 and Walsh in 1772, as well as the famous English physicist Cavendish in 1776, had published their articles devoted to the electrical discharges of these fish and their sensitivity to electrical currents. In 1776 a corresponding member of the Petersburg Academy of Science, the physicist V.D. Wilson, in a letter from London to the Academy, reported his observations on the electric spark generated by the

---

[11] The whole correspondence of Berzelius was published recently in Stockholm (in 1941) in several volumes, Jac. Berzelius Brev. These letters contain interesting data on the history of natural sciences and, in particular, of chemistry, in Russia.

electric eel, .apparently having in mind Cavendish's experiments. In the following year, 1777, an honorary member of the Academy, Zh. G. Magellan, reported in his correspondence with the Academy on a demonstration of experiments with the electric eel performed in the English Royal Society by the famous investigator Walsh. These notes from the scientific Correspondence of the Petersburg Academy of Sciences have a definite bearing on the development of one of the most topical areas of physiological thought in Russia.

It is interesting to note that already at that time the problem of animal magnetism and its practical significance attracted the interest of Petersburg physicians. We find the first indication of it in connection with the Dutchman Bachracht (1724-1806), who was born in Petersburg and acquired his medical training at Leyden University, his expenses being paid by the Russian government. In 1765 he was called before the Medical Board and reprimanded for charlatanism in connection with his use of a magnet for the threatment of toothaches. In his defense, he presented a report and a list of people cured by him, to which the Medical Board replied: "You are not forbidden to treat toothaches; you were called before this Board to be censured for peddling those magnets and selling them at an exorbitant price." At approximately the same time, the first electrical apparatus for therapeutic purposes appeared in the Petersburg hospitals.

The works of members of our Academy at the end of the eighteenth century show that problems of animal electricity were not only discussed in letters with foreign correspondents of the Academy but were also subjected to experimental study. Among the latter we must point out the investigations of the outstanding Russian natural scientist, the honorary Academician D. A. Golitsyn, who, in his Letters Concerning Some Electrical Subjects, published in a separate edition by the Academy of Sciences in 1784, expounds his views on the physics of electricity and also presents data and discussion of the stimulation of the development of chicks by means of electrical treatment of the eggs.

Academician D. Bernoulli worked on the problem of possible resuscitation "of drowned birds" by means of an electric current.

The book by K. Klüge titled Animal Magnetism Presented in its Historical, Practical and Theoretical Aspects appeared much later, in 1818, translated by D. Vellanskiy. And in 1804 Il'ya Gruzinov, future professor of physiology at the Moscow University, defended a dissertation on the subject "On galvanism and its application to medical practice."

As we shall see further on, attention to this problem increased progressively in Russian educated circles. It was especially developed with regard to the nature of animal electricity in the works of A. Filomafitskiy at the beginning of the second quarter of the nineteenth century, when this problem still occupied the center of attention of world science as a continuation of the famous controversy between Volta and Galvani.

In 1787 the renowned Russian Academician and natural scientist V.F. Zuyev (1754-1794) published a short note in the Academy publication New

11

Monthly Reports on "The influence of air on the human body," as well as other articles on physiological subjects. And in the course of the following 15 to 20 years, independent physiological investigations of the first Petersburg Russian scientists began to appear—Sevast'yanov, the two Zagorskiy's (father and son), and others.

At the beginning of the nineteenth century, a large group of representatives of Russian medicine gathered at the Academy of Medicine and Surgery; they, too, participated in the progress of Russian physiology.

CHAPTER II

The struggle between philosophical views around the year 1800 and their significance for the development of the natural sciences, and physiology in particular. The naturalistic views of Russian masons and encyclopedists. Radishchev and his role in the struggle for an experimental natural science in Russia.

During the period around the year 1800, at this critical stage in the development of physiology and of the natural sciences as a whole not only in Russia but also in other countries, there was great significance in the ideological, philosophical struggle which proceeded during this period and established premises for the flourishing of science in the nineteenth century, "the age of science," by the graphic and precise expression of one of the best scientific historians, K. A. Timiryazev. One hundred and fifty years had to pass for science to acquire ample opportunities for development and enter the pathway of an objective, experimental study of nature, the pathway which was marked out in the works of the great English scholars—contemporaries of the philosopher Bacon and the physiologist Harvey. All during the seventeenth and eighteenth centuries an intense struggle went on between this new perspective trend in the study and conquest of nature and a different kind of idealistic, mystical and semimystical speculative views of organic and inorganic nature.

The principal place in this struggle belongs to the French philosopher-materialists of the eighteenth century, and in the first place to their most prominent spokesman—Julien Offrey de la Mettrie (1709-1751). His ideas are set forth in an extremely pointed way in the remarkable treatise entitled Man a Machine (L'homme machine). It is of interest that La Mettrie dedicated his treatise to a very well known physiologist of that period—Albrecht Haller. However, frightened by the materialistic ideas and extreme conclusions of the French philosopher, Haller made all efforts to isolate himself from La Mettrie in the press. This God-fearing Swiss scholar wrote, on the occasion of La Mettrie's book, "Reverence before the Creator, before religion and truth, does not allow me to see without horror and shuddering a creature who dares to rise in rebellion against his Father and Founder."[1]

It was only in 1748 in Leyden, when La Mettrie's book, Man a Machine, a materialistic and strikingly atheistic treatise, outstanding for its time,

---

[1] Quoted from Acad. A. M. Deborin's preface to the collected works of La Mettrie (Sel. Works, OGIZ, 1925).

came out, when from all sides the forces of the idealistic and obscurantists gathered for criticism and rebuff.

The clergy of Holland could no longer breathe the same air with this "impious atheist" and demanded the death penalty for La Mettrie, who had dared to publish such a work in Holland. Having just escaped the vengeance of the French church and his Parisian enemies, who had demanded that he be thrown in the Bastille, La Mettrie did not find peace even in Holland.

This thinker was driven from the country where he had dared to reflect and to print his works, and his enemies came out with a series of books with sharp attacks and retorts against the views he had stated. Thus, in 1749 in Leipzig, Frantzen's German book was published. [2] In the same year, also in Leipzig, the Latin treatise of Trallés was published, and finally, Hollman in 1750 in Berlin published a book in French. [3]

The strong influence of Albrecht Haller, who in the field of physiology held idealistic, natural-philosophical views, was felt in the books of these German authors who refuted the materialistic views of La Mettrie, who called for the re-orientation of physiology on the basis of an objective, experimental study of life processes.

The attacks on La Mettrie's book grew stronger, but at the same time an interest in them grew. Thus, for example, the first translated English edition of the treatise Man a Machine appeared in 1749, and in 1750 a second edition was already needed.

The culminating point of the struggle around the book Man a Machine was the appearance of a booklet by an anonymous author entitled Man More than a Machine. In the same Leyden printing house where La Mettrie's book was published, to please the exultant Dutch priests, this shameful document was hurriedly published immediately upon the appearance of La Mettrie's book.

We quote a translation of the whole title page of the English edition of this book, Man More than a Machine, which made its appearance in 1752. "I. The non-materiality of the soul is proven with incontestable arguments. This truth is presented in a clear and totally different light. II. It is shown that objections to the non-material principle, which are discussed from different ideas, and also on the basis of the observations of medical men, are obviously erroneous. III. The comparison between man and the animals is thoroughly considered, and it is proven that the specific differences between them do not consist in the structure of their bodies. IV. The impious consequence coming from the attitudes of the materialists are refuted; the existence of the Deity is proven clearly and comprehensively. Finally, the necessity of religious worship and its importance for the happiness of man are firmly established."

---

[2] Frantzen. Wederlegung der l'Homme Machine. Leipzig, 1749.

[3] Hollman. Lettre d'un Anonyme pour servir de Critique ou de refutation au livre intitulé "L'Homme Machine," Berlin, 1750.

These four basic propositions of the book Man More than a Machine were concluded with the words "In answer to the malicious and atheistic treatise written by Mr. De la Mettrie and entitled Man a Machine.

The history of this materialistic book of La Mettrie and a number of other brilliant works by him, touching the basic problems of physiology and chiefly the problems of objective study of psychic processes,[4] vividly characterize the atmosphere of ideological struggle in the field of science and especially in the field of physiology, which had an important place in the 1750's and 1760's. La Mettrie's works started the great movement of philosophical materialism which, at the end of the same century, reached a particular high point in the works of the French philosopher-encyclopedists of the period of the French bourgeois revolution, and the views of his opponents had roots in a variety of vitalistic theories, natural-philosophy, and mystical and half-mystical schemes and theories.

This latter trend was especially developed in the works of the German natural-philosophical school, the full flourishing of which dates from the very end of the eighteenth century and the beginning of the nineteenth century. These theories first of all concerned very complicated phenomena—the phenomena of organic nature—and they were especially reflected in the system of medical accomplishments.

In Russia, as in other countries, this natural-philosophical trend was an obstacle for exact science, which was breaking a way through for itself. Only in a struggle with this trend was the right won for there to be an experimental aim in the various fields of the natural sciences, and, in particular, in medicine and physiology.

We should especially indicate the place in this ideological struggle occupied by the masonic movement, which was of considerable importance in the development of Russian social thought. That is, the masonic lodges and circles were the centers where different kinds of natural-philosophical, mystical, and semimystical notions were cultivated, interpreted mainly from the literature of this generation, which was well represented in Germany.

Along with this, among the Russian masons there was a significant group of free-thinkers, to whom these mystical ravings were alien. This group thought highly of the philosophical works of Voltaire, Rousseau, and those French encyclopedists who were guided by the facts and achievements of natural science in their works.

The majority of the masonic idealists came forward as fervent opponents of the representatives of French mechanical materialism, whose works played an absolutely exclusive role in the publicizing of science's achievements in the seventeenth and eighteenth centuries, and they mapped out the subsequent perspectives of its growth.

---

[4] For a detailed analysis of the works and views of La Mettrie, see the work by Kh. S. Koshtoyants. Bibliographical Views of La Mettrie, Moscow, 1928 (Sci. work of Ind.-ped.-inst. imeni K. Libknekht.)

15

The earlier works of La Mettrie, and later the works of Diderot, D'Alembert, Helvetius, and Holbach were of that ideological principle on which grew the classic natural history investigations of Laplace, Lavoisier, and Magendie, who around 1800 laid a solid factual basis for such important areas of science as astronomy, chemistry, and physiology. The works of a number of the philosophers named, and, after them, Cabanis, were particularly significant for the development of physiology, for in them the materialistic basis of many of the most complicated physiological phenomena, including the phenomena of consciousness, occupied an important place.

For the nature of the masons' relations to this group of philosopher-materialists, it is interesting to quote from the records of an associate of N. I. Novikov—T. L. Safonov, characterizing these distinguished philosophers, wrote about them: "Members of the academy of debauchers: 1. Voltaire. 2. D'Alembert. 3. Diderot. 4. Helvetius. 5. Turgot. 6. Condorcet. 7. Laharpe. 8. Lamoignon. 9. Damilavan. 10. Thieriot. 11. Sorsa. 12. Count Argenson. 13. Grimm. 14. Baron Holbach. 15. Lerfa."

His son, P. L. Safonov, probably from his father's words, added to this list: "We must escape from such men and their writings, and by no means read them. [5]

This characteristic writing was not accidental; the persecution of intelligence, the struggle with the "free-thinking deists," as they called the philosopher-rationalists and masonic materialists, was characteristic of the general frame of mind of the noble-official circles of Russian society, which were under great influence of the masonic lodges and groups. This persecution, although it was carried on in the name of a struggle against Gallomania, was really directed against the progressive ideology of the French mechanistic materialists.

Safonov's note is interesting, especially as several of the persons mentioned on the list of "the debauchers of the Academy" were already honorary members of the Petersburg Academy—for example, Diderot, Voltaire, D'Alembert, and Condorcet. Moreover, our Academy, through its members, was especially interested in many of the French scientist-philosophers enumerated in Safonov's list, wishing to include them in its membership. [6] The works of some of the scientists mentioned—for example, Helvetius—had great importance in the formation of progressive-minded people's world outlook, along with the works of Voltaire, Rousseau, Diderot, and others.

These facts are of no minor importance in the general development of Russian social thought. A negative attitude towards the philosopher-

---

[5] Quoted from G. V. Vernadskiy. Russian Masonry During the Reign of Catherine II, Petrograd, 1917, p. 142.

[6] Compare, for example, The Scientific Correspondence of the Academy of Sciences in the Eighteenth Century, pub. house of the AS USSR, 1937.

encyclopedists was greatly cultivated by the masonic groups which wallowed in mysticism; however, a progressive-minded group of the Russian intelligentsia headed by A. N. Radishchev strove for the study of these philosophers. Towards the end of the eighteenth century, in the ranks of our country's intelligentsia, a group of people was already distinctly represented who were supporters of the new philosophical trend of being guided by experiment and real study and analysis of the phenomena all around. And just by this we can explain the fact that in the very first serious appraisal of the works of the physiologist and natural philosopher Vellanskiy in 1812, as we shall see later, the critic proceeds from the philosophy of Bacon.

The resistance to learning of the representatives of rational philosophy and science was manifested in the field of medicine. Medicine was in the field of view of the Russian Masonic movement's most outstanding representatives, and especially the group which was led by N. I. Novikov. This coincided partially with the social ideals of "love thy neighbor," which the masons advocated, and with the practical measures on the organization of medical aid on their estates and in their villages, which several of the members of Novikov's group did.

Seeing in medicine an active science, the masons critically regarded the existing empirical traditions in this field and advocated the necessity of a speculative approach both for an understanding of the nature of illnesses and for the methods of combatting them. The bases of their medical ideas were the speculative theories about man as a "macrocosm" who finds himself in constant interaction with it; about the link between the elements of man's body with the elements of the earth in a vague, alchemistical sense; about the pre-eminence of man's internal world over his external, sensory world; about the perishable nature of life and the necessity of escaping from the "world of sin" and approaching the "mental" life. Books on alchemy were printed in great quantities during the period in the Novikov publishing house in Moscow (or in the so-called Lopukhin publishing house).

The following excerpts from Rosenkreutzer's eighteenth century work "Amor Proximi," which we quote from G. V. Vernadskiy's book The Russian Masonry, give a presentation of the views on medicine of the natural-philosopher and alchemist masons: "True medicine is the heart of the true philosopher... No one can be a true medical man who has not first become a true philosopher. For only from true philosophy is knowledge of the macrocosm drawn, without the basic knowledge of which one cannot become a doctor... Wise men always confine themselves to the center, to the simple truth, but sophists wander about the edge and thus move farther from the goal; wise men become acquainted with the extent of the periphery from the center, but the know-nothings, swarming about the outside, which they look at through glasses and microscopes, never find the basis of the truth, for they do not want to know about the inner spiritual truth."

All this could in no way be conducive to the development of the new, rational medicine and science, nor could the general frame of mind of

17

many masons who viewed the health of man as evil, removing him from "mental" tasks, and who cultivated the basic masonic virtue of "love for death." Although practical alchemy, according to contemporaries, was not highly respected among the Russian masons, nevertheless they accepted and advocated its most extreme theoretical conclusions. They sought a panacea for all illnesses in alchemy.

Novikov—the most prominent theoretician among the Russian masons—gave a great deal of attention to problems of alchemy and medicine. In this respect one of his letters to N. M. Karamzin (1816) is very characteristic; in it he writes, in part: "I am sincerely sorry, my good and honorable friend, N [ikolay] M [ikhaylovich], about your poor health, that you did not tell me about your sickness; perhaps I could have helped you a little, for, with the Lord's blessing, I have a background in medicine, which, though not great, is fairly good.[7]

Novikov's group in Moscow had an influence over the university youth, all the more so since the members of the masonic circles were also professors.

In 1781 an assembly of university students was organized through the efforts of Novikov; this was the first student scientific circle in Russia. This assembly raised for itself a series of important problems in scientific studies, and it was under the ideo-pedagogical influence of Novikov and his assistants. A Pedagogical Seminary, the task of which was to prepare students as teachers and professors, had been created at Moscow University two years earlier, in 1779, also by the efforts of Novikov. Among the students who made up this seminary, who were trained in it and received its material support, was M. M. Desnitskiy, later metropolitan Mikhail Desnitskiy, who, as we shall see later, played an important role in the publication of one of the basic works of the physiologist-Schelling follower D. Vellanskiy, who met with a rebuff from the clerical circles.

It is natural that this influence extended also to the medical department. The members of the group chose their followers among the medical students of Moscow University and assisted them in receiving a medical education abroad. Those sent abroad in this way were Bagrenskiy, Nevezorov, and Kolokol'nikov. M. I. Begrenskiy (1762-1813), a pupil of Moscow University Gymnasium and Moscow University, was directed by Novikov's circle to Leyden University, where he received his doctoral degree. He was so devoted to Novikov in the masonry that he voluntarily went with him to Schlisselburg Fortress, where Novikov was imprisoned.

We cannot dwell in detail on the broad question of the Russian masonry, even in connection with the masons' views on chemistry and medicine—fields to which the masons paid a great deal of attention. It is important only that the masons, having a rich, far-flung network of groups in most of the important centers of the country, could influence the formation of

---

[7] Quoted from G. V. Vernadskiy.

world outlook of youth, and they made use of this widely. Specifically, after the propagandistic and, mainly, the publishing activity of the masons at the end of the eighteenth century, natural-philosophical views were widely spread over Russia. This fact bears direct relation to that significant period in the development of philosophy and medicine in Russia which is connected with the name of the physiologist D. M. Vellanskiy.

The masons' interests in alchemy, with the exceptional significance of alchemy in the history of world chemistry and medicine, also could not help but influence the development of this field of knowledge in our country. The correspondence of the masons, the publishing activity of the Novikov printing house, and the great quantity of books on alchemy which they issued, testify to the sharp interest of the Russian masons in alchemy. The masons considered alchemy the key to the "natural knowledge" of the world and of man, and they were carried away by its theoretical basis.

This enthusiasm for alchemy was so great that it is said that the repercussions of its influence were still felt after half a century. One of Ogarev's letters to Granovskiy testifies to this. In his letter of February 14, 1847, Ogarev, incidentally, wrote: "Chemistry becomes more definite with every year, and it is difficult to go from it into alchemy, as it would be from mathematics. The history of the formation of the planet and organism—those are problems which are solved only by experiment without a touch of fantasy." [8]

But this historically significant process of cleansing the sciences of any touches of fantasy, the process of formation of a science for which the only support is "a staff of experiment" (La Mettrie), was achieved in Russia as in other countries with a stubborn ideological struggle in which the ideas of advanced philosophical thought and experimental science resulted triumphant. The great eighteenth century philosopher-enlightener A. N. Radishchev played an entirely exceptional role in this struggle in the conditions of Russia. We also find Radishchev's name among the names of Russia's well-known masons. However, having entered the masonic organization, Radishchev saw in it the sole form in which he could reveal his social-political activity. The mystical and semimystical philosophical aims which dominated the masonic circles were alien to him from the very beginning. He joined the group of masons which highly valued the philosophical works of Voltaire and Rousseau, cultivated the philosophy of rationalism, and independently raised and worked on the central problems of philosophy, coming near to the successive materialistic conception of the world.

In the evaluation of Radishchev given by V. I. Lenin in 1914, Radishchev's name was found in the chain of the social movement, which, through the Decembrists and the revolutionists-raznochintsy of the 1870's, led to

---

[8] N. P. Ogarev. Letters to Granovskiy, Gertsen and Korsh, Links, No. 1, pub. house Academia, 1932, p. 125.

the mighty revolutionary party which carried on the decisive assaults in 1905 and 1917 on the tsarist butchers, nobles, and capitalists and their backward, reactionary ideology.

Radishchev, in his philosophical and publicistic works, raised high the banner of the advanced materialistic philosophy and science of the end of the eighteenth century and was more than a champion of the revolutionary ideas in the fields of philosophy, anatomy, chemistry, physics, botany, and mineralogy in his philosophical works—in particular On Man, his Mortality and Immortality and The Life of Fyodor Vasil'yevich Ushakov (especially in the second and third parts of this work). Radishchev wrote his basic philosophical work, On Man, his Mortality and Immortality, in prison in Siberia at the very end of the eighteenth century (1792-1796). This work did not come out until 1809. In these works in a living, clear language, free from the vague natural-philosophical schemes, Radishchev showed the omnipotence of the new science, which, remaining within the limits of the harmonious philosophical system of a united world, examines its sections as really essential phenomena of nature, accessible to sensitive analysis. He comes out against scholastics and natural philosophy, and in every way possible he emphasizes the role of experiment and observations.

"The diffusion of enlightenment and general reason has shown that experiments are the basis of all scientific knowledge," wrote Radishchev. [9]

He expressed his methods of approach to the knowledge of nature in the following way: "Let us drive away all our prejudices, all forewarnings, and leading ourselves by the lamp of experience, let us strive, on the way to the fundamental truth, to collect some facts which can guide us to a knowledge of nature. . . But however the progress of testing nature is hindered by various obstacles, the investigator must not seek the cause of a thing, a deed or an action in fancy or, like an ancient fortune-teller, deceiving himself and others, base it on some invention; but trying to learn what the thing, the deed or the action are, he discovers their close and indistinct entailments with other things, deeds and actions; he draws together similar and like facts, breaks them down, examines their similarities, and again breaking down the consequences resulting from that, working from one consequence to another, he will rise and reach the general basis which, as a focus of truth, illuminates the whole pathway to its foundation." [10]

Thus placing so high the role of experiment and observations in the knowledge of nature, Radishchev could not help but appreciate the great significance of those achievements which mankind sought in the field of a more full and perfect perception of the external world via the appropriate implements of investigation, and, particularly, optical apparatuses (Leeuwenhoek's microscope, Herschel's telescope). In artistic form, Radishchev sets forth his interesting thoughts about the similarity and difference of the sensory organs in man and animals, and he concludes

---

[9] Radischev. Complete Works, Vol. II, Leningrad, 1941, p. 50.
[10] Ibid., p. 40.

this comparison with the following thoughts: "The eagle, soaring above the clouds, views from the height of his flight his food concealed under a blanket of grass. Man does not have such farsighted vision as the eagle; millions of animals escape his notice by their smallness; but who is more in possession of his sight than man? He has increased it almost to infinity. On the one hand, he reaches to where he could formerly reach in thought alone; on the other, he exceeds almost the imagination itself. Who can be compared with Leeuwenhoek and Herschel?"[11] Let us compare these thoughts with the negative attitude towards the microscope and the other magnifying optical apparatuses which we already found with the mystics and the natural-philosophers, Radishchev's contemporaries.

Of special interest in the realm of history of views on the evolution of man's psychics—a problem which stands out through the entire new history of physiology in our country—are the views of Radishchev on this question, which he gave at the end of the eighteenth century. He wrote: "The interior of man is uniformly similar to the interior of the animals. The bones are the basis of the body; the muscles are the instruments for arbitrary movement; the nerves are the reason for sensation; the lung breathes evenly in it; the stomach is made for equivalent work; the blood circulates in arteries and veins, beginning at the heart, with its four sections; the lymph moves in its canals, the structure of the glands and all the separate canals, the knee-cap tissue and the fat which fills it, and finally the brain and the acts dependent upon it: understanding, memory, judgment. Then it does not humble man if we say that the animals are capable of reflecting. He who endowed them with perceptibility gave them thought, disposition and passion; and perhaps there are not in man either the sole dispositions or the sole virtues of which resemblances would not be found in animals."[12]

The theoretical views developed by Radishchev in the fields of biology and physiology were unexpected, and were advanced for their time. He not only advocated the advanced biological views of his time in Russia (those of Bonnet, Linnaeus and Wolff), but he even developed them further. Thus, speaking about Bonnet's The Scale of Substances, Radishchev at the same time discarded the angels from it; and criticizing the theory of preformation, which Bonnet held, he strongly advocated the new theory of epigenesis which had developed in the Petersburg Academy.

And as long as we are stopping on Radishchev's original opinions, wishing to show that his philosophical activity was at the earliest stage in the formulation of Russian physiology's ideological content in working out the central philosophical problem of psychical and physical correlation, let us see what Radishchev thought about this. He wrote: "Sensitivity is the property of feeling. Experiments show that it is the property of nerves, and physiologists attribute it to the presence of nerve fluid.

---

[11] Ibid., p. 52.
[12] Ibid., p. 48.

Sensitivity always appears jointly with thought, and this is peculiar to the brain and has its place in it. Without life itself, even these would not be known to us. And thus, it is possible that life, feeling and thought are functions of a single substance, different in different forms, or sensitivity and thought are activities of a different substance into the composition of which, however, goes an electrical force or something similar to it, if not something else. And thus, if we find only thought there where we find sensitivity, if irritability is inseparable from life, then are we not right in saying that these three phenomena of the body are activities of a single substance? For, although we find life without irritability and irritability without thought, nevertheless irritability seems to be an accompaniment of life, which [irritability] is perhaps only the lowest degree of sensitivity, and if sensitivity and thought are not accompaniments of ordinary life, then it is for this reason alone that there are not always organs, nerves, peculiar to them; for there are such substances which are so to speak contiguous to life and sensitivity alone, which for that seem to be deprived of thought because they do not have its organ, the brain."[13]

Radishchev's deep scientific approach to the problem of the nature of the thought processes brought him to a decisive conclusion about the unity of body and soul.

"It is not only superfluous, but also entirely groundless to give to the human body a soul existing entirely removed from it and incomprehensible to it. That which is usually called the soul, that is, life, feeling and thought, is a product of a single substance of which the basic and constituent parts are different and have qualities which are different and not all yet tested. If elements can change so much in their composition, so that they are entirely unlike their primitive state, then how can we come to a conclusion so groundlessly and deny them activity where they are component parts? The successes of the sciences, especially Chemistry and Physics prove that sometime it will not be impossible, by successful experiments, to catch nature in its creative, productive state. And although feeling and thought be forces different from all those known to us, how can we be so quick in our decisions and deny that they are of non-material properties and that they cannot be material, for they apparently contradict it?"[14]

Although in the fourth book of his treatise On Man, his Mortality and Immortality, Radishchev also raises the question of the immortality of the soul, giving this philosophical question its own solution, the deeply philosophical, scientific, historical concept of Radishchev, who was able to view all nature as a whole, from inorganic nature to thinking man, is striking to all of us.

Radishchev's The Scale of Substances is full of deep wisdom and poetic revelation: "Look at everything living around you: extend your curiosity

---

[13] Ibid., p. 88.
[14] Ibid., p. 89.

also to that which we consider inanimate: from the stone, where the only distinct force seems to be cohesion, where the parts, sticking to each other, exist as if one was only placed near another; from the stone to the man, whose composition is so artful, whose elements are of such varying composition, in whom all functions known in nature are formed in one, and show an organization higher than anything, subject to our feelings;. . . from the stone to man the distinct gradualness is worthy of awesome wonder, this clear scale of substances, already long known, in which all of their kinds differ so little from each other, it seems, that it is possible to consider with assurance one a companion to the other; the scale on which granite, ruby, adamant, iron, mercury and gold are like the aloe, tulip, cedar and oak; where in succession these are brothers to the butterfly, snake, eagle, lark, sheep, elephant, and man; the scale in which crystallization and mineralization are already borrowing a vegetative force, in which coral, a sponge, moss differ only internally, even arise from it; the scale in which the vegetative force, spreading its energy in another form, comes little by little to irritability, and from this to sensitivity, where the mimosa and the polyp contribute; the scale where perceptibility settles into sensitivity, joins with mental force; where the orangutan and the Fuegian seem to be the same inside: then all these forces clustering into one and spreading their energy are reflected on the lips of man, in his speech, and drawing him forcibly to social life together, they make him capable of perceiving even a universal founder. O, mortal! Look at yourself! . . your body is splendid in life; deprived of the life spark, it is food for the worms, a part of decay and destruction."[15]

And Radishchev himself understood the novelty of his views and their lack of correspondence with the views of the majority of his contemporaries in Russia. He wrote to his friends from his imprisonment in Siberia (at Ilimsk): "But the circumstances are necessary, they must be overcome, and without Johannes Hus dying in flame, Galileo being taken to the dungeon, your friend being incarcerated in Ilimsk. . . But time, preparation, will remove all obstacles,"—full of faith in the future, he continues further. Indeed, time did its work. Via the difficult way of overcoming mysticism, natural philosophy, and every kind of idealistic quest and vacillation, Russian science solidly came to the way of testing, observation, and the newest experimentation, and an important part in this belongs to the theoretical work done by A. N. Radishchev and his followers.

Radishchev's advanced scientific views at the end of the eighteenth century were not a sole, isolated occurrence in Russia. They reflected the great work connected with the activity of the Russian scientists, his contemporaries and predecessors. The entire gigantic scientific path of M. V. Lomonosov, first of all, led precisely to similar advanced scientific views. Especially outstanding was the work of Radishchev's contemporary Academician Ozeretskovskiy, to whom belongs a series of great scientific-historic works and who did a great deal for the

---

[15] Ibid., pp. 110–111.

popularization in Russia of the latest achievements in the field of science. With the direct participation of Academician Ozeretskovskiy in the early 1870's, the Academy News[16] began to be published; in it was published, particularly, a series of works which bore witness to the high level of scientific demands and to the wide group of readers of problems in scientific history, including biology. Suffice it to say that precisely in the Academy News at this time passages of the great biologist Carolus Linnaeus' works were published.

Thus, at the end of the eighteenth century in Russia, the trend took shape, very clearly expressed, of experimental investigation of natural phenomena, the trend of deep penetration into nature's secrets by scientific methods, and this trend played no insignificant part in the history of the development of Russian physiology. In this very period, Radischev in his philosophical treatises advanced and defended the important idea of the unity and the mutual connection of psychical and physical phenomena which has stood out through the whole history of Russian physiology, finding its concrete expression in the works of Sechenov and Pavlov. But there was still to come a great ideological struggle for the triumph of the objective, experimental observation of nature and its laws, and it flared up with particular force in the first quarter of the nineteenth century and was greatly significant in the history of physiology.

---

[16] It would not be useless for the reader to become acquainted with the text of the title page of this remarkable academy publication. It reads: "The Academy news for [the appropriate year], containing the history of the sciences and their new discoveries; extracts from the works of the famous Academies in Europe; notes from physics and also from scientific history, especially those concerning Russia; authentic and curious descriptions coming with war between parts of the world; new inventions, experiments in Natural History, Chemistry, Physics, Mechanics, and related arts; excellent works, in letters in all Europe, and other notes deserving mention.

CHAPTER III

The development of physiology during the period of natural philosophy. Daniil Vellanskiy and his contemporaries.

As we have indicated, attraction to natural philosophy at the end of the eighteenth century and the beginning of the nineteenth could not help but influence Russian doctors and physiologists. To examine this era of natural-philosophical views in medicine and physiology and the struggle which followed the overcoming of them, let us dwell on the activity of one of the greatest representatives of natural philosophy in Russia—the physiologist D. M. Vellanskiy (1773-1847).

D. M. Vellanskiy occupies an entirely special place among the doctor-thinkers in Russia at the beginning of the nineteenth century. His influence went far beyond the limits of physiology and medicine, and it affected the general path of the development of philosophical thought; it spread not only in Petersburg but also in other cities. D. Vellanskiy had many friends and followers in Moscow. He was a friend of the poet Zhukovskiy and discussed with him the organization in the palace of a class of philosophy; concerning this, he told Zhukovskiy: "Fortunate are the people where philosophy rules and rulers philosophize." He was closely connected with the views of the Schelling philosophers of his time—Vladimir Odoyevskiy and the Moscow University professors M. S. Pavlov and I. I. Davydov. The fact that a group of representatives of the Moscow intelligentsia asked Vellanskiy to give twenty lectures for them for twenty thousand rubles speaks for Vellanskiy's great influence and the interest in him.

Vellanskiy followed the difficult path of a needy, talented youth before he secured such an exclusive role in the movement of Russian scientific thought. His father, Mikhail Kavunnik, a native of Chernigov province, was a leather-dresser, and he could not give any education to his children. Daniil Kavunnik [D. M. Vellanskiy] felt his last name to be a burden, and he acquired a new one from the landlord, Belozerskiy, who sheltered him; Belozerskiy, once reading a French novel, lingered on the word "vaillant" (courageous) and christened the Ukranian lad, who was already at this time working as a doctor's assistant and was dreaming about an education, with a sonorous last name—Vellanskiy. When he had finished at the Kiev academy, the twenty-six-year-old Vellanskiy was sent abroad; there he worked under the direct guidance of the famous natural philosopher Oken, and he heard Schelling's lectures. His three years of study with these teachers had a decisive influence, and in 1805 the mature and confirmed natural philosopher returned to Russia and began intensively propagating natural philosophy and Schellingism on Russian soil. The title of his dissertation alone, "Dissertatio physico-medica de reformatione theoriae medicae et physicae auspicio philosophiae naturalis invente" (St. Petersburg, 1805), speaks for the fact that young Vellanskiy saw in natural philosophy and Schellingism the key to the reorganization of science, including medicine. It is interesting to note that Vellanskiy dedicates his dissertation not to distinguished persons, as many others did, but to "the Russian doctors, my dear compatriots" ("Medicis Russis, clarissimis compatriotis meis").

In the same year, a book by Vellanskiy, Prolusion to Medicine as a Basic Science, was published.

In 1812 Vellanskiy published in Russian his first great work (464 pages) under the title A Biological Investigation of Nature in the Form of Creator and Created, containing the Basic Outlines of General Physiology (St. Petersburg), which is a philosophical generalization on the natural sciences. In this work Vellanskiy sharply criticizes the experimental method in biology, which was becoming better and better known. He declares that "anatomy, physiology, physics, chemistry, mechanics and other sciences based on experiments in their present state, i.e., not illuminated by Schelling's philosophy, are nothing but empty structures."

The fate of these works is extremely interesting. On one hand, their publication, especially the book A Biological Investigation of Nature, met with difficulty because of the sharply negative attitude of the clerics, who feared a philosophical explanation of natural phenomena which did not leave room for the elements sanctified by religious mythology, dogmatism, and worship. Only the intervention of an alumnus of the Novikov Theological Seminary, the metropolitan Mikhail Desnitskiy, who went to the Synod in defense of Vellanskiy, helped his book to come out. These works, after they were published, met with sharp rebuff from the progressive-minded groups, who could not be content with abstracts, or "Philosophy," as they said then; who understood all of the great significance of experimental study of natural phenomena, and along with that, struggled against the characteristic impediment of the Russian literary language by Latinisms, a failing especially of natural philosophers. Precisely in this direction there were reviews in the magazine Lyceum (No. 1, 1806) of Prolusions...; and in the St. Petersburg Herald (No. 4, 1812), of Biological Investigations of Nature.... The review of Vellanskiy's Prolusions... in Lyceum was in its own way topical and opportune. The beginning of the nineteenth century was the beginning of the Pushkin period of Russian Literature. The great force of the people's living language opened a way for itself in literature. Also at this time, the language and the literary style in scientific works, of course, were the center of attention. And from this point of view, both the first and the later works of Vellanskiy, full of Latin words which, according to Gertsen, communicated "orthodox endings and the seven Russian cases," could not help being severely criticized. The critic in Lyceum worte: "For scholars who know Latin it would be better to write in Latin, but there is a great deal in this work which those who do not know Latin cannot understand."

The review in Lyceum sharply raised the question of the literary style of Vellanskiy's work (closely connected with the style of natural philosophy's aims); precisely to this was devoted the review of F. [obskiy] in the St. Petersburg Herald (1812) on Vellanskiy's book The Biological Investigation of Nature .... F. [obskiy] begins his review with the proposition that the book was written according to speculative Schelling philosophy, which was the enemy of experimental philosophy. Making a detailed and critical analysis of a series of problems in physics and physiology set forth by Vellanskiy in a vague, natural-philosophical style, the reviewer leaves it to the reader to call Vellanskiy's book chimera or lofty philosophy. "But—he writes further on—we advise you not to reject the principles of sound logic, and to distinguish true speculation from empty dreams. One must know the history of science and the history of philosophy. Science and the arts are indebted to the method of experiment for their present state. Empty speculation, leading man's mind from delusion to delusion, has not brought him to a single truth since the times of the great reformer of philosophy, Bacon. Thanks to him, man's mind recognized only the path of error."

Only by the intensive high-principled life of progressive-minded Russians, only by their ceaseless struggle against all kinds of speculation, can we explain the fact that a critic of Vellanskiy's work went in the very beginning along the true path, along the path of struggle for the new trend in objective, experimental knowledge of nature's laws, which was organically alien to the philosophy which Vellanskiy advocated in Russia.

F. [obskiy's] review did not entirely reject the role of speculation. It emphasized the difference between substantiated speculation and "empty dreams." And if there was a great deal of "empty dreaming" in Vellanskiy's works, a great many unfounded schemes and analogies of which Oken's natural philosophy was full, then, along with it, Vellanskiy in his works greatly raised the role of theory in the understanding of phenomena of organic nature through a series of successive links connected with phenomena of inorganic nature. Although Vellanskiy repeated Oken's nonsense that the different organs of man could be likened to different animals, nevertheless, his view of man as a part of nature was advanced and was greatly significant in the formulation of the thinking of doctors and philosophers. In his doctoral dissertation Vellanskiy wrote: "In the first part I have presented the state of former and present medicine and have shown the use and the influence of philosophy on medical science. In the second part I have presented proofs that inorganic and organic nature in the objective world are different, presenting opposite poles of the absolute Universe depicted here. Here the organism in general, and the human organism in particular, is drawn from the general state of nature. In the third part, using the foregoing as a basis, I have traced the possibility of medicine's becoming a basic science. Here the pathological state of the human body is briefly drawn from physiological concepts. From the same point I have presented therapeutic evidence, or a method of doing away with disease by the influence of external things on the human organism, which it is possible to prove from its correlation and its unity with all of nature."

As a follower of Oken, Vellanskiy attaches great importance to polarity, the roots of which go far into a particular understanding and universalization of magnetic phenomena. All during his period of scientific activity,

Vellanskiy devoted undivided attention also to questions of animal magnetism, placing very high the theory and practice of the Austrian physician Anton Mesmer (1734-1815), who made wide use of the magnetic forms of treatment which he had worked out himself on almost all illnesses, and, moreover, connected notions of animal magnetism with the vague phenomena of hypnosis. However, Mesmer's various followers brought a great deal of mysticism into the study of animal magnetism. Mesmerism was formulated almost simultaneously with the brilliant period of experimental physiological investigation of electrical phenomena in animal and human organisms, owing to the classical works of Galvani and Volta, and, of course, these two trends were completely alien to each other, both in their methods and in their conclusions. Vellanskiy, as one might expect, paid little attention to the achievements of experimental physiology and propagandized the study of animal magnetism in its mystifying form, as Mesmer's study.

In 1818, Klüge's book Animal Magnetism Presented in its Historical, Practical and Theoretical Content was published in a Russian translation by Vellanskiy. In the dedication of this book "from the publisher," the necessary homage is paid to Mesmer's genius. The book was very successful; after many years it was published a second time in another translation.

In 1840, Vellanskiy, already in Moscow, wrote an independent work on the subject Animal Magnetism and Tellurism, but its publication was forbidden by the censor. The manuscript of this work of Vellanskiy's is preserved in the Leningrad Public Library.

Vellanskiy's interest in questions of animal magnetism precisely in this peculiar form coincides with the interests of a certain group of his contemporaries. Annenkov wrote about Pushkin that in a discussion with the Kazan' poet Fuks he spoke "about the significance of magnetism, in which he fully believes." Prominent philosophers and men of letters—V. Odoyevskiy, Senkovskiy, Grech,[1] N. A. Polyevoy, and other contemporaries of Vellanskiy, not without his influence, of course, were attracted by problems of animal magnetism and wrote about them.

Vellanskiy wrote the first Russian physiology textbook, entitled A Basic Tracing of General and Particular Physiology or Physics of the Organic World (St. Petersburg, 1836), which was dedicated "to Russian youth who are studying the physical and psychical sciences and who wish to have the highest true knowledge of organic Nature and the human being." The influence of German natural philosophy and Schellingism was especially distinctly manifested in this textbook. Vellanskiy disclaimed the cognitive role of experiment, and in physiology in particular, he disclaimed the role of vivisection. Criticizing the so-called mechanistic naturalists, he wrote:

---

[1] Grech's sensational novel of the 1830's, The Black Woman, also dealt with the mysterious phenomena of animal magnetism in the form in which they were represented to their contemporaries.

"They try in vain, by calculations and measurements of observed forms and by the content of things for sensory concepts, to learn the invisible and imperceptible essence of Nature. From such an effort has come only conceited skepticism and shameless charlatanism, of which the first disdains any knowledge which it does not understand, and the second passes off old or insignificant details for new and important work.

"Physiology, which has as its object the investigation of the nature and form of animal or organic bodies, is much poorer than physics, which investigates lifeless or inorganic things. If physics, which investigates only the exterior of nature, does not have the least information about its internal state, then Physiology, which examines only the forms of the organic world, is outside the limits of its purpose, and one can say positively: that there has been no real Physiology at all until our times." And further: "Those who do not understand organic life flatter themselves with the hope of learning about it by dissection of dead bodies, about disease changes and mechanical damage in the animal organism—from which, however, Physiological Science has not been illuminated by the least light. Although age-old experiments attest that one cannot learn the internal essence of organic Nature from its external forms; however, the mechanistic Naturalists are steadfast in their opinion, and they believe that the work done so far in scientific studies has not had enough experimentation or proper skill for achieving the proposed goal, and that geniuses of the future will discover sometime the secrets of Nature hidden from us. . . . But the eternal and infinite essence of the physical and psychical world consists of feasible ideas discovered only by speculation, and not in actual forms of phenomena subject to perceptive investigation."

Vellanskiy's textbook in its content was, of course, far from the experimental physiology of that time. In this textbook there was almost no physiological information proper. The medical students who had to study with this textbook did not, of course, receive the necessary information about human physiology. The same was true of Vellanskiy's lectures. According to those who heard him in the Medical-Surgical Academy, Vellanskiy's lectures were full of enthusiasm, and they were even interesting, but the concrete physiological facts so necessary for their future medical activity did not remain after the lectures.

As is apparent, Vellanskiy spent a long time preparing his textbook of physiology. Two years before the book was published, Vellanskiy sent his work for examination to M. G. Pavlov, a professor at Moscow University. Let us cite an excerpt from Vellanskiy's letter to Pavlov of May 29, 1834, which gives a great deal of characterization of the times and of Vellanskiy himself.

"Last March 17 I sent you a course of my physiology lectures, through G. S. Since I intend to publish my physiology, I want to show it beforehand to those people in the scientific Russian public who can understand and appreciate a work of its kind. It is the fruit of my many years of study and constant efforts in the cultivation of that science of which there was not the faintest notion in Russia before my return from foreign countries, i.e., in 1806.

Organic nature is contained in inorganic, just as the soul is in the body, or ideal existence in real form. Therefore, we cannot understand one without the other: just as, not knowing the anatomical structure of organs, we cannot explain their actions; and the other way around, if we do not understand ideally the living events in the organism, we cannot have important information about the structure of organs shown by dissection of dead bodies. Physiology, setting forth the organic world, cannot be divided from physics, which demonstrates inorganic nature; for the first examines the internal, and the second the external content of one and the same universe, which can only be understood intact.

The ideal of my physiology is the universe, which is presented in its external and internal aspects, and of which the beginning external form was fire and the internal final form is man. The absolute idea of nature in its objective form appears as fire, and man appears in the subjective aspect. Therefore, my Physiology shows fire in the beginning and man at the end. If the models of rational Architectonics, Schelling, Steffens and Oken did not exist, then I could not construct this intellectual edifice. But only he who has his own ability can follow the great originals. . .

I humbly ask you to inform me: how does the course of my physiology lectures seem to you? Your love for true knowledge and noble effort in the dissemination of the small group of Physical sciences in our country is delightful to me. I myself am a great enthusiast for eminent truth; and no opposition can turn me from it. I would like very much to have either opponents or co-workers in the field of physical knowledge. But for thirty years now I have wailed in the Russian scientific world, and it is like a voice in the wilderness. From the beginning the elder scientists have been angry with me, saying with contempt: "What kind of a fledgling is this who has come to us with the ravings of the Germans?" Now the new generation of scientists are fledglings, hatched under old brood hens of decrepit erudition, who have not yet become independent, have not flown out of their nest, and already squeak at the eagles, soaring about the sphere of their vision.

With sincere respect and love for you, I remain your servant. . .

D. Vellanskiy[2]

---

[2] Rumor, a newspaper of fashions and news, published at Telescope, part 7, No. 23, 1834, pp. 345-349. In the same newspaper, in a series of issues from 1834 (No. 38-52), V. G. Belinskiy's remarkable Literary Dreams was published. In an article in No. 39 (pp. 190-194), answering the question of whether there was a literature in Russia, and what to understand for literature, among other very prominent literary works created by Russians, V. G. Belinsky names The Physics of Vellanskiy and Pavlov.

Unfortunately, we do not have at our disposal Pavlov's answer to this letter of Vellanskiy's, but the main thing is that we do not have Pavlov's reference on the purposes of Vellanskiy's physiology textbook; it would have been of great scientific interest.

M. G. Pavlov was one of Moscow University's brilliant professors in the 1820's and 1830's. The image of Pavlov, professor of physics, mineralogy, technology, forestry, rural domestic science, and agriculture, who, standing at the doors of his auditorium, turned to his students with an appeal for knowledge of nature, was well communicated in A. I. Gertsen's My Past and Thoughts. For these were the student years of Gertsen and Ogarev at Moscow University! Pavlov gave lectures on physics in a natural-philosophical style; he was a follower of Schelling in many things. But along with this we must emphasize that he, one of the first Russian philosopher-naturalists, could recognize the narrow-mindedness of Schellingism and the harmfulness of being attracted by speculative theories and abstract "philosophy." In his works Methods of Investigation of Nature (1825)[3] and The Reciprocal Relation of Speculative and Experimental Information (1828),[4] Pavlov came out against excessive attraction to speculative philosophy, and he emphasized the role of experimental science. His work The Reciprocal Relation of Speculative and Experimental Information was written in the form of a conversation between representatives of opposing philosophical directions, and it reflects beautifully the frame of mind and the search of Russian youth in the 1820's. Understanding the great importance of the experimental method (or, as he said, "analytical-empirical") in the knowledge of nature, in contrast to many of his philosopher-contemporaries (including D. Vellanskiy), Pavlov wrote: "consequently, the speculative information composing Philosophy is possible only with the experimental information composing science. Is it now clear to you that the sciences without philosophy can be not entirely nonsense, but Philosophy without science is impossible? If someone thinks to philosophize who does not know the sciences: his philosophizing will be nonsense, shameful for the mind, harmful for the sciences." And in many of his other statements, constantly emphasizing the advantage of a wide synthetic scope of nature in general and, together with this, the insufficiency of a narrowly empirical, analytical approach to the knowledge of nature in general, the great thinker Pavlov highly valued experimental investigation as a stage in the knowledge of nature.

In the light of this very quick reference to M. G. Pavlov, great interest is provoked by the question of how Pavlov regarded Vellanskiy's physiology textbook, where there was propagated, as we have seen, a complete negation of the experimental method. Vellanskiy's appeal to Pavlov in the spring of 1834 is all the more interesting, since in August of 1833 Vellanskiy was in Moscow and saw Moscow professors, including Pavlov, and held long discussions with them. Sakulin, in his monograph dedicated

---

[3] Journal Mnemosyne, pt. 4, 1825.
[4] Journal Athena (published by M. Pavlov), pt. 1, No. 1 and 2, Moscow, 1828.

to V. Odoyevskiy,[5] quotes an excerpt from a letter of Vellanskiy's in which he, sharing with N. Rozanov his impressions about the meetings in Moscow, wrote: "The Moscow scientists feel all the importance of philosophical science, although not even one of them understood my Physics." To this Sakulin added: "And, of course, this reference could concern M. G. Pavlov most of all."

Pavlov's philosophical statements, especially his caustic criticism of pure "philosophy" without a scientific basis, and his positive regard for the role of an experimental direction in the knowledge of nature of course provoked a sharp reaction. Indeed, in the pages of the Moscow Telegraph, Athena, Son of the Fatherland, and Northern Archives appeared widespread controversies, very important in the history of Russian science—actually concerning the central problem of the role and significance of experiment in science and philosophy. The articles in the Moscow Telegraph defended the old aims of the speculative "philosophers;" as usual, they belittle the role of experiment, sharply criticizing the views of Pavlov, who had taken a decisive step forward in comparison with his earlier natural-philosophical views.

Thus, within Moscow University ripened the philosophical trend which was opposed to the long-lasting, uncritical perception of the vague natural-philosophical systems of Oken and Schelling. These polemics continued right up to the middle of the 1830's, and in the works of A. I. Gertsen, a pupil of Moscow University, these polemics, as we shall see later, concluded with the triumph of the advanced ideas of objective knowledge of nature's laws. Just as the struggle in France for the philosopher-encyclopedists' objective, experimental method of studying nature triumphed, owing to the concrete works of the chemist Lavoisier, the physiologist Magendie, and other naturalists, in Russia the matter begun by Pavlov was developed a great deal because of the activity of foreign and native naturalists, and especially that of the Moscow physiologist Aleksey Filomafitskiy. Aleksey Filomafitskiy began his brilliant activity in Moscow University as a herald of the omnipotence of experimental science in 1835, when the philosophical polemics described above had not yet lost their sharpness.

Let us return to D. Vellanskiy. His conviction of the correctness of his views is striking. Even in his first works Vellanskiy declared: "My soul does not quake in the least from the cloud of passions of the learned 'evil-wishers.'" Not deviating a single step from his natural-philosophical views during three decades, Vellanskiy in 1832 placed his challenge in the Northern Bee (No. 133), in which he pledged that he would pay a thousand rubles to anyone who could prove erroneousness in even one of his propositions developed in Experimental, Observational and Speculative Physics.[6]

---

[5] P. N. Sakulin. From the History of Russian Idealism. Prince Odoyevskiy. (2 volumes). Vol. 1, Moscow, 1913, p. 123.

[6] In the biographical reference to Vellanskiy in Critico-Biographical Dictionary of Russian Writers and Scientists by S. A. Vengerov, there are inaccuracies: first, from where is it taken that Vellanskiy declared the prize to be five thousand rubles, and second, it is not indicated that the challenge was printed in the Northern Bee.

In March of 1833 the Moscow Telegraph reprinted the challenge with a short but interesting addition: "A challenge by academician D. M. Vellanskiy. In the Northern Bee, No. 133, the following declaration—worthy of the curiosity and attention of all lovers of science—was printed:

Experimental, Observational and Speculative Physics, a work of academician and Professor D. Vellanskiy, was published late in October, 1831. From the scientific public not a single response has yet followed this work, which decisively refutes the whole system of the ordinary study of physics in its theoretical sense and presents science in another form, conforming to the simplest basis of its ideal arrangement. The author considers his work the first work in physics literature in the Russian Scientific World, and he asks informed people to subject even a few articles from it to impartial critical analysis.

The author worked 8 years on this production, and was preparing it for 20 years; and therefore, an exact survey of it must be of no little difficulty. Moved by love for true knowledge, the author proposes to Russian scientific people: join with him in interpretational polemics, on some subject expanded in his physics. If the polemicist destroys the theoretical constitution of this subject and in place of it creates a better substantiated intellectual structure, then the author will give him a thousand rubles as a reward and will acknowledge his theory with gratitude. If the opposing statement is not drawn from the highest principles of the speculative concept and the author proves its groundlessness, then in that case the polemicist must give the author half of the reward he has proposed, that is, five hundred rubles currency.

The subjects which the author would like to argue are: light, weight, heat, magnetism, electrism, chemism, and galvanism, which in this particular book are set forth with very weak and inconstant hypotheses. Farther on, Vellanskiy refers to the difficulty for unprepared readers of understanding his Experimental, Observational and Speculative Physics and points out what has composed a brief extract from this book which would be printed in Son of the Fatherland, and he continues: 'The author is studying general physiology, or organic physics, which without a preliminary account of inorganic nature could not be presented in its own importance, and of which a basic tracing can be completed during the course of this year.' "

Having given a reprint of Vellanskiy's "challenge," the Moscow Telegraph wrote: "It is interesting to observe: what kind of action produced so original an announcement? As we know rather well our scientific and literary world, we could predict to the Author that. . . but we will refrain from this for the time being."

Vellanskiy's challenge evidently was accepted by a serious "polemicist" who worked over the book three years, and, preferring to hold back his name, he anonymously published in 1834 the first part of his critique, entitled An Analysis of the Physics of Mr. Vellanskiy and Other New Authors, Produced in 1834 (St. Petersburg, 1834, part 1). Now, more than 100 years later, it would be interesting if our physicists were to examine this discussion from the point of view of the developmental history of basic concepts in physics.

It is interesting to quote the full title of Vellanskiy's book: Experimental, Observational and Speculative Physics, Giving an Account of Nature in the Material Aspects, Acting Forces and Founding Principles of the Inorganic World—Composing the First Half of the Encyclopedia of Physical Knowledge. Vellanskiy wrote in the dedication: "Dedicated to the Russian-Slavs, my dear compatriots and competitors, who work in the dark, unstable and narrow field of the scientific world," and farther on: "to the wise, truth-loving, magnanimous and enlightened people who prefer lucid philosophical knowledge and the positive truth of speculative criticism to the dark ignorance of haughty profanation and to the splendid nonentity of conceited skepticism." Vellanskiy's Experimental, Observational and Speculative Physics, like other similar works of those times, includes not only information on physics in our modern understanding but also contains factual data and theoretical conclusions on the laws of nature in general. In Vellanskiy's book, moreover, material and conclusions regarding organic nature and physiology prevail. The preface to it begins with the following words. "According to the significance of the physical being and spiritual existence in man, all his knowledge concerns physics, giving an account of Nature and History, showing the developments of man's soul." Understanding so peculiarly the problems of physics and underestimating the perspectives of physics in the fundamental reorganization of man's activity (for example, in the field of technics), Vellanskiy wrote: "Physics is not so necessary for technology as it is for Anthropology and Psychology, which without a speculative knowledge of nature cannot be reduced to a systematic form. ..."

Thus, Vellanskiy's book was rather an encyclopedia of nature in which there was an especial preponderance of general theoretical conclusions and a discussion of the problems of organic nature's essence. And over this whole work one of Vellanskiy's basic philosophical propositions rules, full of deep content: "Each being and substance is a certain member in the composition of the general world, and a real knowledge of such things can come only from an understanding of the whole world structure, where the importance of each thing is basic."

Four vast sections, 900 pages, of Vellanskiy's Experimental, Observational and Speculative Physics give a large amount of factual material

---

[7] A review entitled "An Analysis of Vellanskiy's Physics" was also written by the well-known writer of this time O. I. Senkovskiy (Baron Brambeus). See Works, 1858, vol. 4, p. 17. Also, his story Satan's Great Exit (Works, vol. 1, pp. 394-395): Satan, demanding that the hole in the ceiling of Hell be closed up so that no light could penetrate there, pulled out of a barrel "two thick books: Speculative Physics of V*** and Schelling's Course on Speculative Philosophy; he opened them, examined them, closed them again, and suddenly flinging them in the face of his architect, said: Here! . . . take these two books and stop up the crack in the ceiling with them: no light could pass through these speculations."

from the field of "elementology" (light, gravity), cosmology, geology; in these sections are detailed accounts of such important problems as "electrism," "magnetism," "chemism" and "galvanism;" in all the sections, right along with interesting factual data, Vellanskiy sets forth his natural-philosophical views about the unity of natural phenomena, the role of speculation, and about the limited importance of experiment in the knowledge of nature. In his work, Vellanskiy, in addition to giving the views of Oken and Schelling, especially frequently gives an account of the views of Steffens—an extreme Schellingist. [8]

The pages devoted to "electrism," in connection with an account of the history of the discoveries of Galvani and Volta and their successors, are of special interest to physiologists.

This book of Vellanskiy's is difficult to read and understand, but it is considerably easier than his A Basic Tracing of General and Particular Physiology or Physics of the Organic World. Vellanskiy's reservations, in the text of the "Challenge" quoted above, about the incomprehensibility of its exposition, are not accidental. The text of Vellanskiy's works is difficult to understand for us now, but it was really difficult for his contemporaries, for whom Vellanskiy's phraseology was not strange and whose thinking was more receptive to the characteristic speculative schemes of that time, to understand him.

The situation of incomprehensibility and isolation for Vellanskiy grew more and more intense, and it reached its high point in the early 1820's. Vellanskiy came under fire from two sides: from the reactionary groups and from the advanced representatives of rational philosophy. Just at that time began the correspondence between Vellanskiy and a known Schelling philosopher (also involved in the masonry through Martinism), Vladimir Odoyevskiy. One of Vellanskiy's preserved letters to Odeyevskiy very clearly characterizes Vellanskiy's position in this period.

We quote the complete text of D. Vellanskiy's letter to V. F. Odoyevskiy, dated July 17, 1824. [9]

"Your Excellency, Sir Vladimir Fyodorovich! I have frequently received opinions flattering to me from persons I do not know, from different parts of Russia; but the letter from your excellency has delighted me the most. Almost twenty years ago I first announced to the Russian public new knowledge of the natural world based on a theoretical concept which, although it was conceived by Plato, was formed by Schelling and matured under him. Such knowledge I attribute only to physical subjects, not equating them to any occurrences in the field of man's soul;

---

[8] Heinrich Steffens, a Schellingist and a natural philosopher, was occupied a great deal with problems of geology and paleontology. K. Marx heard his lectures in Berlin University as a student.
[9] First published in 1864 in the journal Russian Archives (nos. 7 and 8, pp. 804-805), from which we quote it.

however, some of our scholars who cannot either understand or refute my propositions have tried to present them as blameworthy in a moral and religious sense. As far as the dark circumstances for enlightenment in our country, I have not feared empty censure. But since the time when obscurantism began to guide the Russian Feb's chariot, I have been horrified at the clouds surrounding it, and I am remaining inactive. The aphorisms of your excellency placed in Mnemosyne I have read with the greatest pleasure, and I admit that of all the Russian scientists I know, you alone have understood the real meaning of philosophy. Our public in its education follows mainly the French pattern; and it is very difficult to acquaint the public with the high spirit of natural philosophy. Therefore, I also believe that your method of promulgating Mnemosyne[10] is the best. Children must first be occupied with toys in order for them to later be shown something important. You can find a great deal of material for your publication in the German magazine which is put out by Oken: 'Isis, oder Encyclo-pedische Zeitung von Oken.' It was started in 1817 and continues now. Of all the European magazines Isis is perfect. I do not have left a single copy of my dissertation in Latin, and for a long time there has been no more of Prolusion. By accident I obtained a copy in which someone had translated words, many of them very incorrectly. In place of the dissertation I am sending you the Review of philosophical science, the translation On Light and Darkness and the physiological program for which I almost suffered under the former minister of public enlightenment, Prince Golitsyn. He did not allow me to teach Gallic cranioscopy, which he had been told was against the Christian religion! Wishing to express to your excellency my most sincere gratitude for your kindness to me, I remain your most humble servant, Danilo Vellanskiy, Councillor of State and Academician of the Imperial Medical-Surgical Academy in Saint Petersburg."

The letter from Vellanskiy to V. Odoyevskiy becomes especially interesting when it is compared with other documents of the time. First of all, we see from the letter that at this time nothing happened, so that Vellanskiy was compelled to be "inactive"—i.e., his philosophical views met a sharply negative attitude. But from where did this "obscurantism," which began to "guide the Russian Feb's chariot" and which so horrified Vellanskiy, come? The answer to this may be found in some reports of this same period, memoranda of the trustee of the Kazan' scientific area, M. L. Magnitskiy (addressed to the minister of ecclesiastical affairs and public enlightenment, A. N. Golitsyn),[11] which were directed against new ideas in philosophy and science. Several months before Vellanskiy's

[10] Mnemosyne—a collection of works initiated by V. Odoyevskiy, in verse and prose, which had as its main object the elucidation of philosophical problems. Mnemosyne was the first scientific-literary collection in Russia and came out in 4 booklets during 1824-1825.
[11] "Two opinions of the trustee of the Kazan' scientific district, M. L. Magnitskiy." Russ. Arch., 1864, no. 3, columns 325-327.

36

letter to V. Odoyevskiy, in a letter of May 9, 1823 to the minister, Magnitskiy attacks the contemporary philosophy, and, taking as an object of criticism the book Principles of Logic by an ideological friend of Vellanskiy, Professor Ivan Davydov of Moscow University, he demands decisive measures. This letter is so characteristic of Magnitskiy's dismal activity and, along with it, brings us so close to the circumstance which marred Vellanskiy's creative life, that we are quoting a long excerpt from it. From Kazan', Magnitskiy wrote to Petersburg:

"Owing to the permission given to me by your excellency in the Main College Board, and with Professor Davydov's opinion about the program, I have the honor of presenting notes for his book which he is publishing under the title of Logic; the book is a classic in Moscow University.

The notes include in brief the whole meaning of our destructive present-day philosophy, from Kant to Steffens, [12] whose name is not yet known to any of us, except for his fanatical followers and the small number of their opponents, while he is a very dangerous principal of Schelling philosophy, of which the whole infernal secret is opened and displayed in the notes I am presenting.

Along with this, I have the honor of presenting an excerpt from a book which I obtained not long ago, about the secret knowledge of the illuminators, in which it is presented for attestation precisely of the excerpts. In this excerpt, those articles which support this presentation are mentioned.

Imagining the notes presented with this excerpt, your excellency undoubtedly deigns to be convinced from the places mentioned in it that present-day philosophy is none other than present-day illuminatism, indebted only to its new name for Christian governments' allowing the public teaching of it and even paying salaries to its disseminators.

I have devoted five years to an indefatigable study of this subject and to a useless wail against the inevitable and close danger by which the Lord's church and the state government are threatened, from the open spreading of destructive illuminatist principles in the popular education; presenting incontestable proof, I for the last time have still made up my mind to entreat your excellency with all that is sacred to strike this terrible monster which is quietly undermining our altars and throne by open teaching of principles in all our universities and in all the higher colleges where departments of philosophy and politics have been established; for until now, only in Kazan' University have the facts been given out for instruction in it, in all strictness, and philosophy has been taught in an accusatory form.

The time has already passed [i.e., three years before] when we considered these studies as only harmful theories of free-thinking professors; since that time rebellious forces have already overturned several thrones, and now three States teach these destructive principles, and one of them—the head of this infernal union, opposed

---

[12] This is the same Steffens about whom we spoke above.—Kh. K.

as an enemy to the holy union, in the middle of its parliament—solemnly explains that it recognizes that state power is initiated by the people. If this impious dogma of Marat in Kunitsyn province frightened us in his time, then does it not frighten us when it comes from Canning, according to whom numerous forces and the commanding English fleet can be moved on all seas, for reinforcement of its rule?

And thus, God's enemy has needed only three years to carry its pursuits from the chair of Kunitsyn to the shaking of Naples, Turin, Madrid, Lisbon, and to this solemn confession of the English Parliament; from the single line of a professor to 200 bayonets and 100 battleships, to the States being steeped in blood.''

These quotations from Magnitskiy's letter show what kind of a threat was hanging over enlightenment and science in Russia in this period. The activity of Vellanskiy, as one of the recognized authorities in the field of philosophy and also in that part of it which concerned the regularity of nature, of course called forth the resistance of the reactionary circles. We have already noted that the clerics tried to prevent the publication of his A Biological Investigation. . . in 1812 and that only the persistent defense by the metropolitan Mikhail Desnitskiy in the Synod led to the publication of Vellanskiy's book. We learn from Vellanskiy's letter to V. Odoyevskiy that the same minister of public enlightenment, Prince Golitsyn, to whom M. L. Magnitskiy turned, forbade Vellanskiy to read his physiology lectures on "Gallic Cranioscopy," about which someone had told him "that it is against the Christian faith."

From a comparison of all these facts with the evidence, it follows that Vellanskiy's philosophical activity for its time had also a great positive side, since it was directed against inertness, religious dogmas, the gross heavens, and stagnation of thought. His philosophical works, idealistic in their basic purposes, however, inculcated a wide system of views of the phenomena around as a single process in which separate phenomena are deeply connected and act reciprocally.

Vellanskiy propagated the connection between physiology and philosophy in Russia, just as his contemporary—the very prominent physiologist of that period, Johannes Müller—did in Germany. In 1826 Müller's well-known work Zur Vergleichenden Physiologie des Gesichtsinnes des Menschen und der Thiere nebst einem Versuch über die Bewegungen der Augen und über den menschlichen Blick was published, in which J. Müller, proceeding from natural philosophy, formulated a number of fundamental propositions which later on provoked a great controversy in the elaboration of the true aims in the field of the physiology of sense organs. In the very beginning of this work J. Müller entered into a defense of speculative natural-philosophical principles in physiology and emphasized the limited importance of experiment in the knowledge of physiological phenomena. Precisely in this work J. Müller laid the basis of that "physiological idealism" which many later followed (in spite of the fact that in his later years Müller himself incinerated his own earlier natural-philosophical works).[13]

---

[13] Du-Bois Reymond reports this in his long speech dedicated to J. Müller. See Reden von Emil Du-Bois Reymond, 1887, no. 2, p. 158.

It is known that almost 40 years later Ludwig Feuerbach subjected J. Müller's views to severe criticism, and, as V. I. Lenin wrote, "ranked him with the 'physiological idealists'. . . . The idealism of this physiology consisted in the fact that, investigating the importance of the mechanism of our sense organs and their relation to sensations, pointing out, for example, that the sensation of light results from various influences on the eye—he was inclined to conclude from this a negation of the fact that our sensations are forms of objective reality. L. Feuerbach very neatly caught this tendency of one school of naturalists toward 'physiological idealism,' i.e., toward an idealistic interpretation of the known results in physiology. The 'connection' between physiology and philosophical idealism, chiefly a Kantian trend, has been exploited by reactionary philosophy for a long time now."[14]

There was already formulated in the above-mentioned work of Müller the so-called "law of specific energy of sense organs," which up to our times was a basic premise of physiologists and philosophers (chiefly German), who persistently denied the authenticity of our sensations and drew a narrow line between sensory perception and the world around us. We shall return later to this problem, the strict scientific solution of which was given by a leading figure of world science, V. I. Lenin, in his philosophical "theory of reflection," and by Sechenov in his psychophysiological investigations.

For the history of the development of Russian theoretical thought, it is extremely important to note that, upon the appearance of this idealistic treatise by the physiologist J. Müller, the progressive Russian organs of the press regarded it very reservedly and critically. Thus, the Herald of the Natural Sciences and Medicine, in one of its first numbers,[15] in 1828, featured an article on J. Müller's work, criticized his general natural-philosophical views, and later gave a detailed account of basic psychophysiological conclusions. Special attention was given to the "energy of the sense of sight." As the author of the article wrote, according to Müller it appears that "we do not know the essence of external objects, nor of that which we call the world; we know only the essence of our feelings." In conclusion the author wrote, not without emotion: "Ugh! They found even a single reality with difficulty. But let us stop at this, and this already supplies us with the complete idea about this dreamy philosophical contemplation which does not give credence to the daily evidence of senses and which encloses itself in a vague dream in which the foreseer seeks nature, instead of observing and investigating it."

The dramatic nature of Vellanskiy's proposition consists in the fact that a criticism of his views came from two sides. Such was the logic of events between two eras in the history of science. Already the fate of Vellanskiy's first major work was very significant in this respect. As

---

[14] V. I. Lenin. Works, vol. 13, pp. 248-249.
[15] "The principles of natural philosophy applied to vision and to optical illusions by Professor Müller." Herald of the Nat. Sc. and Med., No. 8, 1828, pp. 466-470.

D. M. Vellanskiy (1773–1847)

we saw, it met rebuff from the clerics and sharp criticism from the representative of the new objective trend in science and philosophy.

V. F. Odoyevskiy, a friend and contemporary of Vellanskiy, gave an especially vivid characterization of these contradictory frames of mind in the "searching for truth" of Russian youth of the 1820's and 1830's. He wrote:

"My youth was passed in that era when metaphysics were in the same general atmosphere as the political sciences are now. We believed in the possibility of such absolute theory, by means of which it would be possible to build up (we said construct) all the phenomena of Nature, just exactly as we now believe in the possibility of such social reform which would completely satisfy all man's wants. . . Be that as it may, then all nature, all man's life seemed clear enough to us, and we were a little condescending to physicists, to chemists, to utilitarians, who rummaged in crude matter. Of the natural sciences only one seemed to us worthy of the attention of philosophy—anatomy, as a science of man, and especially the anatomy of the brain. We settled down to anatomy in a practical way, under the guidance of the famous Loder, with whom many of us were favorite pupils. We cut up more than one cadaver, but anatomy naturally directed us to physiology, a science which was just beginning then, and of which the first fruitful development emerged, we must admit, with Schelling, and later with Oken and Carus. But in physiology at every step we naturally came across questions which were unexplainable without physics and chemistry; and even many places in Schelling (especially in his Weltseele) were dark without natural knowledge; and thus, the proud metaphysicians, even to remain true to their name, were brought to the necessity of being set up with flasks, receivers, and similar drugs, necessary for crude matter."[16]

Kh. I. Loder (1753-1832), to whom Odoyevskiy refers, was a professor of anatomy at Moscow University. He was not only a brilliant professor of anatomy and an organizer but also a great thinker. The preserved letters from Goethe to Loder, and also references to the philosophical trend of Loder's lectures, testify to the broad views by which he attracted his talented and keen pupils who studied anatomy not just for future medical activity but also in the search for the laws of nature. Loder created the excellent anatomical theater of Moscow University, where Odoyevskiy and his friends hastened to hear Loder's lectures and prepare cadavers (corpses), and almost simultaneous with them N. I. Pirogov (who entered the university in 1824) was in the university in the very same place where, at the end of the century, there was built the still-standing two-story building of the Physiological Institute in the name of Sechenov (the department of physiology and microbiology of the first Moscow medical institute).

Although the whole university was steeped in traditions of the past, this part of it is nevertheless especially dear to a physiological historian.

---

[16] V. F. Odoyevskiy. Russian Nights, Moscow, 1913, pp. 8-9.

In this new building there is now something sacred to Russian physiology—
I. M. Sechenov's private study, with many of his instruments and things.
Sechenov entered the university in 1851, and he even found the old
building and the Loder anatomical theater where he studied anatomy as
a student. And returning to the university as a professor after almost
half a century, he did scientific work and taught in the new building of the
Physiological Institute on the same spot.[17]

V. Odoyevskiy and his philosopher-friends, besides their anatomical
studies with Loder, avidly studied all the latest natural-scientific
literature, and especially works on physiology. The physiologists Carus
and Bichat were their real teachers. Along with Goethe and Schelling,
Odoyevskiy considered Bichat and Carus mankind's greatest thinkers.
Bichat's book Physiological Investigations on Life and Death,[18] published
in Paris in 1800, became the manual for the Russian philosopher-
idealists. In Bichat's system his assertion of the qualitative difference
of the living and the impossibility of systematizing the laws of organic
nature with the laws of inorganic nature particularly attracted V.
Odoyevskiy and his associates, who stood for philosophical idealism.

In order to have an idea of the deep, many-sided interest of V.
Odoyevskiy and his friends in the natural sciences, it is sufficient to
familiarize oneself with the ninth chapter of Russian Nights. Various
problems in chemistry, physics, astronomy, physiology, and medicine
are discussed here, in the form of a dialogue between incorrigible
natural philosophy (Faust) and his opponent, striving to begin on the path
of experimental science (Viktor).[19]

However, study of the natural sciences could not give the proper result
with such an enormous, almost fanatical attraction to Schelling's idealistic
natural philosophy, which was so characteristic both for Vellanskiy and
for V. Odoyevskiy. This attraction met a sharply negative attitude from
the progressive-minded youth, who were proceeding to a knowledge of
the laws of nature and society by other paths. In this atmosphere,
naturally, conflicts were bound to arise which were reflected in the

------

[17] The new anatomical theater of the university, which existed until
1926 where the university's Chemical Institute is now located, was built at
this time. It is not without interest that much later on the spot of this
second Anatomical Theater of the university, according to the plans of
Professor A. F. Samoylov, is the Physiological Institute of the biology
department, but before its surrender to the physiologists it was given
to the chemists (early in 1930).

[18] M. F. Bichat. Recherches physiologiques sur la vie et la mort.
1800. Russian translation by Bibikov, St. Petersburg, 1865.

[19] V. Odoyevskiy's thoughts were carried far away by occupation with
the natural sciences, and he can correctly be considered the father of
Russian scientific-fantastic literature. He wrote "The year 4338 (Petersburg letter)" (See V. Odoyevskiy. Romantic Tales. Pub. Breakers, 1929,
p. 346), amazing in its fantasy; it is the best scientific-fantastic work in
world literature.

dialogue "The Ninth Night" (Russian Nights, by V. Odoyevskiy). But the controversy which took place between V. Odoyevskiy and his cousin, the poet and Decembrist Aleksandr Odoyevskiy, is especially interesting. We know about this controversy from Aleksandr's letters to Vladimir Odoyevskiy, one of which Vladimir Odoyevskiy received almost at the same time as the above-mentioned letter to him from his associate Vellanskiy (July, 1824).

Vladimir Odoyevskiy set forth his philosophical views in his letters to Aleksandr Odoyevskiy. In answer to these letters, Aleksandr Odoyevskiy, in part, wrote: "My dear Volodya [nickname for Vladimir], you couldn't be a better philosopher! I read and reread your letter and I understood how an enlightened cornet of the household troops of the Horse Regiment can hardly understand the profound speculations of the unintelligible Schelling, dressed in the manner of Davydov by his favorite pupil-dreamers. I read and read, and Schelling philosophy was pitch dark to my strained mind"... (the letter of March 2, 1823). From a letter written October 10, 1824, we learn that Vladimir and Aleksandr Odoyevskiy separated from each other in view of Aleksandr's sharp censure of Vladimir's attraction to Schelling's abstract system and verbal exercises. "Exclamation after exclamation!—he writes to Vladimir—But if the flame burns in your soul, then not puncturing completely the hard dome of your skull, it would find at least a chink, to throw out a spark. Where is it? Apparently you are roasting on the fire of Schelling, and not giving off light."[20]

In his declining years, evaluating the entire peculiarity of the epoch in which he passed his student years, V. Odoyevskiy wrote, addressing future generations: "It is you, the new generation, whom the new sun awaits, you!—and you do not understand our sufferings! You do not understand our age of contradictions! You do not understand this Babel, in which all ideas have been mixed and each word has taken on a meaning opposite to itself! You do not understand how we lived without beliefs, how we lived by suffering alone! You would laugh at us!—Do not hold us in contempt! We were poor doomed men whom Providence cast into the first crucible to rectify the sins of our fathers; for you it has preserved a skillful stamp to raise you to its revelry."[21]

The successes of analytical science, or as they said then, empirical science, gave rise to great uneasiness in the circles of followers of D. Vellanskiy and V. Odoyevskiy. The achievements in experimental physiology called forth especial confusion. The followers of Vellanskiy and Odoyevskiy felt that analysis of nature leads to skepticism, to a complete dissociation of the tie between man and nature, and finally to a loss of man's most precious sense—the sense of beauty.

These sentiments were conveyed in an especially vivid way by V. Odoyevskiy in the seventh chapter of Russian Nights ("The

---

[20] We quote excerpts from letters from the edition: A. I. Odoyevskiy. Complete Collection of Poems and Letters. Pub. house Academia, 1934.
[21] V. Odoyevskiy. Romantic Tales, p. 345.

43

Improviser"). Doctor Sigeliel', who possesses a special secret power, shares his ability to see everything, know everything, and understand everything with an enamored youth, Kipriyano, who has turned to him for help. And this leads to terrible consequences for Kipriyano. Having received from Doctor Sigeliel' his secret initiation, Kipriyano runs to his sweetheart, Charlotte, and . . . (oh, curse nineteenth century physiology!):

"Through the cell membrane, as through muslin, Kipriyano saw how the three-sided artery, called the heart, began to palpitate in his Charlotte; how the red blood rolled out of it, and reaching the capillaries, produced this tender whiteness which he used to admire so much. . . The wretch! in her beautiful eyes filled with love he saw only a kind of camera-obscura, the retina membrane, a drop of disgusting liquid; in her pretty steps—only the mechanism of levers. . . The wretch! he saw also the gall bladder, and the movement of the food-receiving mechanism. . . The wretch! for him, Charlotte, this earthly ideal, before whom his inspiration had offered prayers, became an anatomical preparation!

In horror, Kipriyano left her. In a nearby home there was an image of the Madonna, to whom Kipriyano had formerly run in moments of despair, whose harmonious appearance had calmed his suffering soul; he ran up, threw himself on his knees, and prayed; but alas! there was no longer any picture for him: the paints stirred on her, and he saw in the work of the artist only a chemical ferment.

The wretch suffered incredibly; all sight, hearing, smell, taste, touch—all his senses, all his nerves acquired a microscopic capacity, and in a certain focus the least speck of dust, the smallest insect, nonexistent for us, crowded him, turned him out of the world; the twittering of a butterfly's wing rent his ear; the smoothest surface tickled him; everything in nature was decomposing before him, but nothing united in his soul; he saw everything, understood everything, but between him and people, between him and nature was an eternal abyss; nothing in the world felt for him."[22]

These peculiar and very strong lines of Odoyevskiy were a sharp criticism not only of analytical physiology but also of analytical science in general. The criticism of the analytical trend in the knowledge of nature was an integral, component part the philosophical views of both Odoyevskiy and Vellanskiy, since their philosophical clearness of purpose had as its main point the synthetic perception of the world.

Precisely these philosophical views led to an idealizing of the scientist who examined the phenomena of nature in general, the scientist who harmoniously combined the analyst, philosopher, and poet. Full of national pride, Odoyevskiy considered the ideal of the scientist of the future to be the genius of Russian science, M. V. Lomonosov. Odoyevskiy wrote: ". . . you kneel before the man unknown to you, who was a poet,

---

[22] Ibid. pp. 220-221.

44

a chemist, a grammarian and a metallurgist, who before Franklin brought lightning to the ground, and wrote a history, and observed the movement of the stars, and did mosaics cast in glass, and in every field moved science far ahead; you kneel before Lomonosov, this native representative of versatile Slavic thought, when you learn that he, equally with Leibnitz, with Goethe, with Carus, hid in the depths of his soul that secret method which studies not separated members of nature, but all its parts in total, and harmoniously draws to itself all varied knowledge. Then you will believe in your dark hope about the completeness of life, you will believe in the approach of that era when there will be a single science and a single teacher. . ."[23]

Precisely this ideal opens before us the positivism which is so notable in the system of philosophical views of V. Odoyevskiy and his associates, who were occupied with scientific problems. One cannot recognize as very progressive the striving to set off the idea of synthesis, the idea of reciprocal connection of phenomena against crude empiricism, an unprincipled decomposition of nature, and a reduction of the laws of complex phenomena to simple ones. This is the positivism of activity of Vellanskiy, in whom, just as in the views of his teacher, Oken, we see not only the "nonsense which results from the dualism between science and philosophy" (Engels)[24] but also the profound idea of the general connection of phenomena and the high appraisal of the role of theory in scientific knowledge of the world and man's practice (especially in the field of medicine).

In their philosophical views, Vellanskiy and V. Odoyevskiy reflected the poignant quests for truth of the whole generation. Along this path passed such a titan of thought as V. G. Belinskiy. Even now, after more than a century, one cannot read without agitation the remarkable lines of his Literary Dreams, where Belinskiy sets forth his view on nature as the "breath of a single, eternal idea, manifesting itself in innumerable forms, like a great spectacle of absolute unity in endless variety."[25] In 1834, in his literary debut, although Belinskiy, too, gives the complete idealistic system of his views on nature, in this system the fruitful thought about the unity and reciprocal tie of all natural phenomena dominates. And this makes Belinskiy's views of this period related to the views of Vellanskiy and V. Odoyevskiy. But after ten years, in an article dedicated to V. Odoyevskiy,[26] Belinskiy, mentioning all the profundity and

---

[23] Ibid. pp. 421-422.
[24] K. Marx and F. Engels. Works, vol. 14, 1931, p. 409.
[25] V. G. Belinskiy. Works, Moscow, vol. 1, 1881, p. 15. See ibid., p. 282: in a review of A. Drozdov's book Trial of a System of Moral Philosophy (1835) Belinskiy touches upon the same questions and discusses the question of the correlation between experiment and speculation and their importance, and he emphasizes the dominant importance of speculation (1835).
[26] Belinskiy highly valued V. Odoyevskiy as a writer, and especially as the author of Russian Nights. Belinskiy wrote about his works: ". . . they display in him not only a writer with great talent, but also a man with a deep passionate drive for the truth, with a fervent and sincere conviction, a man who is troubled by questions of time and whose whole life belongs to thought" (Works, 1881, pt. 9, p. 70).

interest of the philosopher's views, along with it points out their narrowness, calls for a unity of synthesis and analysis, and emphasizes the great importance of empirical, analytical facts, without which it is inconceivable to construct a system of views on nature. But we shall return to this later.

The following generation of Russian philosophers and naturalists, standing on the solid-materialistic paths of the knowledge of nature, held high the banner of theory, and in their work, the ideas of unity and the link of natural phenomena, the unity of synthesis and analysis, theory and practice, came to a brilliant conclusion. A. I. Gertsen, in his Letters on the Study of Nature (1845-1846), gave standards which were unsurpassed for their time for the dialectical-materialistic examination of nature.

CHAPTER IV

Two ideological trends in philosophy at the beginning of the nineteenth century, Magendie and Bichat. The struggle against natural philosophy and idealism in physiology in Russia and in other countries. The first Russian experimental physiologists.

At the beginning of the nineteenth century, France's capital, Paris—where François Magendie (1783-1855) [1] carried on intense experimental work in his modest physiological laboratory; where Xavier Bichat (1771-1802) did experiments, performed autopsies, and wrote his amazing treatises in the hospital Hotel Dieu; where the doctor-innovators Corvisart and Laennec established traditions of objective methods in diagnostics and therapy—became the mecca of new medicine and physiology. Youth from all the countries of Europe, and also from America, came here to study with famous teachers and their followers. Doctors from Russia came here.

In the history of physiology the activity of Magendie and Bichat had an absolutely exclusive importance. Both of them were innovators in concrete study, in the description of various phenomena in the healthy and diseased body of animals and man, not previously known to science. Their names are connected with the very bright period of the beginning of experimental science in the nineteenth century. But the names of these two famous French physiologists are also connected with two mutually exclusive systems of views on the essence of life, on the essence of physiological processes.

In his textbook of physiology, Magendie persistently maintained that the vital problems in knowing the laws of activity of organisms "cannot be learned by empty indoor speculation; only an exact knowledge of physics, numerous experiments on healthy and diseased bodies and strict logics can lead to this."

Comparing the composition of living and nonliving bodies, Magendie observed the similarity and differences in their character, and, even be-

---

[1] Although this is also well known, let us nevertheless remember that Magendie carried out his best work in a private laboratory, and only in 1831, after almost 50 years, did he acquire a laboratory at the Collège de France. In Magendie's laboratory a genius of physiology, Claude Bernard, worked and studied.

fore Veler solved the synthesis of urea, he wrote: "Many of the observed differences [organic] will probably disappear completely in a short time. Thus, for example, we must note that along with the fact that animal bodies completely destroyed cannot be rebuilt, chemistry has succeeded in obtaining substances which are found only in organic bodies. In due course, it is entirely possible that this will go even farther."

In just the same way, strictly and sharply criticizing contemporary idealistic aims, he approached the problem of mental activity and the functions of the brain. "Physiology—he wrote—obtained from religion the consoling faith that consciousness is God's paradise; but even the laws of logic emphasize the necessity of studying mental activities just as if they were the result of the activity of an organ." And further: "A group of facts shows that the brain is the material organ of mental activity." However, Magendie considered the study of mental processes basically beyond the limits of physiology, and the object of study of a "special science—Ideology or Psychology."

It is very characteristic for Magendie that for the study of problems in psychology he referred the reader primarily to the works of Bacon, Locke, Condillac, Cabanis, and other scientists and philosophers who raised the question of links between the soul and body, and thus in these questions he was under the influence of the French materialistic philosophical school.

Besides the textbook mentioned, where a criticism of idealism and wordy-descriptive physiology is given with such brilliance, and models of an experimental approach to physiological problems are demonstrated, Magendie wrote a number of other works which were important in the history of physiology. Of them, we must mention the book Leçons sur les phénomènes physiques de la vie (1836-1842), in which, in Claude Bernard's words, Magendie was "the first physiologist to write a book on the physical phenomena of life."

This book, which raised the problem of the study of physico-chemical phenomena of separate organs and tissues and which was written under the profound influence of Laplace, with whom Magendie was personally acquainted, had concrete historical importance as a document directed against the prevailing views of the idealist Bichat, who believed that the life principle was diffused in all tissues.

Of great importance also was the magazine Journal de physiologie expérimentale (1821-1831), which was organized and edited by Magendie and which united the majority of physiologists of that time who followed the path shown by Magendie of working out the problems in physiology by experiment.[2]

---

[2] It is not without interest that the first Russian author to print an article in Magendie's journal was the well-known astronomer I. M. Simonov (1794-1858). The article concerned the problems of vision; Magendie pointed this out in his textbook of physiology. "These changes in the shape

The works of Magendie, his books and journal, were thus the conclusion of the great work which was done by the brilliant group of French philosophers and scientists in the eighteenth century who struggled for a materialistic understanding of life phenomena, against all remnants of the scholastic science of the feudal system.

Precisely this struggle, as one of the aspects of the struggle of the eighteenth century bourgeoisie, advanced France, in the person of Lavoisier and especially Magendie, to the position of the country in which nineteenth-century scientific physiology first appeared. From here it spread to other countries too, and first to Germany, where natural philosophy had prevailed so completely in the first quarter of the nineteenth century.

And if the immortal work of the thinkers who proceeded along lines of a scientific knowledge of nature (Galileo, Bacon, Descartes, Newton, Le Roy, French materialists) put physiology in France on the path of Lavoisier and Magendie, the path of true scientific knowledge of regularities in a living thing, then the work and views of philosophers of the idealistic wing formulated another trend of development of physiology in France at the beginning of the nineteenth century. In this respect we must note the philosophical school which came into the history of science under the title of the Montpellier school. A number of doctors, anatomists, and physiologists, for the most part from the medical department at Montpellier— Bordeu (1722-1776), Grimaud (1750-1789), Barthez (1734-1806), Chaussier (1746-1828), Louis Dumas (1766-1813),—developed vitalistic views on the nature of processes which take place in an organism. Grimaud, the great anatomist and predecessor of Bichat in the creation of a study on animals and organic functions, developed, for example, the notion of particular digestive forces; Barthez, negating the attempts of physical and chemical explanation of physiological phenomena, set out on the path of recognizing the existence of a special "life principle." Denying the physico-chemical interpretation of life phenomena, the vitalists put forth a proposition of a "super-mechanical force." Xavier Bichat (1771-1802), who was the creator of the new trend of vitalism, played an important role in the further development of this trend in France. In his two treatises Physiological Investigations on Life and Death and General Anatomy in its Application to Medicine and Physiology, Bichat, analyzing and criticizing various vitalistic directions—Stahl, van Helmont, the doctors of the Montpellier school (Grimaud, Barthez), the German vitalist Blumenbach—advances his own understanding of the living thing, the special characteristics inherent in the living things, placed in the separate tissues and in the separate organs. His study on life characteristics flooding the various parts of the body gave new nourishment to vitalism, for the great difficulties and

---

of the eye, or in the position of the crystalline lens are sometimes attributed to pressure on the eyeball by the rectus and oblique muscles, a contraction of the crystalline lens, the ciliary processes, etc. Mr. Simonov, the famous Russian astronomer, now maintains that it is not necessary for the eye to change in form; he bases this case on calculation (see my physiological journal, vol. IV)." (A Brief Basis of Physiology, by F. Magendie, Moscow, 1830, vol. 1, p. 76).

contradictions in the question of where and how to localize a particular life principle (a question which also disturbed Stahl, van Helmont, and many others) were solved in the teaching that life characteristics flow about the whole body, determining in each given part the characteristics of the given tissue, the life characteristics for the given organ, of two forms. Bichat defined them in the following way: "Examining the characteristics of each living organ, we can divide them into two kinds: some are found in direct dependence upon life, appear and disappear together with it, or rather they compose its principle and essence; others are indirectly connected with it, and apparently depend rather on the organization, on the structure of the parts. The ability to have a sensation, the ability to contract simultaneously are life characteristics of tissues; the latter characteristics, it is true, are strengthened under the influence of life, but they nevertheless remain in organs even after the cessation of life, and only the decomposition of these very organs stops the appearance of these characteristics." And further: "One cannot say digestedation, respiredation, separatedation, exhaledation, etc., because digestion, respiration, separation, exhalation are results of functions coming from the same general laws: we must say the same thing about the phenomena of heat . . . The assimilation of substances heterogeneous to our organs is one of the main results of sensitivity and movability," etc. [3]

Bichat considered these characteristics as manifestations of a special life force, and he sharply attacked all attempts at physico-chemical approaches to an understanding of life phenomena. "The invariability of laws controlled by physical phenomena makes it possible for all sciences studying them to submit them to calculation, whereas no mathematical science can present formulas which could apply to life phenomena. It is possible to calculate the return of a comet, resistance for a liquid flowing along an immobile canal, the speed of flight of a projectile, etc., but to calculate together with Bordelli the strength of a muscle, with Keill the speed of circulation of the blood, with Jurine, Lavoisier and others the quantity of air entering a lung; it is the same as constructing a building on unstable sand, solid in itself, but slowly falling because of the lack of a solid foundation." [4]

The above-mentioned works of Bichat were widespread and greatly influential because in his works he simultaneously gave brilliant models of the application of experiment and in a new way raised a series of questions in physiology (for example, about the interrelations of animal and vegetative functions), anatomy, and pathology. Along with this, Bichat's influence went also along the line of his basic theoretical views.

As we can see, Bichat's system and his views on the path of development of physiology were diametrically opposed to Magendie's views. If Magendie awaited the "Newton of physiology," if he was inspired by Galileo and Descartes and considered the ideal for physiology to move this

---

[3] M. F. K. Bichat. Physiological Investigations on Life and Death (translated by Bibikov). St. Petersburg, 1865, p. 93.
[4] Ibid., pp. 65-66.

P. A. Zagorskiy (1764–1846)

science along the same path which the physics of Galileo and Newton had followed, then Bichat directed physiology along another path, declaring the following: "From this it is easy to conclude that the science of organic bodies must use methods completely different from those of the science of inorganic bodies."

"Physiology would have greater successes if everyone did not bring into it notions borrowed from the sciences which, although they are called auxiliary, are nevertheless completely separate from it. Physics, Chemistry and the others are contiguous because the same laws govern their phenomena; but a great space separates them from the science of organic bodies because a great difference exists between their laws and the laws of life. To say that physiology is the physics of animals is to give an entirely untrue notion concerning it; on the same basis I would say that astronomy is the physiology of the Stars," declared Bichat. [5]

This was an epoch full of contradictions in the field of science and its ideological direction. In Germany, Oken with his natural philosophy continued to live in some minds; Goethe greatly furthered this; Schellings's ideological system, in spite of the ideological discord of his followers, put forth deep roots in the science of nature and prepared the ground for the Hegelian idealistic philosophy of nature; the factual material of great importance in Bichat's works and the charming personality of this brilliant youth could not help but attract attention to his idealistic views on life; along with this, the early works of Kant and the works of Laplace, as if bringing back the images of Copernicus and Galileo, assaulted the sky itself and stirred man's mind with his duty and the complete possibility of coming to know the laws of the universe, disregarding the question of God's place in it; Lavoisier looked into the very essence of material processes of the world and dealt a very strong blow to idealism, proclaiming the principles of preservation of a substance, while Lavoisier and Laplace, by their experiments on the consumption of oxygen by animal organisms, were freeing from "life forces" the phenomenon of respiration (the very name of which is close to the word for soul in many languages). Their friend Magendie, following the tradition of Harvey, studied the physicochemical and physical essence of many processes carried on in the living body and drove out of physiology the "soul," the "life force," as its everlasting enemies.

The struggle for new paths in medicine and physiology went on in this historical framework in our country also. The principal danger for the development of science in Russia in this period was the German natural philosophy, chiefly in the form of Schellingism. The forces of the principal organs of the progressive press, which formed the world outlook of the Russian intelligentsia, were directed against Schellingism. Among these organs, at the end of the 1820's, the journal Herald of the Natural Sciences and Medicine occupied a conspicuous place; it was first printed in the publishing house of Moscow University in 1828. The publisher of this journal was a teacher at the university—the doctor, later professor of medical chemistry and pharmacology, Aleksandr Iovskiy.

---

[5] Ibid., p. 68.

In a series of articles entitled "The system of natural philosophy or German philosophy," the journal subjected to especially pointed criticism the attempts at instilling "Schelling philosophical study" into medicine (and physiology) [6]: "There where the activity of the imagination is valued, the language of the natural philosophers can still be allowed; but in the sciences, where dignity of thought is measured by the dignity of its application, probably only clarity and determination are tolerable."

The journal called its readers, Russian doctors and physiologists, to follow the paths mapped out by Galileo, Bacon, and Newton. Giving an enthusiastic comment about the successes and direction of the new physics and chemistry made on the basis of the experimental method, the author of the review Latest Physiological Investigations for 1829 (no. 6 and 7) wrote: "How well it would be to say the same thing also about physiology, this very important sphere of our knowledge, that it, too, has the same direction, that it has undergone the same transformation as the physical sciences. But alas! Among us they still believe that physiology is nothing but a game of the imagination; we see even books in which the physiological opinions set forth could be excused only in the time of Galileo. Among us they still believe that physiology must have its own contrasting beliefs in one or another assumption; what it studies must follow one or another theoretical sect. Among us they still call to witness the ancient dreams as absolute truths. We regret this, and it depends on us to raise the banners of true life science also in the snows of the North."

Other progressive journals in the 1820's—1840's also called Russian scientists and doctors to the struggle against natural philosophy and Schellingism. Thus, in the "Miscellany" section of the journal Library for Reading (Vol. 27, 1840), in a paragraph entitled "Magnetization of needles by means of a nerve," the author not only sets forth the contemporary state of the question of the nature of animal electricity, but he also lashes out at the rest of the natural philosophy views, which hindered the working out of correct scientific notions in Russia in the field of physiology. Citing Faraday's latest investigations, the author writes: "Would it not be better, instead of speculative nonsense, to read attentively these dissertations which constitute an epoch in science, and to acquaint the Russian reading public with their content? Unfortunate speculation is the cause of all evil: we are behind in facts, in information, in science, only because two or three dreamers who in passing heard about the German philosophers have taken it into their heads to convince the present generation, as if they had discovered everything by their intellect, without the help of experiments, and that for this reason it is not worth the work to become acquainted with experiments and positive facts. . . The harm which speculation has done and is still doing to positive enlightenment is incalculable. And there must be an end to these trifles." [7]

Under the direct influence of the great philosophical work done by the progressive Russian thinker-encyclopedists, in conditions of an increas-

---

[6] Herald of the Nat. Sci. and Med., No. 3, 1828, p. 801.
[7] Library for Reading, 1840, vol. 27, "Miscellany," pp. 88-89.

ingly great rise of interest in the actual, concrete laws of all nature and the human organism in particular, in the 1830's the intoxication by natural philosophy and German romantic idealism passed, and young Russian scientists sought new paths of learning nature's objective laws. Skorichenko, historian of the Military-Medical Academy, characterizes this epoch correctly:

"Natural-philosophical medicine (its own kind of medical romanticism) decisively lost all its influence and credit in our Academy. When during the cholera epidemic one doctor presented an argument in which he advanced as the cause of the disease the irritating influence of some combination of the moon and a planet, especially Mars, on the nervous system of the people, "which can be understood only in an electro-magnetic relation" (he also explained the political events in Europe by the same thing), the confederation regarded the author's philosophy completely negatively. The best evidence of what we have said are the accounts of the Academy's young doctors who were sent abroad by the Academy or went there by their own means. As early as the late 1830's and early 1840's, having met the German doctors' world outlook, backward and stuck in the mud of metaphysical utopias, the former students of our Academy in their accounts testified to the low level of medical and general education of the German medical world. [8]

Even in the early period of the development of scientific medicine in Russia, the first Russian scientist-doctors expressed markedly their critical regard for the natural-philosophical, speculative trend in interpreting the problems of biology and medicine which prevailed in Germany. Prokhor Charukovskiy (1790-1842), a professor at the Medical-Surgical Academy, in the preface to his original book General Pathological Diagnosis From Symptoms, or the Study of Disease Symptoms in General, wrote in 1825:

"It is true that Shprengel's diagnosis, translated by Zatsepin, was published last year; but doing complete justice to the worthy and indefatigable works of Shprengel, very useful in the early parts of medical and other sciences, one must admit that its physiological and pathological content, except for incorrect hypotheses and unfounded reasoning, has almost nothing else that is original."

Prokhor Charukovskiy was not alone; there was also his brother, the well-known scientist-doctor Arkhip Charukovskiy, and many other doctors who raised for themselves the problem of mastering contemporary science and creating principles of Russian medicine and experimental physiology precisely through a critical appraisal of the content and methods of contemporary European science. Full of a desire to connect science with the interests of their people, and themselves being under the influence of the philosophical ideas of advanced Russian thinkers, these pioneers of medicine and biology blazed independent trails. Their first original medical works, which also included elements of physiology, called forth the pride of progressive public figures.

---

[8] History of the Military-Medical Academy; 1898, pp. 392-393.

An article in the Petrashevskiy file by one of the prominent people in the Petrashevskiy circle, Balasoglo, is very demonstrative in this respect; Balasoglo, appealing to the pride of the Russian people, wrote in 1845: "What, can it be that we still do not have the people . . . Compare the Russian Gogol' with the all-European Eugène Sue and ask how the foreigners spoke of the Encyclopedia of jurisprudence of Nevolin; be curious and compare all European methods for publicity in science even with Charukovskiy's book of popular medicine..."[9]

The struggle with Schellingism in the field of medicine and physiology was a characteristic feature of the theoretical activity of doctors and physiologists in this period. Thus, for example, in 1848 in Kazan', Professor Lindgren published a work on the very topical subject A Test of the Nosology of Eastern Cholera. Discussing the actual problem of cholera, Lindgren draws his conclusions on abstract philosophical arguments such as "this, as if to say, is a vitalistic notion on the eastern cholera, which some perhaps doubt; for this reason I do not abandon it agreeing in general with the idea of the organism which expresses the striving, uniform (einheitlich) value in the form of self-preservation, and only in this way do I think to answer the problem, presenting the disease as a fact, i.e., without an examination of the causal moments."[10]

Or, comparing the urgent emptying of the bowels in animals with symptoms of cholera, Lindgren wrote: "In the running of animals during hunting there are phenomena from a mental (seelisch) reason, in cholera from a physical reason, and precisely in the running the moment of unity—the soul, filled with fear, with a moment of indication by the nervous system—reconciles itself with the moment of separation, with precisely an atomistic change of principles; in cholera, on the other hand, the moment of separation—the affected change of principles—is reconciled also by the nervous system with the moment of unity, with the idea of the organism, or with the soul."[11]

It is natural that the scientific-medical thought of the country could not pass a similar statement of a professor and doctor, which held science back. The Military-Medical Journal (No. 1, 1849, pt. 13) carried a very detailed critical analysis of this work by Lindgren. The author of the article wrote, in part: "It is strange, even sad, to think that at the present time, with an experimental, analytical trend in science, there appears a book, almost in the middle of the nineteenth century, which wishes to explain cholera—this enigmatic disease which occupies the lucid minds of so many scientists—in a philosophical way! The history of the sciences shows us how pernicious was the intrusion of Schelling's transcendental philosophy into the bounds of medicine in general and how much work it took to restore medicine to the degree of a factual, positive science. The honor of this wise analytical reform belongs to the French."

[9] The Case of the Petrashevskists, vol. 2, p. 19, Pub. house AS USSR, 1941.
[10] Military-Med. Journal, part 53, No. 1, 1849.
[11] Ibid.

In Germany itself the natural-philosophical school had to give way to the new progressive experimental method under the influence of changing ideas which through the works of the great French materialists—philosophers and scientists—were raised to such a height in the period of the French bourgeois revolution at the end of the eighteenth century and the beginning of the nineteenth.

In the field of physiology the exclusive role belongs to Magendie, the teacher of Claude Bernard. In the history of physiology the name Magendie is connected with the name of a great seventeenth century physiologist, William Harvey, whose objective method was so brilliantly developed by Magendie. In the beginning of the nineteenth century Magendie's textbook of physiology, which set forth the bases for experimental physiology, was translated into a number of languages, including Russian and German. The translator of the German edition of Magendie's book, by the way, wrote in his preface:

"The translator is convinced that Magendie's reproaching physiology for the fact that it more often follows forms of the power of imagination than the sober method of experiment bears an even greater relation to the physiology which prevails in Germany. In Germany there are still physiologists who wish to demonstrate the science of life completely independently of experiment, a priori. Magendie named this natural-philosophical physiology, and he also gave it yet a completely different name—"romantic physiology." Although in Germany these natural-philosophical views have generally been abandoned, nevertheless there are still many opponents of the new trend. Attachment to old notions, a scholastic inclination to make deductions from these notions, aversion to everything new, a partiality to the existing, insincere shame, and base envy are unfortunately the basis in Germany for the fact that a new thing in science is considered harmful, the same as an attack on the good, long-standing rights of the people or ruler. Science does not know feudalism and does not know unfailing power, but knows only good heads. Just because Magendie was a young and clever revolutionary in science, in which he did not inherit established principles of experimental investigation, but wanted to build them himself, the translator considers it praiseworthy to contribute to the spreading of this new and really correct method in Germany."

The experimental method persistently worked its way into a number of countries, including Germany. Thanks to the tireless work of the great Czech scientist Jan Purkinje (1787-1869), the first European institute of experimental physiology was organized in Breslau; it was the breeding ground of the experimental method in Germany and in other countries.

Thus, the new experimental, strictly scientific principles of physiology took shape on the paths shown by the great reformer of physiology, the English scientist Harvey, in the cooperative work of scientists from different countries and peoples.

The best experimental-physiological laboratories of France and Germany, and first of all the laboratories of F. Magendie, J. Purkinje, J. Müller, and later, C. Bernard and K. Ludwig, served in the subsequent

A. P. Zagorskiy (1805–1888)

place of growth of experimental skill of the prominent Russian physiologists, and also of the physiologists of other countries in the Old and New World.

At the end of the eighteenth century and especially at the beginning of the nineteenth century, our Russian scientists, including physiologists, began to appear on foreign scenes. The first Russian physiologist in the Academy of Sciences was from 1807 on an active member of the Academy and professor at the Medical-Surgical Academy, P. A. Zagorskiy (1764-1846).[12] He left behind a number of valuable special investigations in the field of anatomy and published in 1801 the first Russian textbook on descriptive anatomy—Textbook on Knowledge of the Human Body. During the last years of his life Zagorskiy worked on a compilation of his Anatomical-Physiological Dictionary. He combined the departments of anatomy and physiology, but he devoted little attention to the latter. In the field of anatomy he was original, but in his teaching of physiology he adhered to the existing foreign textbooks, particularly Prokhaska's, which was later translated into Russian by D. Vellanskiy (Physiology, or the Science of Human Nature, St. Petersburg, a number of editions, the last, 1822). Naturally, under these conditions the experimental method could not be of proper scope.

D. Vellanskiy's direct successor in the department at the Medical-Surgical Academy, A. P. Zagorskiy (1805-1888), son of Academician P. A. Zagorskiy, stimulated very fruitful activity directed at the overcoming of the speculative, natural-philosophical trend in physiology which Vellanskiy had cultivated. There are indications that in 1837, having become a professor at the Medical-Surgical Academy, A. P. Zagorskiy introduced experimental methods into the teaching of physiology, and his great service lies in this.

A. P. Zagorskiy received his scientific preparation in Dorpat University, together with N. I. Pirogov. Together with them at the same place was A. M. Filomafitskiy, who, as we shall see in the next chapter, working in the physiological laboratory at Moscow University, laid the basis for experimental physiology in Russia.

In his Diary of an Old Doctor, N. I. Pirogov wrote exceptionally vividly about the years of preparation for the title of professor at Dorpat University which many young Russian scientists in the 1820's and 1830's undertook, and he wrote about his friends, the physiologists A. P. Zagorskiy and A. M. Filomafitskiy.[13] And although the German students jokingly called the Russian youths sent to Dorpat for preparation for professional activity "Professors in Embryo," these "embryos" developed rapidly, and, re-

---

[12] There is detailed information about the life and activity of P. A. Zagorskiy in the collection Fifty Years of Service as a Professor by Academician Petr Andrevich Zagorskiy. St. Petersburg, Academy of Sciences Press, 1838.

[13] About A. M. Filomafitskiy see N. I. Pirogov. Works, pub. in 1916, vol. 2, pp. 503-504, 690.

58

turning to Russia, they not only advanced science in Russia but were also very influential in the development of world science. This primarily concerns the giant of world surgery N. I. Pirogov, and in the history of physiology in Russia, the name of his friend A. M. Filomafitskiy will always shine brightly. Both of these names are connected with Moscow University.

As we have indicated above, A. P. Zagorskiy, taking upon himself the teaching of physiology in the Medical-Surgical Academy, carried out this work on new principles, and experimental physiology began to force its way into this very old Russian educational institution as early as the 1840's.

In Petersburg University, until 1863 physiology did not have either an independent teacher or an independent laboratory. During the 1830's to 1850's, the well-known professor S. S. Kutorga for a quarter of a century taught a course of zoology (of an encyclopedic nature), in which, along with general morphological information, he gave information on physiology also. However, among Kutorga's works there is only one article of a physiological nature, devoted to the system of Lafater and Gall. [14] This was the situation with physiology in the first half of the nineteenth century in Petersburg. The case was somewhat different in Moscow; precisely during the first half of the nineteenth century physiology was making great progress at Moscow University.

---

[14] "On the System of Lafater and Gall." Library for Reading, 1845.

CHAPTER V

Physiology at the end of the eighteenth and beginning of the nineteenth centuries at Moscow University. Aleksey Filomafitskiy—the founder of experimental physiology in Russia. Physiology Published for the Use of My Students by Filomafitskiy. V. Basov and his classic works on the physiology of digestion.

As early as 1776, medical students at Moscow University attended a course in physiology. The first to introduce it at Moscow University was Professor A. Keresturi, a Hungarian by nationality. Demonstration of experiments on live animals was included for the purpose of initiating his students into the laws of function of the human organism.

Later on M. I. Skiadan (who died in 1802), a professor at the faculty of medicine, was in close contact with the teaching of physiology at the University. Skiadan was a colorful figure in Moscow at the end of the eighteenth century. I. F. Timkovskiy writes about Skiadan: "He enjoyed an extensive practice in Moscow and belonged to the type of men who read their reference books while riding in their carriages. After the death of Professor Shaden he occupied the latter's position temporarily but called the Kantian philosophy warmed-up cabbage soup, 'crambe biscoctum.' He was of medium height, rather stout in his old age, with a white round face; he had pleasing speech, with a high pitched voice and gracious enunciation. When I was once in need of a source on legal anthropology, he called to my attention Physiology by Haller."[1] Skiadan's work on "The causes and effects of the passions of the soul, and a method of tempering and restraining the same for the purpose of a happy and peaceful life" (Moscow, 1794) was translated from the Latin by his contemporary, Professor Foma Barsuk-Moiseyev.

Foma Ivanovich Barsuk-Moiseyev (1768-1811) was appointed as extraordinary professor of Moscow University in 1795 and lectured on physiology, pathology, and therapy. He defended a dissertation entitled On Respiration[2] in 1794. This was the first defense of a dissertation in Russia. It was attended by a large public audience, in addition to numerous members of the teaching staff and students of the University. The real name of Barsuk-Moiseyev was Moyza. His first work of a philosophical nature (on the Supreme Beatitude of Man..., St. Petersburg, 1785) appeared under the name Foma Moyza. According to his biographers he

---

[1] Biography. Dictionary of the Professors of Moscow University. Moscow, 1855, part II, p. 417.
[2] "Dissertatio Medica-physica de respiratione."

DISSERTATIO

MEDICO-PHYSICA

DE

RESPIRATIONE,

QUAM

PRO

GRADU DOCTORIS

Honoribus que in arte Medica rite ac legitime ccnfequendis
elaboravit et in Auditorio majore Caefareae Mofquensis
Univerfitatis folenniter defendit

THOMAS BARSSUK-MOYSSEIEW.

XXXXXXXXXXXXXXXXXXXXXXXXXXXXXXXXXXXXXXXXXXXXXXXX

MOSQUÆ,

Typis Caefareae Mofquenfis Univerfitatis apud Chriftianum
Rüdiger et Chriftophor. Claudi.

1794.

*Титульный лист первой диссертации по физиологии на степень доктора
медицины, защищенной в 1794 г. в Московском университете
Ф. Барсук-Моисеевым*

Title page of the first dissertation in physiology for
the degree of doctor of medicine, defended in 1794
in Moscow University by F. Barsuk-Moiseyev.

derived the first half of his surname, (Barsuk), from an anagram of the word "bursak."*

For his time Barsuk-Moiseyev was a well-educated person, in perfect command of Latin as well as of European languages. This aided him greatly in his important contributions to the development of physiology and medicine by translations into Russian of the most important books of that time. In 1796 his translation from the Latin of Physiology, or the Science of the Nature of Man, by F. Blumenbach, provided the first textbook in physiology for Russian physicians. In addition, Barsuk-Moiseyev translated 13 other large volumes (from Latin and French) dealing with the various fields of medicine, including pharmacology.

In the early period of development of physiology at the Moscow University, we must mention Professor Il'ya Gruzinov, who defended his dissertation in 1804 on the subject On Galvanism and its Application in Medical Practice. Like his contemporaries in other universities, he lectured not only on physiology but also on anatomy, pathology, and various clinical subjects. Early in July, 1812 (i.e., only a few days after the invasion of Russia by Napoleon's forces), at a gala session of Moscow University, Il'ya Gruzinov presented an address "A message on the newly discovered locus of the origin of the voice in man and in animals."

When, in our times, we read this speech with its somewhat peculiar title, we are first of all struck by the opening part of the speech of this scientist, full of faith in the strength of Russia and in her future.

From the scientific standpoint this short speech is especially interesting, for, in the first place, it is an expression of Gruzinov as an original experimenter.

Giving an appraisal of the state of the problem at that time, he points out that it had already been studied by a number of outstanding figures of antiquity (Galen) as well as of modern times (Haller, Cuvier and others). He courageously proclaims that he disagrees with all his predecessors and brings forward a new viewpoint. "Some scientists have compared this organ with a musical wind instrument, others with a stringed instrument; still others considered it a combination of the two. These three opinions were defended by the greatest scientists of all nations; each is based on proofs which clearly testify to the zeal in the search for truth as well as to the sharpness of intellect of those who proposed them. In giving proper credit to the work of all these students of nature who endeavored to dispell the darkness which concealed the place where such an interesting phenomenon as the voice is generated, I nevertheless must declare my own doubt concerning all these viewpoints. Having devoted myself to the examination of all these views, I have found that none of them presents satisfactory proof. I found that in the production of the voice, nature functions entirely differently from the way assumed by anyone up to this day. In order that you

---

*Antiquated expression meaning seminarian.

may not doubt this opinion, I intend to consider these views one by one and present the proofs for their rejection."

These proofs were by no means speculative, for Gruzinov presents the results of his observations on patients, on live animals, and unusual (and daring) experiments on human cadavers. Gruzinov describes his experiments as follows: "I am convinced that the human voice originates in the chest, at the lower end of the wind pipe, at its posterior membrane. In experimenting on cadavers I would blow up the windpipe through its branches and, on tightening the posterior membrane, I was able more than once to obtain perfect sound of the voice very similar to that obtained from the living; I obtained this without tightening the vocal cords and even after their transection.

"In this way I succeeded in producing changes in the voice characteristic of various human feelings and am convinced that under proper conditions anyone is capable of performing these experiments with equal success. I found that the voices of the female sex are higher in pitch, finer and purer because the rings of the windpipe as well as its membranes are significantly thinner and smoother than in males. I have also noticed that the voice becomes hoarse when the posterior membrane of the windpipe fails to be smooth due to a preceding inflammation. A hoarse voice also appears even when the posterior membrane is smooth but not evenly stretched." If one imagines efforts of the experimenter in the surroundings of the morgue, with sounds emitted by cadavers during such startling experiments, one cannot fail to evaluate this physiologist, Il'ya Gruzinov, as a most courageous scholar-innovator, who loved science.

But the endeavors of this dedicated man were interrupted by the extreme conditions of the War of 1812. He soon departed in the capacity of a volunteer surgeon with the Moscow Guard, took part in various campaigns, rendered medical service under fire at the battle of Borodino and, while with the fighting forces, fell gravely ill with typhus and died in 1813 at the age of 32.

During the years 1813 to 1835 the teaching of physiology at Moscow University was in the hands of one of the most active professor-physicians of the first quarter of the nineteenth century, Ye. O. Mukhin (1766-1850). Like his predecessors, Mukhin lectured on physiology as well as on other subjects, such as anatomy, toxicology, forensic medicine, and medical policework. Mukhin also lectured on physiology and anatomy at the Moscow Medical-Surgical Academy. His published works, many of which are voluminous, are devoted to his basic fields of interest—anatomy and surgery. We give as examples The Basic Principles of Bone Setting (1806) and The Science of Ligaments and Muscles (1812).[3] In 1817 Mukhin published a speech in Latin on the physiological problems of location and function of sensitivity; this interest in physiology is

[3] Treatise on the ligaments—syndesmology; treatise on the muscles—myology.

indicated also by the fact that only two days before his death he asked for the new edition of Liebig's chemistry text. [4]

The years of Ye. O. Mukhin's professorship are of great interest for the history of physiology in Russia. In May of 1828 a graduate in medicine of Moscow University, Aleksandr Iovskiy, began the publication of one of the most notable Russian scientific journals, The Herald of Natural Sciences and Medicine [Vestnik Yestestvennykh Nauk i Meditsiny]. This journal devoted a great deal of attention to the newest achievements of physiology and to its development in Russia. From issue to issue, in a section under the title "Medicine in a broader sense," Iovskiy presented a series of valuable notes on "The newest achievements in physiological research." We see in the Herald (1829) a detailed presentation of the classical work of Charles Bell on the structure and basic laws of function of nervous conductors, supplemented by remarkably executed drawings from Bell's works. In another series of issues are presented the brilliant experimental investigations of Magendie and other French investigators, dealing with the various basic fields of physiology. [5] Many of the findings of special research in the area of physiology of the nervous system, circulation of the blood, and digestion are set forth here with all their details, interesting even to specialists. Perhaps even now, for those young physiologists for whom the original English works of Charles Bell are difficult, we can and should recommend the articles entitled "On Charles Bell's natural nervous system," included in Herald of the Natural Sciences and Medicine (1829). In the same publication there are also beautifully written biographies of the great workers of that period in the field of medicine and physiology, among them the biographies of the physiologists Bichat and Spallanzani.

The Herald carried detailed abstracts on the sensational physiological experiments performed at the beginning of the nineteenth century on bodies of executed criminals by means of galvanic stimulation of muscles and nerves ("The effect of galvanism on the lifeless body of man"). The experiments of the Turin physicians Vassalo, Julio, and Rossi may be compared with the above described experiments on cadavers performed by the Moscow physiologist, Gruzinov, for the impressiveness of their effects. It suffices to cite here the description of one of the experiments with galvanic stimulation of certain cranial nerves in the cadaver of an individual an hour after his death from hanging: "All muscles gradually entered into states of horrible contortions; fury, horror, despair, grief and a repulsive smile were represented in the expression of the multilated face of the murderer. At such a sight, many of the spectators felt compelled to leave the auditorium, driven by the terrifying ugliness; and one of the spectators even fainted." [6]

The ideological influence of this notable Russian periodical was of special significance. The Herald of the Natural Sciences and Medicine

---

[4] Quoted from 175 Years of the First Moscow State Medical Institute. Gosmedizdat (State Medical Publishing House), 1940, p. 66.

[5] Having travelled abroad in the 1820's, Iovskiy had a chance to acquaint himself personally with the investigations of Bell and also Magendie.

[6] Herald of Natural Sciences and Medicine, 1829, no. 2, p. 234.

played a tremendous social role in the history of Russian science, emerging as an apostle of new directions in experimental science in the third and fourth decades of the nineteenth century, when so many prominent workers in the fields of philosophy and science were under the spell of "nature" philosophy, Schellingism, and philosophical "romanticism." This was the great service rendered by A. A. Iovskiy, who both edited the Herald for five years (1828-1832) and authored many of its brilliant articles.

From 1835 to 1843, A. Iovskiy served as Professor of the Medical Faculty of Moscow University, occupying the chair of pharmacy and pharmacology. Beginning in 1826 he taught medical chemistry in the capacity of an associate. As N. I. Pirogov reminisces in his Diary of an Old Doctor: "In the evenings I often visited the associate in chemistry, Iovskiy...," who used to tell "...about the scientific life of German and French Universities, joking with me about our backward scientists who had outlived their time." This was in 1826 and 1827.

In connection with the decision of the government to send young Russian university graduates abroad for the purpose of preparing them for professorial careers, in 1827 the Medical Faculty of the Moscow University selected N. I. Pirogov, among others. Of great historical value are the lines in the Diary of an Old Doctor in which Pirogov tells of his first conversation with Professor Mukhin concerning this trip. To Mukhin's proposal to choose a definite field of science in which he would like to specialize, Pirogov replied that he would choose physiology as a specialty. Thus, the interests of a great Russian surgeon in this early period of his life were concerned with physiology. Of course, only chance circumstances turned young Pirogov from physiology—his chosen speciality. In response to Pirogov's suggestion, Mukhin, himself a professor of physiology, "made a long face" and briefly and clearly decided "No, you may not choose physiology. Take something else."[7] If not for this incident, the glorious name of Pirogov would have shone within the brilliant galaxy of Russian physiologists.

A. Zagorskiy from Petersburg and A.M. Filomafitskiy (1807-1849) from Khar'kov arrived at Dorpat University together with Pirogov to prepare for a professorial career in physiology.

Having successfully concluded the preparatory course at Dorpat University, A. Filomafitskiy transferred to the laboratory of the famous physiologist, Johannes Müller, where he worked on a series of problems in experimental physiology. After such extensive scientific preparation, in 1835 Filomafitskiy became a member of the teaching staff of Moscow University and Mukhin's successor in the course of physiology. The most important period of development of the Moscow physiological school is closely linked with A. M. Filomafitskiy's name. From the time he began his educational activities, great progress was made in separating

---

[7] N. I. Pirogov. Works. Kiev, 1916, vol. II, p. 418.

physiology from the aggregate of anatomy, pathology, therapy, forensic medicine, etc., and physiology was introduced into the curriculum of the University as "Physiology and Comparative Anatomy" and into the curriculum of the Faculty of Medicine as a course "Physiology of the Healthy Person."

In the year of 1836 the first Russian textbook in physiology was published by a follower of Schelling's philosophy, D. Vellanskiy. During the same year the professor of physiology of Moscow University, Filomafitskiy, published the first volume of his textbook under the title Physiology Published for the Use of My Students [Fiziologiya Izdannaya dlya Rukovodstva Svoikh Slushateley]. This represented a direct opposite to Vellanskiy's text. Filomafitskiy ardently defended the experimental method in physiology which had but recently appeared in various European countries. In his book Filomafitskiy constantly refers to the results of his own experimental investigations (only partially published as separate works) and frequently enters into controversy with European authorities, among them his contemporary and teacher, Johannes Müller, as well as Schultz. Filomafitskiy's text was the first original and critical summary of the field of physiology in the Russian language and unquestionably belongs among the best examples of scientific literature in our country.[8] This book was greatly valued by its contemporaries and was awarded the Demidov prize of the Academy of Sciences in 1841. A reviewer, academician K. Baer, wrote that Filomafitskiy's textbook was on a level with the best contemporary texts on physiology, and he emphasized the originality of the author's views.

Besides the scientific significance of Filomafitskiy's textbook, it must be emphasized that this volume was written in vivid and, in places, artistic language and is free from the nebulous and long foreign (or Latinized Russian) words and phrases which were so abundant in the scientific literature of that period and which were so characteristic of Vellanskiy's book.

The great vivifying force of the Pushkin period of Russian letters affected even scientific literature, and, thanks to it, science became nearer and nearer to the broad masses of youth starved for knowledge. Through the efforts of the first Russian physiologists (Filomafitskiy in Moscow, Kalenichenko in Khar'kov), the chairs of physiology at universities were not only delivered from natural-philosophical reasoning, cultivated mainly by foreign professors, but became centers of the propagation of science in the living native tongue.

A. Filomafitskiy and D. Vellanskiy were two opposites. Even if their books had not appeared simultaneously, each of them would have been subject to the most severe criticism by the other. After reading Filomafitskiy's Physiology Published for the Use of My Students, which was directed against the natural philosophy, any reader would have condemned

---

[8] Part I appeared in 1836; parts II–III appeared in 1840; a second edition of this work appeared in 1844.

66

Vellanskiy's scientific writings, including his textbook of physiology. On reading the latter, one clearly senses that the basic conclusions are directed against the physiologists who turned in the direction of experimental, rather than speculative, exploration of nature. Filomafitskiy was the most outstanding representative of experimental physiology in Russia during the fourth and fifth decades of the nineteenth century.

Did these two remarkable contemporaries, who headed facilities of physiology at the best Russian universities and expounded two different trends of development of this science, ever meet? In his Diary, Pirogov remarks that Vellanskiy was among the professors of the Petersburg Academy of Sciences who examined the young scientists going to Dorpat. Thus, it is probable that the first meeting of Filomafitskiy and Vellanskiy occurred in Petersburg at the examination in physiology preceding Filomafitskiy's departure for Dorpat. This assumption is all the more likely, since a candidate for professorship in physiology could not have achieved his appointment without an examination in the given subject. This was in 1827. Much later, in the 1840's, Vellanskiy visited and even lived in Moscow. Did these representatives of two opposing ideological trends in science ever correspond? All these questions await further investigations and are of no little significance for the history of development of science in our country.

Thus, when the reverberations of the natural-philosophical exaltations of I. I. Davydov and M. G. Pavlov had hardly subsided in the lecture halls of Moscow University; when the traditions of empirical casuistry were still strong among University professors, including those in medicine; when the philosopher, M. G. Pavlov, having liberated himself from the tenets of Schellingism, attempted to speak up in favor of the experiment in the exploration of nature; the brilliant young professor of physiology, Aleksey Filomafitskiy, appeared in 1835 and proceeded to criticize severely the concepts of natural philosophy and to proclaim the experimental method of study of nature as the only correct one.

Only a historical juxtaposition of the work of A. Filomafitskiy at Moscow University with the thinking of other advanced Russian men can reveal the significance of this remarkable Russian physiologist. The fascinating pages of his textbook of physiology, devoted to the struggle against the casuistry of natural philosophy and to the promotion of the experimental method and concrete thinking, are interwoven with the soul-searching experiences and struggles which involved the heroes of Young Moscow, published by A. I. Gertsen, a group which included such men as Belinskiy, Granovskiy, Ogarev, and of course, Gertsen himself. This was a significant epoch. These were men intimately related to each other; this was an integrated ideological trend.

Let us listen to the ideas which were heard in the halls of Moscow University in the 30's and 40's of the nineteenth century in the lectures of the physiologist Filomafitskiy:

"There are two ways of exploring the phenomena of life, the empirical and the experimental. According to the former, investigations begin with the general and by way of analysis one gradually approaches the particulars; by the second method, we begin with the particulars and then arrive

67

A. M. Filomafitskiy (1807-1849).

at the whole. The first method is followed by the so-called natural philosophers, who reject any experimentation and observation and endeavor to reduce all phenomena to a single origin invented by their wit. "Natura construi debet," they proclaim, and, being fascinated more by the play of their imagination and wit than by truth, they frequently endeavor to interpret phenomena on the basis of their principles in spite of the obvious results of experiments and direct observations. To be sure, such a method of investigation contains much fascinating poetry, but for beginners it may do more harm than good. Here are the reasons. 1) by accustoming them to an abstract perception of things, such a method debases in their eyes the dignity of experimentation and unbiased observation; 2) by presenting proofs based exclusively on judgment, it dulls a sense of healthy criticism which demands positive proof derived from experimentation; 3) it gives rise to systems and theories which stand frequently in contradiction to experimental and direct observations. I speak here of natural philosophy as it concerns physiology and medicine. The other method of exploration of the phenomena of life is the method of experimentation. Here the scientist is guided by observation and experiment, and he endeavors to explore all phenomena of life individually. He observes the latter at various times and under various conditions. But this is not enough. He submits them to experimentation, during which he chooses the necessary and varied conditions, and by repetition finally discovers what is substantial and permanent and what is incidental in the phenomenon studied."[9]

Further on, he again emphasizes the "advantages" of the experimental method: "The extent to which this method of investigation is important and indispensable, in the natural sciences in general and in medicine and physiology in particular, is demonstrated to us by the history of these sciences. Medicine would still be enveloped in the darkness of ignorance were it not for physiology which, by consistently elaborated and perfected experiments, has shed its light on the various branches of medical science. And physiology itself would have remained for long a game of unrestrained fantasy and mysticism had not the lucid minds of some physiologists opened this new path of experiment and observation."[10]

In that period, these statements sounded both like a revelation and a battlecry. As if having in mind his adversaries while appealing to his young listeners, Filomafitskiy used to remark in his lectures; "In short, if we desire to obtain some concept of life and not satisfy ourselves only with opinion, proposition or play of imagination, then there is only one path available to us, the path of experiment and observation. This is the path chosen by me, gentlemen, in my endeavors in physiological science, and I shall follow this path in my teaching. I shall not sing you lullabies, as Goethe calls hypotheses, in order to lull you and to conceal the deficiencies of my subject. I shall frankly admit what we do not know and shall gladly communicate what we do know. I shall not present proofs

[9] A. M Filomafitskiy. Physiology Published for the Use of My Students. Moscow, 1836, vol. I, pp. 15-17.
[10] Ibid., p. 17.

that have not been subjected to healthy criticism. You shall not hear from me propositions which may not be proved by experiment or strict logical judgment. If circumstances permit I shall do my utmost to repeat experiments performed by others and to proceed with new ones when necessary.[11] To be sure, this method will strip many concepts of the rainbow-colored flowers with which the natural philosophers had adorned them. At the start such a path may appear dry and thorny to you; but do not despair! In exchange for poetic flowers you will acquire a rich store of observations and experiments and each of these, when at the bedside of a patient, will appear to you far more precious than the abstract casuistry of the natural philosophers. At times I, myself, shall offer you explanations by the first and second method for comparison and in order to demonstrate that truth always bears in itself the seal of simplicity, brevity and conviction."[12]

Filomafitskiy's faith in the significance of experimental science was limitless. In discussing, in his textbook of physiology, the central problem of the nature of life and failing to offer a satisfactory explanation, Filomafitskiy wrote: "Let everyone try to solve this riddle in his own way; one may search for the source of life in the chemical process or in the electrical one; one may explain the process of life by selected affinity and polarity of the parts; or, armed with scapel and microscope, one may endeavor to penetrate into the depth of organic matter and search therein for the source of life; or one may endeavor to explain this secret by exploring the laws and phenomena of excitability in the healthy and ailing organism. All these will enrich physiology with a multitude of highly valuable facts. Maybe it is not given to those living today to achieve the ultimate goal of this path, but we do not know where the limit of our knowledge lies and how far our endeavors can lead us in the exploration of the mysteries of life, and therefore we shall never stop on the path of experiment and observation but shall always go forward!"[13]

A physiologist who had chosen the path of experimentation had to develop in every possible way the methods of vivisection so indispensable for physiological investigations. Indeed, Filomafitskiy must be recognized as the first ardent protagonist of vivisection and the surgical trend in physiology. As we shall see further on, a close and serious relationship was established between the physiologist Filomafitskiy and the surgeon Basov as the symbol and basis of the scientific approach which in later years accounted for the fame of Pavlov, the creator of the surgical method in physiology.

In contrast to Vellanskiy, who denied the role of experiment in physiology and with it vivisection on animals, Filomafitskiy consistently emphasized "the necessity of vivisection and experiments on animals." He states: "Since the opportunity of experimentation and observation on humans is extremely limited, this deficiency must be necessarily compensated by experiments on animals. Many sentimental physiologists call these experiments cruel. They avoid them with disgust and even ask:

---

[11] Ibid., p. 17.
[12] Ibid., p. 20.
[13] Ibid., pp. 122-123.

70

are we really in the right when we perform bloody experiments, and are these experiments sufficiently useful for science and the good of mankind to make up for the suffering of living beings? Of course an experiment performed by inexperienced hands and without clear purpose must be called an act of cruelty, especially if an animal continues to suffer unnecessarily after an acute operation. But in the hands of a skilled and dedicated investigator these same experiments are essential to science and to the salvation of mankind. And does not such an aim enoble the dedicated scientist who has set the truth as his highest goal? And if people in general so frequently torment and kill animals just for their own satisfaction, does not the physiologist have a greater right to take the life of animals if he is moved only by his search of truth and usefulness to mankind?"[14]

Indeed, as may be seen from the opinions of his contemporaries and from the literature that has survived, A. Filomafitskiy made broad use of the experimental method in his teaching and in his research. The animals on which Filomafitskiy experimented were frogs, dogs, and pigeons. His usual method of observation were vivisections; he also used optical equipment. In particular Filomafitskiy was one of the first in Russia to use the microscope for the study of the blood corpuscles, (the instrument being put at his disposal by Shikovskiy, professor of botany at Moscow University). Most interesting for that period were Filomafitskiy experiments on the consequences of transection of the vagus nerves with particular reference to the cough reflex. Filomafitskiy presents numerous experiments to substantiate his conjectures on the difference between electrical and neural excitation. Apparently he also investigated the problems of the chemistry and mechanical aspects of gastric digestion. We shall discuss in more detail later his investigation of the effect of a series of anesthetizing substances (including ether and chloroform) on the organism.

The extent of Filomafitskiy's original experimental investigation should not be judged by the relatively small number of special articles he published. The results of the numerous experimental investigations he conducted in laboratories abroad as well as at Moscow University are abundantly represented in the three volumes already mentioned of his textbook on physiology. A careful scrutiny of the results presented by him demonstrates that Filomafitskiy was one of the outstanding representatives of experimental physiology of the first half of the nineteenth century.

On the basis of his own experimental data, Filomafitskiy made a critical evaluation of the results and conclusions of the most outstanding experimenters of his time. Thus, while he presents the results of the work of many physiologists who were concerned with the nature of the process of digestion (among them Schultz, in whose laboratory Filomafitskiy worked), he expounds his independent viewpoint in the basis of his own very interesting experiments. In presenting the generally accepted views

---

[14] Ibid. , pp. 17-18.

of Schultz on the processes of the gastric digestion, Filomafitskiy wrote: "However, no matter how correct his (Schultz's) idea on the subject may be, and no matter how brilliant are the conclusions drawn from the experiments and observations, a careful study of his development of an idea will unavoidably lead one to the realization that he was excessively carried away by the idea so that his proofs are often biased in favor of the subject, and for this reason I have felt it necessary to point out this weakness to the reader."

He is just as critical of the impressive work of the American physician, Beaumont, who was deservedly considered one of the originators of strictly scientific research on the physiology of the digestive processes.

Filomafitskiy's ideas on the nature of the respiratory process are of particular value. In 1836 he presented in detail the views that had been held up to that decade concerning the sources generating animal heat, and for the first time in world literature he expressed the idea that the sources of animal heat, i.e., the center of the true processes of respiratory oxidation, are not to be sought in the lungs, as was done by his contemporaries, but rather in the physiological-chemical transformation of tissues in the organisms. "Consequently," wrote Filomafitskiy in 1836, "the source of animal heat is partly in the lungs and partly in the animal-chemical processes of the living organism that are governed by the nervous system." He developed these ideas further in 1838, i. e., 30 years prior to the investigations of Paul Bert, whose name is connected with the first basic formulation by his contemporaries on the tissue origin of animal heat and of oxidizing processes.

When these statements are added to the fact that Lomonosov preceded Lavoisier by 17 years with his data on the scientific basis of the oxidizing processes, it becomes obvious that the scientists of our country were indeed responsible for providing a new solution to a central problem in physiology, the nature of the respiratory process.

Filomafitskiy's views on the nature of the nerve process are no less original. His textbook contains a chapter entitled "The difference between electricity and the living nerve process." In this chapter we read: "The discovery of galvanic electricity in 1790 provided an excellent opportunity for a most precise investigation of the excitability of nerves. Although many physiologists, especially the English ones, were drawn by the striking similarity between the function of a living active nerve and electricity and considered the two to be identical, the most conclusive experiments repeatedly performed with equal success by many physiologists, including myself, leave no doubts as to the fact that electricity and the origin of nervous activity are entirely different agents. This can be proved by the same experiments that Wilson, Philip, Weinhold, Hastings and Kremer present in defense of nervous electricity. One has only to examine these experiments from a real and accurate viewpoint, i. e., to consider electricity as an external influence that generates the living nervous impulse or life force; then all the phenomena observed in the nervous system and in the whole organism during these experiments can be explained just as readily but more naturally than by confusing these two functions."[15]

Filomafitskiy's distinctive and clearly expressed opposition to the unaminously acknowledged electrical theory of the nervous process was based not only on a number of his own experiments and observations on the nervous system but also on his completely original concept of the nervous process as a whole. In the conclusion of his text partly on the physiology of the nervous system, Filomafitskiy develops the idea that the processes of distributing excitation along the nervous stem and transmission from one part of the nervous system to the other (from the sensory nerves to the motor) follow the same pattern as the processes of blood circulation. It seems to me that the idea of circular movement of the nervous process belongs entirely to Filomafitskiy. Here is how he presents his idea:

"If we have accepted and proved the constant activity of the reproductive system as expressed by the transformation of organic matter (see my Physiology, Part I, pp. 125-141), for the same reason must we not then also accept the constant activity of the nervous system which governs the entire organic process of nutrition and elimination. How can there be constant nervous activity—triggered by constant external influences—unless it is accepted that some of this triggered activity immediately acquires more nervous activity brought to the periphery by the motor nerves?

"This activity cannot be reversed along the sensory nerve and directed away from the brain—its source—i.e., it cannot be directed from the center to the periphery; otherwise, the two opposite effects would neutralize each other. Because of their fine structure the nerves alone cannot produce a sufficient amount of nervous impulses: they serve only as conductors. Thus the store of impulses is depleted on the one hand by the activity of the sensory nerves and is replaced, on the other hand, by the motor nerves which carry the nerve impulse directly from the brain – its source. If we accept these logical conclusions, we must also accept the circulation of the nervous impulse as comparable to the circulation of blood in the circulatory system. Obviously, every nerve taken individually with the brain constitutes a complete circulatory system, and consequently there would be just as many separate systems of nerve impulses as there are nerves in our body. Do we not find the same in the circulatory system of the blood? Is there not an artery and a vein for each area? Does not each area represent an individual circulatory system, the aggregate of these systems converging in the heart, just as the nerves converge in the brain?

"I anticipate numerous objections to this theory of nervous circulation. and I myself have many; but I shall not mention them in order to obtain an inquisitive reaction from my compatriots, physicians and physiologists alike. Any objections against my views are bound to awaken in me new

---

[15] Ibid., vol. III, pp. 57-58.

73

ideas and will prompt either further development of this theory or possibly its complete rejection."[16]

These ideas may appear naive and futile at first glance. But they contain a remarkable foresight of future scientific development. Nowadays we are well aware of the enormous significance of circular processes in both simple and coordinated neural-reflex acts. Even by a purely comparative consideration of Filomafitskiy's statements, we would be impressed by the wisdom of this physiologist of the 1840's; such a comparison has already been made in our days by one of the most brilliant physiologists of the twentieth century, A. F. Samoylov, in his articles on the circular rhythm of excitation and on Harvey's discovery of circulation.

The importance of Filomafitskiy's textbook was enormous. It was used in the training of future Russian physicians and physiologists, and there is no doubt that this text was used by I. M. Sechenov, who first took up physiology at Moscow University. Consequently, the pages in which Filomafitskiy expounds his views on the role of the brain acquire a special significance. Here we encounter passages which seem to echo the ideas developed 25 years later in Sechenov's brilliant monograph Reflexes of the Brain, on the role of the will in inhibition ("delay") of reflexes ("reflected or sympathetic movements"). Like Sechenov, Filomafitskiy dwells on the most important fact that voluntary movements do exist and that the human will is capable of delaying or accelerating reflected (reflex) movements, and he searches for the cause of this phenomenon in the brain. Thus Filomafitskiy wrote: "It is obvious that the cause for these different phenomena lies in the brain; but what role does it play here? All sympathetic movements are notably involuntary and occur most often as a result of stimuli that we do not perceive or feel. Let us remember furthermore that during sleep contact with some object evokes a movement which in a waking state would not have occurred at all or would have been performed voluntarily. Considering all these circumstances, we are justified in concluding that a state of rest or unconsciousness favors the transition of a nerve impulse from one fiber of a primary stem to another while a state of consciousness inhibits such a transition. Such a conclusion will appear even more probable to us if we recall the reverse and opposite relationship between sympathetic movements and voluntary ones. The activity of attention and will may restrict and even abolish sympathetic movements: the convulsive movements evoked by tickling may be curbed by will power. When a stimulus is anticipated, an individual is prepared for it and reacts to it calmly: Scaevola conversed with Porcen while his hand lay in fire; conversely, a person deep in daydreams startles at the slightest noise or at a light touch of the hand. Here all is reduced to the following law: the stronger of two stimuli acting on a nerve will elicit a reaction; in this instance, the will is stronger than the stimuli that produce sympathetic reactions."[17]

However, neither Filomafitskiy nor his contemporaries were able to solve the mystery of the inhibitory influence of the brain on reflex

---

[16] Ibid., vol. III, pp. 197-198.
[17] Ibid., vol. III, pp. 177-178.

movements. As we shall see, this discovery is to be credited to I. M. Sechenov. We feel it is very important to establish the historico-logical link between the disvovery of the inhibitory centers by Sechenov and the ideas which matured at the laboratory of Moscow University in the works of its most outstanding representative, Aleksey Filomafitskiy.

Filomafitskiy's book, Treatise on Blood Transfusion (The Only Means for Saving Life, in Many Cases) printed by Moscow University in 1848, is a brilliant illustration of the development of experimental physiology in Russia. Nearly 100 years have passed since this book was published.

Blood transfusions as a physiological and clinical method were subjected to scientific analysis and clinical tests in articles and books by many scientists and physicians. However, the experimental data, the theoretical generalizations, and, finally, the very drawings of blood transfusion equipment contained in Filomafitskiy's Treatise to this day amaze the reader by their depth and perception.

This brilliant treatise was written by Filomafitskiy not as a review of the literature but rather as a report on his own exceptionally interesting experiments in the field of blood transfusion. In his experiments, dogs were bled until they reached a "fainting" state, and they were revived after administration of defibrinated blood from other animals.

In 1847 Filomafitskiy began an experimental investigation of great scientific and practical value on the influence of sulphuric ether vapors on the animal organism when ether had been proposed as an inhalation anesthesia by the American physicians Jackson, Morton, and Warren, at the end of 1846. An interesting record is preserved in the archives of Moscow University "On the allocation of the sum of 500 silver rubles for experiments and observations on the newly discovered method of painless operations by means of inhalation of sulphuric ether vapors."[18] This record contains, among other, the following communication from the Medical Faculty to the administration of the University. "In response to the communication of April 28th, the Medical Faculty has the honor to report to the administration of the University that the faculty intends to obtain from the mentioned administration the sum of 500 silver rubles for the performance of experiments on inhalation of sulphuric ether vapors and to assign this sum, in accordance with the rules for credit and debit, to Dean and Ordinary Professor Filomafitskiy."

We are nearing the centennial of the great discovery of methods of combatting pain and relieving the physical sufferings of man. In this connection, it is especially interesting to study the documents which describe the attitudes toward this problem in Russia and the role of Russian scientists in the development of this most important scientific achievement.

First of all, these documents testify to the extreme speed of the reaction in Russia to the American physicians' discovery. October 16, 1846,

---

[18] Archives of Moscow University. File no. 213 of the administration of Moscow Imperial University for 1847.

is the date of the first application of sulphuric ether inhalation anesthesia. On that day the New York surgeon, Warren, first used ether anesthesia in an operation to remove a tumor. In the very first volume of the journal The Contemporary (1847), authorized for printing on the 30th of December, 1846, and supplemented during the process of printing by communications of new events in science, in the "Miscellany" section for February, there appeared an item under the heading: "Sulphuric ether as a means of eliminating pain during surgery," giving a detailed description of the brilliant results of the application of ether as a pain-killing substance. The author of this item lists all communications from the foreign medical press up to January 1847. In other words, this journal gives the very latest information concerning this most important scientific and practical discovery.

The concluding lines of this article in the The Contemporary are of interest. "After all these experiments, science cannot dismiss this important discovery. A small dose of ether acting on the lungs eliminates pain. But further investigations are still in order to ascertain whether this potent remedy is not harmful to health." [19]

It is of historical significance that, concurrently with the American investigator, this important scientific problem was being solved by the great Russian scientist-surgeon, N. I. Pirogov. As early as April 4, 1847, Pirogov reported to the Academy of Sciences on his discovery of a new method of anesthesia, the so-called "rectal ether anesthesia," and in his communication he notes the advantages of his method over the method of inhalation proposed by the Americans. [20] During the same year, Pirogov published in the Russian, French, and German languages the results of his physiological and clinical experiments on the effect of ether anesthesia. [21]

Finally, as may be seen from the cited archive sources, on April 28th of the same year the Medical Faculty of Moscow University succeeded in obtaining a subsidy for experimental investigations of ether anesthesia. Having obtained the funds for experimentation on the effect of pain-relieving substances, Filomafitskiy invited Inozemtsev and Pol', professor-surgeons of the University, to collaborate with him, and he developed a vastly important research project in close association with his friend, N. I. Pirogov. While the experimental work proceeded in the surgical clinics and physiological laboratory of Moscow University, N. I. Pirogov was applying his method of anesthesia in operating on wounded soldiers in Dagestan (at the siege of Saltee).

In a short time, Russian science demonstrated to the whole world new paths towards the scientific solution and practical application of ether anesthesia as a pain-killing remedy. In 1847 the Military-Medical Journal,

[19] The Contemporary, 1847, vol. I. "Miscellany" section, pp. 132-133.
[20] Bull. de la Classe Phys.-Mathem. de Acad. des Sc. de St. Pet., 1847, vol. VI, no. 7 (127), p. 97.
[21] N. I. Pirogov. Practical and Physiological Observations on the Effect of Ether Vapors, 1847.

in reporting "On the surgical aid rendered to the wounded during the siege and occupation of Saltee," proudly writes: "Russia has preceded Europe by our procedures during the siege of Saltee and has demonstrated to the whole civilized world both the feasibility and the unquestionable benefits of ether anesthesia for the wounded, on the battlefield itself. We hope that from now on ether will be included in the physician's kit as being just as essential as the scalpel during his service on the field of battle."[22]

On the 21st of December, 1847, in the presence of the Dean of the Medical Faculty, A. Filomafitskiy, N. I. Pirogov performed his experiments on the effect of chloroform as an anesthetic

Filomafitskiy did a great deal of work on testing the effect of sulphuric ether and other volatile substances on animals. But his exceptionally important contributions to the development of the theory and practice of anesthesia were interrupted by his untimely death at the age of 42. His interesting work "A physiological view on the use of ether, chloroform and benzine to reduce nervous activity" was published after his death.[23]

This article is noteworthy primarily for first raising the question of the physiological mechanism of analgesics. Before describing his own experiments and conclusions, Filomafitskiy reviews the anatomical-physiological knowledge concerning the nervous system that could, in his opinion, "orient us towards a correct approach to all experiments performed with ether and other substances which deaden nervous sensitivity." This review summarizes the most advanced views in the field of physiology of the nervous system at the end of the 1840's and also expresses his own original views. Here he again presents his concept of the circular nature of nervous activity. "When considered in its entirety, the nervous system may be compared to a ring which has no beginning and no end; a blow inflicted to any part of it will affect all of it." He discusses the problems of the relationship between the somatic and autonomic nervous systems; the nature of pain; the sequence in which various parts of the nervous system cease to function at death, during sleep and narcosis; and arrives at some sound conclusions which have not lost their freshness even for contemporary neurophysiology. On the basis of his experiments, Filomafitskiy also stresses the generalized effect of substances "that deaden nervous sensitivity" and gives a number of practical suggestions as to cases where the use of these substances may be contra-indicated.

He concludes this brilliant article, so closely linked with the most pressing medical problems of this day, with the following statement. "Every physician (surgeon, obstetrician and therapist who has carefully studied the foregoing should unhesitatingly and with every hope of favorable results use ether, chloroform and benzine for the alleviation of pain. Thus, through the use of these substances, medicine now has a new method for attaining its principal and sole aim, to relieve the suffering of man-

---

[22] Military-Medical Journal, part 40, no. 1, 1847.
[23] Ibid., SPb., 1849, part 53, no. 1, p. 31.

kind." These are the last words of Filomafitskiy's last work before his death.

A brief editorial comment in the Military-Medical Journal in connection with the above quotation attests to both the timeliness and originality of Filomafitskiy's work. It states: "These articles express his judgment much too positively in favor of ether, chloroform and benzine; recent reports of death after the use of these substances compels us to be more cautious."

Immediately below the text of this article, the editors published a brief obituary: "The Professor of the Imperial Moscow University: State Counselor Aleksey Matveyevich Filomafitskiy, who labored for science and inspired gratifying hopes for the medical literature, died on January 22nd of this year. The above article on 'The physiological view on the use of ethers, chloroform and benzine to reduce nervous activity' is one of his last works."

Filomafitskiy must be given particular credit for being the first to include demonstrations of animal experiments in lectures on physiology. This was highly appreciated by his students and by his contemporaries on the Medical Faculty of Moscow University. At his lectures, 103 years ago, Filomafitskiy exhibited dogs with artificial fistulae that had been made by his brilliant contemporary, Professor-surgeon V. A. Basov.

Thus, thanks to Filomafitskiy's efforts, Moscow University may be considered the cradle of experimental physiology in our country, both in the field of research and in teaching methods.

V. A. Basov (1812-1879) was a contemporary of Filomafitskiy's at Moscow University in the department of surgery. He was one of the best Russian physician-scientists. It was a struggle for him to obtain a university education and attain scientific achievements. He was born of a poor family in Orel, taught school, and entered Moscow University at a relatively late age. For a long time after his death, he was remembered in Moscow as humane and as a physician who donated his services to the poor.

In 1842, a year before the publication of the article by the French scientist Blondlot, Basov made an artificial fistula in a dog's stomach and thus laid the foundation for the surgical method for the study of digestive processes which attained its brilliant perfection in the classical works of I. P. Pavlov.

In view of the fact that, beginning with Heidenhain's review, in Hermann's summary of the physiological achievements in the nineteenth century, the Frenchman Blondlot is consistently credited as the author who first proposed the operation for a permanent gastric fistula, it is essential to present here some accurate data concerning Basov's priority in this important problem for the history of physiology.[24] Blondlot's

---

[24] The importance of V. Basov in the development of world physiology was not fully appreciated even in our country. Thus in the famous Critico-bibliographical Dictionary of Russian Writers and Scientists by S. A.

V. A. Basov (1812–1879).

work, "Traité analytique de la digestion" ("Analytical treatise on digestion"), in which the surgical procedure for making a fistula in the stomach
is described, was published in Paris in 1843. In the same year, Basov
published an article in French, "Voie artificielle dans l'estomac des
animaux" ("Artificial access to the stomach of animals"), in the Bulletin of the Moscow Imperial Society of Nature Students, which had a
rather extensive circulation abroad.

This classical work also appeared in 1843 in Russian under the title
"Notes on the artificial access to the stomach of animals," in the Petersburg journal Memoranda in the Field of Medical Sciences [Zapiski po
Chasti Vrachebnykh Nauk], and as a separate reprint. It is especially
important to emphasize that Basov read a paper on this operation at the
meeting of the Moscow Society of Nature Students on November 17, 1842,
and that the Bulletin de la Société Impériale des Naturalistes de Moscou
for 1842 published an abstract of Basov's report in French which mentions
that in presenting his paper Basov exhibited his dogs with permanent
fistulae that had been made several months earlier. From Basov's report
it is obvious that in November he exhibited a dog that was operated on
in September.

Thus there remains no doubt that Basov's work was new and original
and that it constituted a landmark in the physiology of digestion, as did
the investigations of the American physician-physiologist Beaumont, who
studied the gastric processes of a Canadian trapper, Alexis St. Martin,
who had a permanent opening in the stomach as a consequence of an
accidental injury.

In view of the close historical relationship between the investigations
of Beaumont and Basov, it is interesting to note that the report of Beaumont's classical experiment that was published in 1834[25] reached Russia
that same year, and an article under the heading: Observations on the
stomach of an American," giving a detailed description of Beaumont's
observations over a period of nine years on the processes of digestion
in the stomach of his patient, was published in Vol. 4 of Library for
Reading (1834). In conclusion, the author of this article wrote: "On
reading this report—which we ardently recommend to the attention of
our physicians—it is hard to decide which is more astonishing: Beaumont's
diligence in studying the functions of this not quite sweet-smelling organ,
or the patience of a man who for nine consecutive years permitted him

---

Vengerov, the item devoted to Basov indicated his activities as a physi-
cian-surgeon but does not mention the significance of his work on the
surgical production of an artificial fistula of the stomach—an achievement which marks an era in science; however, the list of his publications
includes this article.

[25]W. Beaumont. Experiments and Observations on the Gastric Juice
and the Physiology of Digestion. Boston, 1834. Because of this work,
Beaumont was recognized as the founder of physiology in America.

to putter around in his stomach! . . . But this case presages that in time speculators will appear in Europe who, for money, will have windows made in their stomachs for the Medical Academy to observe, if it be true that such windows do not prevent a person from being well, happy and even married." (St. Martin married during the period of Beaumont's observations of his stomach).

It is important to note that Basov, an outstanding physician of that period, understood the significance of Beaumont's experiments, and he was also the first to realize that it would be impossible to sit and wait for new accidental stomach injuries and that it would be necessary to perform operations on the stomach of animals.

Basov's brief communication on his work, covering less than seven pages, is a classic scientific work. The following quotation from his report to the Moscow Society of Nature Students testifies to the depth of Basov's approach to the solution of the experimental surgical task. He wrote: "It is well known that evidence is an indispensable condition for a truth to become convincing; and every science can attain perfection only when the truths it proposes are evident, when they are tangible. The more complex a phenomenon, the more circumstances capable of hiding it from the investigator—the greater the need for evidence. Gastric digestion is such a phenomenon. It has been recognized that the reason for so many theories on the digestive process is the great number of conditions governing this process in mammals; also, there can be no doubt that the contradictions regarding this vital process have arisen and continue to arise because of the lack of sufficient opportunities to conduct direct investigation and experimentation on the digestive processes in the stomach. It is for this reason that Beaumont's observations and experiments on digestion in an accidentally perforated stomach of a living man may be designated as the beginning of a new era in the research on digestion. Considering that the opportunity which presented itself to Beaumont is exceedingly rare; that his observations remain as legends that have not been witnessed by any one else; that not all problems of gastric digestion have yet been solved; that even if they had been solved new problems could arise with the further development of the sciences—all these considerations led us to wonder whether it would not be possible to recreate this opportunity at will rather than by accident, by intentionally making an artificial opening in the stomach of animals? The eight experiments performed by us during this year on dogs answer this question in the affirmative."

After this introduction Basov describes in detail every step of the operations, as well as the preliminary results of his observations on dogs which had undergone surgery satisfactorily. We have already mentioned that Basov exhibited the dogs on which he had operated during the presentation of his 1842 report. But even prior to that time, Basov had shown the dogs to Filomafitskiy, who, in turn, as we have mentioned before, used them at his lectures on physiology at the Medical Faculty of Moscow University. We learn of this important stage in the history of physiology in our country from Basov's own article, which he concludes with the following statement. "We do not consider these experiments to be perfect in all respects. However, they do serve our purpose, i.e., they do demonstrate that it is possible to make an artificial access to the stomach of animals for the purpose of direct observations and experiments on gastric digestion. Some of these observations and experiments have already been demonstrated at Professor Filomafitskiy's lectures at Moscow University; and, as is known, he is credited with introducing demonstrations of physiological experiments on animals during lectures at this University." At the end of the article Basov expresses his firm belief in the enormous significance of physiological experimentation for surgery and therapeutics. This could not have failed to exercise an influence on the development of experimental medicine and the growth of interest in physiology on the part of physicians.

At that time a number of valuable books in physiology and pharmacology were published in Moscow. We must mention first of all the translations of the books by the greatest physiologist of that time, Magendie, whose text A Brief Outline of Physiology was first published in two volumes in 1830. This book was translated by two students, Ivan Glebov (subsequently a professor of physiology at the Moscow University) and Lunin. Another book by Magendie, Pharmacography,[26] appeared in 1840 in a translation by F. A. Al'bov, a student of the Moscow Medical-Surgical Academy.

A translation from the German of Eble's Handbook of Human Physiology was also published in 1840 in Petersburg. The Russian version of this book was met with a broad response, as can be judged from the numerous critical reviews. The famous author, Senkovskiy (Baron Brambeus),[27] devoted a special article to Eble's book. A brief review in The Library for Reading[28] was also devoted to this book; this review is so characteristic of the history of development of Russian physiology that we shall quote from it rather fully. The anonymous reviewer (possible Senkovskiy, an active contributor to The Library for Reading, or V. Maykov) wrote: "One may doubt in general the usefulness of translating textbooks in physiology from the German. With all due respect for the erudition, love of truth and conscientiousness of German scientists, one must nevertheless acknowledge that among European physiologists the Germans have the least talent for producing a useful book on physiology. They are too vague for such a task. Individual experiments, observations and investigations are excellently performed with great skill and unusual patience; their beautiful work and discoveries constantly broaden the horizon of human knowledge. But when it comes to organizing these very precise and ingenious experiments, observations and discoveries into a systematic whole in book form, they are unable to confine themselves to the positive, the precise and the definite. The innate German dreaminess instantly carries

---

[26] As noticed by the critics, the translation of this book is greatly defective from the standpoint of style (see Library for Reading, 1840, vol. XLII, p. 32-33. [Koshtoyants proceeds to give some examples of spurious translation which in an English translation would appear meaningless.]

[27] Senkovskiy. Works, vol. IV, p. 17.

[28] Library for Reading, 1840, vol. XLII, pp. 41-42.

them away into the nebulous regions of conjecture. They joyfully embark on the dangerous path of casuistry, drawing daring conclusions from conclusions; facts are replaced by words without concrete knowledge; and finally the whole is transformed into unfathomable chaos. In a science as yet so insecure as physiology, this unfortunate passion is ruin . . . . Eble's textbook of physiology is recognized as one of the best German books in the field. And yet what do you find in it? 'A woman,' says he, 'represents the negative side of life [what is that?], giving form, appearing [a word without any positive sense], who, in her organic movements [again, what is that?] reveals a great susceptibility to stimuli and an organic resistance, with a quickness for learning but with limited decisiveness [please try to understand that!]. A choleric temperament consists of an equally high level of excitability and of vital activity [just empty words!] and represents speed and strength of organic movement and speed in development of organic learning.' Had the sphinx spoken in such riddles, Oedipus would never have attained fame for his acumen. What a chore it must have been to translate with precision this ugly delirium of mystic natural philosophy!''

Eble's textbook of physiology appeared in the Russian translation at a time when the Russian reader had already had the opportunity to familiarize himself with physiology through Filomafitskiy's original text. This first Russian textbook of physiology was free of any natural-philosophical nonsense and invited daring experimental exploration of the physiology of man and animals.

The journal The Contemporary was born in that period of publicizing ideas and findings in experimental physiology. Thus, in the first volume of this remarkable journal (1847), the editors (I. Panayev and N. Nekrasov) published a translation of an article by E. Littre, "The importance and achievements of physiology." This was the beginning of the outstanding activity of The Contemporary in the history of Russian physiology, and we shall refer to it again.

The scientific endeavors of Filomafitskiy and Basov raised experimental physiology in our country to an unprecedented height. Thus both assured the great significance of Moscow University in the history of development of physiology and experimental medicine in Russia.

But the role of Moscow University was not limited solely to this aspect of progressive development of science. Within its walls, the deep theoretical and philosophical work continued, constantly directing the development of the natural sciences in Russia and, particularly, the important role played in the development of physiology.

We have already noted the broad scope of the endeavors of the professors and students of Moscow University (M. G. Pavlov, V. Odoyevskiy) attained through discussions concerning the basic problems of idealism and materialism, of synthesis and analysis, and other philosophical concepts directly touching upon the central problem of insight into the laws of nature.

This was the nucleus that culminated in the remarkable articles of Aleksandr Ivanovich Gertsen, which appeared in 1845-46 under the title Letters on the Study of Nature [Pism'a ob izuchenii prirody]. These Letters threw a new and bright light on the path of development of philosophical thought in our country and gave a new impetus to the development of experimental science and of strict scientific ideology.

These Letters by A. I. Gertsen are an incomparable contribution to the general picture of the standing of science in our country in the 1840's. The brilliant combination of Filomafitskiy's and Basov's works created a firm foundation for experimental physiology, while the philosophical works of Gertsen already pointed to the theoretical path which Russian science, including such an important field as physiology, was to follow. All these extremely important events occurred within the walls of Moscow University.

CHAPTER VI

The level of theoretical problems in the field of physiology from 1830 to 1850 in Russia. Letters on the Study of Nature by A. I. Gertsen and their significance for theoretical natural science.

The second quarter of the nineteenth century had an entirely exclusive significance in the development of physiology. During the 1830's and 1840's results were achieved in related fields of the natural sciences which provoked a radical reorganization of physiology.

The decisive factors in this reorganization were the discovery and description of the elementary structural and functional unit of complex organisms, the cell; the establishment of the possibility of synthesizing in the chemist's flask substances which were products of the vital activity of organisms; and, also, the rising interest in the history of life on the earth, mainly under the influence of discoveries in paleontology.

Giving a general plan of the principal stages of the history of physiology in connection with the history of biology as a whole, F. Engels wrote: "Harvey, owing to his discovery of the circulation of the blood, made a science out of physiology (of man, and also of animals); zoology and botany nevertheless remained sciences which collected facts, until paleontology was born – through Cuvier – and quickly following were the discovery of the cell and the development of organic chemistry. And only owing to this, morphology and physiology became possible as true sciences."[1]

Under the influence of these scientific achievements in the field of natural science, extremely important theoretical questions once again arose before physiologists. The works of the great Russian philosopher A. I. Gertsen played an important role in the organization and deep synthetic solution of these questions which greatly influenced the subsequent path of development of Russian physiology.

In this period, A.I. Gertsen, who had retired to a secluded place near Moscow, wrote his famous Letters on the Modern State of Science. In

---

[1] F. Engels. The Dialectics of Nature. K. Marx and F. Engels. Works, vol. 14, Gosizdat, 1931, p. 439.

the villages of Pokrovskoe and Sokolovo, near Moscow, during 1844-1845, Gertsen wrote a series of articles which formed a treasury of Russian philosophical thought, entitled Letters on the Study of Nature.

Exactly 100 years have passed since in the April book Notes of the Fatherland for 1845[2] the first letter of this series of letters entitled "Empiricism and Idealism" was published. The thoughts expressed by Gertsen both here and in the following seven letters were full of profound novelty for contemporary theoretical science.

The 1840's were especially important in the history of the struggle for dialectical materialism in theoretical science. K. Marx began to study problems of science almost at the same time as Gertsen.

V.I. Lenin in his article "Recollections of Gertsen" wrote:

"In Russia under serfdom in the 1840's he could rise to such a height that he stood on a level with the greatest thinkers of his time."[3] Farther on, Lenin wrote: "The first of the Letters on the Study of Nature - 'Empiricism and Idealism' - written in 1844, shows us a thinker who even now is head and shoulders above the abyss of modern naturalist-empiricists and the multitude of themes of present-day philosophers, idealists and semi-idealists."[4]

In the philosophical works of Gertsen, who closely approached dialectical materialism, we see a number of very important general conclusions about the correlation of science and philosophy, about the role and correlation of synthesis and analysis, and about the successes in the various fields of the natural sciences and their perspectives for development, especially the very important theoretical principles for the correct solution of the basic physiological problem of the correlation between soul and body.

Summing up the state of science in his time, Gertsen wrote: "It is very brilliant; that about which we hardly dared to dream at the end of the last century has been accomplished or is being accomplished before our very eyes. Organic chemistry, geology, paleontology and comparative anatomy have blossomed out in our times from small buds into huge branches, and they have borne fruit which has exceeded the most daring hopes... The naturalist, armed with a microscope, pursues life to its last limit, follows its hidden work. On this threshold of life the physiologist has met the chemist; the problem of life has become more definite, better resolved; chemistry has compelled us to look not on the forms and their modifications alone - it has taught us to examine organic bodies in the laboratory for their secrets."[5]

---

[2] Notes of the Fatherland, vol. 39, No. 4, sec. II, pp. 81-104 (the second letter, "Science and nature - the phenomenology of thought," was also in this number).

[3] V.I. Lenin. Works, vol. 15, p. 464.

[4] Ibid.

[5] A. I. Gertsen. Letters on the Study of Nature. OGIZ, 1944, pp. 1, 12.

This brilliant analysis of the reorganization of biology and such an important branch of it as physiology which Gertsen made in 1844 on the basis of achievements in science in the 1840's, by the depth of its thought and its concrete content, had something in common with the passages quoted above from The Dialectics of Nature of F. Engels, relating to the 1870's.

Having been brought up on the most progressive philosophical traditions of that epoch connected with the names and activity of the Decembrists, Gertsen early was able to free himself from the empty natural-philosophical theories, philosophical romanticism, and mysticism which had taken root in Russia through the works of German writers. From his early youth he was drawn by the example of his relative A. Yakovlev, an atheist, who was called "The Chemist" by his family and friends. Entering the physico-mathematical department at Moscow University, A.I. Gertsen visited Yakovlev in his home on Tver Boulevard and here, on his advice, became acquainted with the best works in natural science of the 1820's - by Cuvier and De Candolle. Under the influence of A. Yakovlev, Gertsen became convinced that without the natural sciences, "somewhere in the soul there remains a monastic cell, and in it a mystical core which can spill igornant water over all understanding." Speaking of Yakovlev, Gertsen gave a characterization of his atheism which is extremely valuable for the general history of the development of Russian theoretical thought: "The Chemist's atheism went beyond theological realms. He considered Geoffroy St. Hilaire a mystic, and Oken simply harmful. With the same scorn with which my father summed up Karamzin's History, he dismissed the work of the natural-philosophers. 'They themselves invented the first reasons, the spirtual forces, and then they wonder why one cannot find them or understand them.' " [6]

According to the first, youthful work of Gertsen on the theme Analytical Account of Copernicus' Solar System [7] (1828), which was his dissertation, it is evident that Gertsen at that time was not yet free from the influence of philosophical idealism and romanticism. This refers both to the content and to the so characteristic form of exposition which he himself later derided. Professor Perevoshchikov, reading the treatises by the philosophizing naturalists of this period, who used long phrases and Latinized Russian words, not without reason spoke of a "bird's tongue." But Gertsen quickly broke away from this captivity of philosophical romanticism; they did not succeed in making him a "philosophical monk," and his subsequent philosophical works, including first of all Letters on the Study of Nature, were full of novelty, of fighting spirit, and in their form they could be ranked with the best examples of Russian artistic prose.

Gertsen's philosophical views were closely connected with the preceding stage of Russian philosophical thought. They were the key to overcoming those deep contradictions from which his predecessors, completely under the influence of Oken, Schelling, and Steffens, could not break away.

_____

[6] A.I. Gertsen. My Past and Thoughts, vol. 1, chap. 6, GIKhL, 1937, p. 198.
[7] A.I. Gertsen. Works, vol. 1, pp. 91-105.

The enormous importance of Gertsen's works for the history of science in Russia (and physiology in particular) lies in the fact that Gertsen connected his philosophical works with the most pressing problems of science and with theoretical questions about the ways and methods of the knowledge of nature. Thus, polemicizing with the followers of Schelling and Oken, he wrote: "The naturalists, Schelling's followers, have taken the formal side of his study; they have not grasped the spirit which fills his writings; they have not been able to fan the sparks of deep contemplation which he had scattered everywhere into a bright stream of flame. No, they have constructed from his views some kind of strange metaphysical-sentimental structure; their scholastic dryness combined in them with pure German gemütlichkeit. Not that they pseudo-scientifically or systematically have given accounts of the philosophy of nature according to the principles of Schelling: they have taken two or three general formulas, dry and abstract, and have calculated all phenomena, all the universe, on them. These formulas are as if a measure in the recruiting offices: whoever rises to it comes out a soldier. Even those natural philosophers who were greatly beneficial to the factual part of their science did not avoid either formalism or sentimentalism. Take, for example Carus: he was of infinite benefit to physiology, but what does he write in his general views, in his introduction? What kind of verbiage, what thoughts! One feels sorry that a sensible man compromises himself so. Above all of them stands Oken, but one cannot entirely eliminate even him. In the nature of Oken it is awkward and tight, and above all, there is no less dogmatism than in the others; the wide and voluminous thought is apparent, but Oken is at fault for this very thing, that it is apparent as a thought; it is as if he has used nature to corroborate itself."[8]

Gertsen applied all the power of his logic and persuasive artistic expression to show the groundlessness of the idealistic attempts to depreciate the importance of experiment and observation (empiricism). That which Pavlov, who understood the necessity of the unity of empirical facts and generalized conclusions from those facts, conjectured took on the form of a complete philosophical conception of the unity of synthesis and analysis, experiment and speculation under Gertsen. Some remarkable lines of the first letter from his series Letters on the Study of Nature are dedicated to this.

"Idealism," wrote Gertsen, "arrogantly thought that it had only to make some scornful statement about empiricism and it would disperse like dust. The highest natures of the metaphysicians were in error: they did not understand that at the foundation of empiricism was a broad principle which was difficult for idealism to shake. The empiricists have understood that the existence of an object is serious; that interaction of feelings and the object is not a deception; that the objects surrounding us cannot but be real, because they exist; they have turned with confidence to that which exists, instead of searching for that which ought to be, but which, strangely enough, is nowhere! They have accepted the world and

---

[8] A.I. Gertsen. Letters on the Study of Nature. Gospolitizdat, 1944, pp. 31-32.

88

feelings with the simplicity of a child and have called to the people to come down off nebulous clouds where the metaphysicians have been busy with their scholastic nonsense; they have called them to the present and the real; they have recalled that man has five senses, on which is based his principle relation to nature, and they have expressed in their view the first moments of sensitive contemplation - the necessary, sole precursor of thought. Without empiricism there is no science since there is none of it even in one-sided empiricism. Experiment and speculation are two necessary, true, real degrees of one and the same knowledge; speculation is nothing more than higher, developed empiricism; taken in contrast, exclusively and abstractly, they also do not lead to analysis without synthesis or synthesis without analysis. Correctly developed, empiricism must certainly shift to speculation, and only the speculation based on experiment will not be empty idealism. Experiment is chronologically first in the matter of knowledge, but it has its limits beyond which it either loses its way or turns into speculation. These are two Magdeburg hemispheres which seek each other and which, after they meet, will not be pulled apart by horses."[9]

In the same year, 1844, when A.I. Gertsen wrote these lines, his friend V.G. Belinskiy published in Notes of the Fatherland a critical article on the works of V. Odoyevskiy, in which, examining the question of the role of analysis in the knowledge of nature and the correlation of synthesis and analysis, he came to the following important conclusions:

"Everything that he [Okoyevskiy - Kh. K.] says about the predomination of experimental observations and petty analysis in the natural sciences - all this is partly true; nevertheless, one cannot agree with him that this happened through moral corruption, through disposal of life: rather, one may believe that for the natural sciences the time has not yet come for general philosophical principles precisely on a lack of facts which can be obtained only by experimental observations, and that this modern empiricism must also in due time prepare a philosophical development for the natural sciences. This division of knowledge also has the same sense, after which one who has studied mathematics considers he has a right not to have notions concerning history, and another who has studied political economy considers it his duty to be ignorant in the theory of art. But that one must see in this only a progressive, and consequently temporary state, change, and not stagnation, as a precursor of near death - the words of Faust himself show this, that all feel and recognize the insufficiencies of general principles in the sciences and the necessity of knowledge as something of value, as the sciences of life, of being, of reality in the broad sense of the word, and not as sciences now about this subject, now about that."[10]

As he deeply appreciated the enormous importance of experimental science for a true, comprehensive knowledge of nature, paying a tribute of respect to the works of the naturalists and the doctor-experimenters, Gertsen at the same time cautioned them against breaking away from theory and synthesis.

---

[9] Ibid, pp. 14-15.
[10] V.G. Belinskiy. Works, Moscow, 1881, pt. 9, p. 62.

Gertsen wrote: "The naturalists are ready to experiment, to toil, to travel, to expose their life to danger, but they do not want to give themselves the work of thinking and making judgments about their science. We have already seen the reason for this fear of thought; abstractness of philosophy and customary readiness to pass into scholastic mysticism or empty metaphysics, its imaginary reticence, its satisfaction, not in need of either nature or experiment or history, these were bound to alienate people who dedicated themselves to science. But since any onesidedness produces weeds along with fruits, the natural sciences, too, have had to pay for the narrowness of their views, in spite of the fact that their views were cramped by the narrowness of the opposite side. Fear of trusting thought and the impossibility of awareness without thought have been reflected in their theories: they are personal, unsteady and unsatisfactory; each new discovery threatens to destroy them; they cannot develop, and they are replaced by new ones. Taking each theory as a personal matter, outside the subject, as a convenient accommodation of details, the naturalists open the door to appalling skepticism, and sometimes even to startling nonsense." And further: "The naturalists and medical men always refer to the fact that it is not for them to theorize when they have not yet collected all the facts and performed all the experiments, etc. Perhaps the material collected is really insufficient, and this is even probable, but saying that the facts are endless in number and that as long as they are not collected one cannot come to a conclusion all the same does not interfere with putting the question in an appropriate form and developing the real requirements and true notions of the relations between thought and life."[11]

The public lectures on the psychology of animals given by an outstanding professor of zoology at Moscow University, K.F. Rul'e,[12] served as grounds for A.I. Gertsen's deep philosophical analysis of the problem of the evolution of man's consciousness, which he made in 1845.[13] Concerning the correlation between the psychology of man and that of animals, Gertsen wrote at that time: "The psychology of animals has attracted incomparably less attention to itself on the part of scientific naturalists that the animals' form. Animal psychology must complete, must crown comparative anatomy and physiology; it must present a subhuman phenomenology of developing consciousness; its end is at the beginning of

[11] A.I. Gertsen. Letters on the Study of Nature, p. 25.
[12] K.F. Rul'e was one of the most brilliant figures at Moscow University during these years. As early as the 1840's in his university and public lectures, Rul'e set forth advanced, evolutionary ideas in the field of zoology. As far back as the beginning of the 1850's, Sechenov, hearing lectures at the university by professors, including Rul'e, reminisced about him in his Autobiolgraphical Notes: "Then, enthusiasm was turned to a professor of zoology, Rul'e, who loved to philosophize at his lectures, and lectured eloquently." It is very important that Rul'e, along with his basic zoological and paleontological research, devoted much attention to the nature of animal instincts and may be considered our founder of zoopsychology.
[13] The article was printed in the newspaper Moscow Gazette.

human psychology, into which it flows, as venous blood flows into the lungs to receive its breath and to become the red blood flowing in the arteries of history."[14]

The problem of the origin and development of consciousness constantly disturbed Gertsen. The central matter in this very important problem for Gertsen was the conclusion that consciousness is a material process, and its explanation, specifically, consists in the exposure of the characteristics of the physiology and chemism of the nervous system.

As far back as the beginning of 1845, in his letter to Ogarev, Gertsen, raising the most important questions on the correlation of physiology and chemistry, compared the views of the eighteenth century French encyclopedists and the chemist Liebig and came to very valuable conclusions. "In one place Liebig says: It is impossible to imagine either a single strong feeling or a single strong activity without a change in the qualitative composition of the brain. This is far from what the French were saying in the eighteenth century: 'Thought is a secretion of the brain.' No, this only shows us man von einem Guss."[15]

For Gertsen, as "the eye is the only instrument of vision," so "man's brain is his instrument of consciousness of nature." Gertsen wrote, "Thought is natural, as an extension, and is a degree of development, like mechanism, chemism and organics, only higher."[16] Here we see an attempt by Gertsen to go bravely far beyond the limits of Hegel's philosophy of nature. Gertsen obliterated the point raised by the German philosopher-idealists, where the sphere of psychic phenomena begins: he put a comma here and included the range of spiritual phenomena in the general chain of natural phenomena. Gertsen wrote: "Human consciousness without nature, without the body, is thought which does not have a brain to form it or an object to provoke it."[17] This concise sentence is full of novelty for its time, and it was a program of action for future investigators of the nature of consciousness - both philosophers and physiologists.

The philosophical quests and assertions of Gertsen's friend, the great Belinskiy, were in the same direction. In 1847 in a small article, a kind of review, Belinskiy wrote: "Long ago the philosophers themselves agreed that 'nothing can be in the mind which has not first been in the feelings.' Hegel, recognizing the correctness of this statement, added: 'except the mind itself.' But this addition is almost suspicious, like an outcome of transcendental idealism. Man has not directly or by pure thought become conscious of the fact that he has a mind, but he observed it first of all from his own actions, in which his mind was reflected, but which, besides, he recognized by his mind only through feelings."[18]

---

[14] A.I. Gertsen. Selected Philosophical Works, OGIZ, 1940, pp. 222-223.
[15] Ibid., pp. 230, 231.
[16] A.I. Gertsen. Letters on the Study of Nature. Gospolitizdat, 1944, p. 178.
[17] A.I. Gertsen. Sel. Philos. Works, OGIZ, 1940, p. 179.
[18] V.G. Belinskiy. Sel. Philos. Works, OGIZ, 1941, p. 453.

In a letter to V.P. Botkin, dated February 17, 1847, analyzing the views of Comte, the author of "positive" philosophy, V.G. Belinskiy wrote:

There is no doubt that action, i.e., activity of the mind, is a result of activity of the organs of the brain, but just who has observed the action of these organs during the activity of our mind? Will it be observed some day?[19] One must not separate the human spiritual nature from the physical nature as something peculiar and independent from it, but one must distinguish them, as a field of anatomy and a field of physiology are distinguished. The laws of the mind must be observed in the activity of the mind. This is a matter of logic, of science, directly following physiology as physiology follows anatomy. To the devil with metaphysics: this word stands for supernatural, and is consequently nonsense; but logic, by its very etymological meaning, signifies both reason and word. It must go its own way but only not forget even for a minute that the subject of its investigations is the blossom, the root of which is in the earth, i.e., the spiritual subject, which is none other than an activity of the physical subject. Free science from the spectres of transcendentalism and theology, show the limits of the mind in which its activity is fruitful, draw it away forever from all that is fantastic and mystical - here is what the founder of a new philosophy will do, and here is what Comte will not do, but which he, together with many outstanding minds similar to his own, will help the man so summoned to do."[20]

The excerpts cited from the philosophical works of Gertsen and Belinskiy show how high the Russian thinkers rose over the general level of world scientific thought in a most important problem of science, and, precisely, on the question of the nature of consciousness. These excerpts are indicative also of the fact that constructive criticism and the overcoming of the limits of Hegelian philosophy in the works of Gertsen and Belinskiy unavoidably affected the central problems of natural science too, and among them such an important problem as the correlation between the soul and the body, which was a touchstone not only for all philosophy, but also for theoretical physiology. The Russian physiological school, which in the works of Sechenov and Pavlov factually substantiated the idea of the unity and interdependence of the soul and body, had deep roots in the splendid period of the 1840's, when the moving philosophical ideas of Gertsen and Belinskiy were enunciated.

Gertsen was not content with the character of his contemporaries' generalizations on the nature of the neural process. He wrote: "You are awaiting, for example, an explanation of how the general receptor of feelings transmits the operations of your soul to the nerve, and the nerve to the muscles, but instead of an idea, they pass on to you the image of a musician, of taut strings, transmitting an artist's fantasy; a simple

---

[19] Only now is science able to give some answers to these questions which troubled V.G. Belinskiy 100 years ago.

[20] V.G. Belinskiy. Sel. Philos. Works. OGIZ, 1941, pp. 158-159.

question becomes complicated; this is such that one may again reduce it to something similar, and the original object is entirely lost in the likeness: this is the same method by which a man's portrait alongside similar copies is reduced to a picture of fruit.[21]

The significance of the lines quoted from Gertsen's Letters is not only historical. Directed against the formal, scholastic explanation of complicated natural phenomena which his contemporaries who were educated in the school of philosophical idealism (chiefly German) gave, these lines even today ring like a reproof to some idealist-physiologists, who try to contrast scientific knowledge of the essence of the neural process with empty forms and comparisons. Thus, a direct descendant of the German philosopher-idealists of that period, the Hamburg biologist Baron Uexküll, recently[22] speaking about the functions of the nervous system, precisely "passes on the image of a musician, of taut strings, transmitting an artist's fantasy," and other similar nonsense, a hundred years after Gertsen's criticism of these views and in spite of the great amount of factual material in the field of neurophysiology which has become well known in the world after the work of Sechenov, Pavlov, and Sherrington.

Gertsen constantly followed the successes of physiology, chiefly the physiology of the nervous system. Not without the influence of his outstanding father, A.I. Gertsen's son, Aleksandr Aleksandrovich Gertsen (1839-1906) chose as his specialty physiology and devoted his work principally to questions of the physiology of the nervous system.[23] A.A. Gertsen's physiological investigations were published as early as the beginning of the 1860's. The quests of the great Russian physiologist I.M. Sechenov attracted his attention right away, and just two years after Sechenov published his discovery of the inhibitory centers in the brain, A.A. Gertsen published his research on that subject, in Turin.

Aleksandr Ivanovich Gertsen alertly followed the development of scientific works by his son and consequently also the development of the physiology of the nervous system. In the sharpest period of his excessive enthusiasm for the thought of the possibility of reducing to elementary reflexes the complex acts of animal and human behavior, the cautioning voice of the great philosopher who had so profoundly raised the problem of the correlation of synthesis and analysis was heard. In a letter to his son of July-August, 1868, he wrote:

"Dear Aleksandr. I carefully read your pamphlet on the nervous system. I am writing to you meaning neither to disprove you nor

---

[21] A.I. Gertsen. Letters on the Study of Nature. OGIZ, 1944, p. 22.
[22] This nonsense by Baron Uexküll, who laid claim to "innovation" in biology, was set forth in a book, Bedentungslehre, which was published in 1940.
[23] A.A. Gertsen's special works were printed mainly in French and Italian. Those which were printed in Russian are: 1) The General Physiology of the Soul (1890); 2) The Physiological Activity of the Nerve and the Electrical Phenomena Accompanying It. Scientific Review, vol. 8, No. 3, 1-17, 1901; 3) Physiological Discussions. St. Petersburg, 1901.

to give any other solution to the problem. I only wish to bring up some weak aspects in your method, which seems to me too narrow.

There is no fundamental difference in views between us, but it seems to me that you are solving a problem which goes beyond the limits of physiology in too simple a way. Physiology has realized its problem with fortitude, breaking man down into endless actions and counteractions and reducing him to a crossing, a vortex of reflex acts. Let it now permit sociology to restore him as a whole. Sociology will wrest man from the anatomical theater and return him to history."[24]

Letters on the Study of Nature and the other philosophical articles of Gertsen sounded like an alarm appeal to the mastery of science. The article by Gertsen which we quoted above, dedicated to the public lectures by the zoology professor K.F. Rul'e, had as its epigraph the words of Pliny the Elder. "Ignorance of nature is the greatest ingratitude," and it began with the following words: "One of the principal needs of our time is a generalization of veritable, serious information on science. There is a great deal of it in science, and little of it in society; we must push it into the stream of public consciousness; we must make it accessible, we must give it a living form, as nature is living; we must give it an outspoken, simple tongue, like its own tongue, with which it unfolds the endless wealth of its essence in majestic and harmonious simplicity. It seems almost impossible for us to foster a really powerful mental growth without science; no sphere of knowledge so disciplines the mind to a resolute, positive step, to humbleness before truth, to conscientious work, and what is even more important, to conscientious acceptance of the consequences which result, as the study of nature; we would have begun our education with it in order to cleanse the adolescent mind of prejudices to let him grow up on this healthy food and then reveal to him, strengthened and armed, the world of man, the world of history, from which the doors open straight into reality, into his own concern in contemporary problems."

We see an enthusiasm for the natural sciences in the poet N.P. Ogarev, a friend of Gertsen. Ogarev's notebooks, which show his persistent striving to master chemistry, are preserved in the Lenin Library; in the Library are four of his notebooks entitled Anatomical, Physiological and Therapeutic Studies ("Etudes anatomiques, physiologiques et therapeutiques"). From Ogarev's letters of 1847 to T.N. Granovskiy it evidently follows that Ogarev was deeply interested in problems of applied and theoretical science and medicine and worked on them. He asked that the derivatives of plants, particularly medicinal herbs, be obtained for him; he did experiments in applied chemistry in order to raise the productivity of the soil and established a farm, and he took the trouble "to make artificially natural wine, namely, Madeira." "Until now I have been working at the decomposition of this wine," he wrote to Granovskiy,

---

[24] A.I. Gertsen. Complete Works and Letters, ed. by M.K. Lemke, Gosizdat, 1923, p. 5.

"and not entirely unsuccessfully. There are hopes and prospects for the possibility of selling it at 50 kopeks currency per bottle, so that with the help of the authorities we may turn it into the national drink and largely replace destructive vodka. Therefore, I am troubling about it as about a civic act."[25]

Not only the socioeconomic aspirations of Ogarev, and also of many other progressive-minded people in the 1840's who saw in science a way of raising productivity in backward agriculture in Russia, but also great problems of theoretical importance drew him to the natural sciences.

Also in 1847, in a letter to Granovskiy, fascinated by the natural sciences and inspired by the omnipotence of experiment in the knowledge of nature, Ogarev wrote: "The history of the formation of planet and organism - here is a problem which experiment is solving without a dash of fantasy. For the sake of this problem, I wish to work as long as life lasts, and in the method of pursuit I am going carefully."[26]

The 1840's were a valuable period in the development of philosophical thought in Russia. The creative philosophical activity of Belinskiy and Gertsen illuminated the field of theoretical science with a new light. The philosophical works of Belinskiy and Gertsen paved the way for a new period in Russian philosophical thought which was connected with the name of N.G. Chernyshevskiy, and they were at the same time a powerful stimulus for the development of the natural-historical sciences, which especially flourished in the 1860's - the period of the glorious activity of N.G. Chernyshevskiy and of the brilliant group of Russian naturalists, headed by the physiologist I.M. Sechenov.

[25] N.P. Ogarev. Letters to Chernyshevskiy, Gertsen and Korsh. Links, No. 1, 1932, p. 125.
[26] Ibid., p. 124.

CHAPTER VII

The early period of development of physiology in the Universities of Khar'kov, Kiev and Kazan'.

Khar'kov University was founded in 1804, and the first teachers of physiology and related disciplines were foreigners. The early development of these disciplines at Khar'kov University is of special interest, since this is where Filomafitskiy began his studies.

In a eulogy delivered at the funeral of Ya. Vannoti (1774-1819), who was a professor of anatomy, physiology and forensic medicine, Filomafitskiy spoke warmly of him as a university professor and a dedicated scientist. No original investigations are credited to Vannoti. We only know about a few of his speeches, among which one bears the interesting title "A word on the probable curability of all diseases" (1818).

At this early period in the history of Khar'kov University, physiology was not yet offered as an integrated independent discipline with a predominance of experimental methods. Thus, in order to continue his education and further his scientific training, Filomafitskiy enrolled at Dorpat University.

Vannoti, like many other professors of that period, lectured in a language that most of the students did not understand. But in 1838 a special professor was assigned to teach physiology at Khar'kov University, and the outstanding physiologist-scientist, I. O. Kalenichenko (1805-1876), was the first to deliver lectures in Russian. He was of peasant origin, and only upon graduation from the Khar'kov University in 1829 was he relieved from "poll tax." His articles on botany, geology, and physiology were published in various journals in Russian during the years of 1837 to 1863. He travelled extensively in Russia and abroad.

By 1842, A. P. Walter, a professor at Kiev University (1817-1889), had already published the results of his experimental investigations—the earliest work on the influence of the sympathetic nerves on the blood vessels. His paper, "On the significance of the sympathetic fibers contained in the sciatic nerve of the frog," was published in 1843 in the Report of the Medical Surgical Academy (St. Petersburg); and a year earlier it had appeared in the German language in Müller's Archives of Anatomy and Physiology bearing the signature A. Walter—Russian physician. One can hardly overestimate the significance of this work. It undoubtedly deserves a place of honor in the history of

Russian physiology as the first to put on an experimental basis the most important problem on the relationship between the sympathetic nerves and the regulation of blood circulation.

In his investigations Walter used one of the most perfected microscopes of that period, which was designed by Plessl; he was the first to combine microscopic observation of reactions of the blood vessels with stimulation and elimination of the sympathetic nerves, and, preceding the classical works of Claude Bernard by 11 years, he proved the vasoconstrictive function of the sympathetic nerves. In the work that he performed in Vienna, Walter was helped by the Czech scientist Chermak, who provided him with the Plessl microscope.

Walter obtained his training at Dorpat University and studied under N. I. Pirogov. The latter aroused Walter's interest in related anatomical and physiological problems and, specifically, in the physiology of capillary circulation. His career at Kiev University began in the capacity of assistant to Professor N. I. Kozlov (1814-1889), who was on the faculty of the department of physiological anatomy.[1]

In subsequent years, Walter, having been appointed professor of anatomy, also taught physiology (1862-1864), pharmacology, therapy (1859-1861), etc. Walter's physiological investigations did not stop with his first brilliant work. Beginning in 1862, he published an extensive series of investigations on heat generation in animal organisms. Through his contact with Academician F. V. Ovsyannikov in St. Petersburg, Walter regularly sent his "Thermophysiological Essays" to the Bulletin of the Academy of Sciences from 1864 to 1867. Among these, his work on heat generation in the organism at death merits special attention.

Walter's activities were highly versatile and fruitful. He devoted his doctoral dissertation to the problem of the causes of plica polonica which was prevalent among the poor in Byelorussia and Latvia, and he slashed at the ignorance of the doctors who did not carry on the needed battle against this disease. As an anatomist he assembled an enormous collection of Slavic skulls, which was subsequently given to the Krakov anthropologist Kopernitskiy. He founded and published a special journal called Contemporary Medicine [Sovremennaya Meditsina] to acquaint Russian physicians with achievements in medicine and biology. Walter loved Kiev University, where he worked for 30 years. In his will he states: "I wish to be buried in Russian soil, near my dear Kiev University."[2]

---

[1] N. I. Kozlov was an important figure in the history of Russian medicine. His popular articles on medicine had already appeared in the Library for Reading in the 1830's. He is also known as an outstanding worker in the field of Russian medical education. His most outstanding achievement in scientific research is the experimental application of the then unknown histochemical method for the study of pathological processes.

[2] These data are taken from the Critico-biographical Dictionary by S. A. Vengerov, vol. IV, 1895.

Up to 1858, the Englishman V. F. Bervy lectured on physiology at Kazan' University; he had been appointed full professor of physiology and pathology at the University on the recommendation of the Moscow governor-general, Prince Golitsyn. The basic tendencies of development of experimental physiology were entirely unfamiliar to him. Bervy had been a naval doctor, and before his appointment to the faculty of physiology he had made two trips around the world. He had never worked in any physiological or other scientific laboratory, and what he knew of physiology was only from books. His discussions on specifically physiological subjects were anachronistic, even for those times. For example, in his discussion, "On excitability as a phenomenon of organic life" (1851), Bervy states: "Excitation is not something that really exists, something exogenous, something additional and distinct from the organic mass; excitation is only a subjective concept, i.e., an idea based on contemplation as to how external nature activates an organic body."

Bervy used his lectern to spread the most reactionary philosophical views in direct opposition to the new physiology which was breaking through at the leading Russian universities.

At the same time the chair of physiology at Kazan' University was occupied by Professor A. A. Sokolovskiy (1822-1891), who was subsequently a professor of pharmacology at Moscow University. In 1858 he published a brilliant article in the Scientific Memoirs of Kazan' University "On the effect of various remedies on the nervous system in the application of Du Bois-Reymond's theory on sedation and excitation of nerves." In this work Sokolovskiy presented with exceptional thoroughness the most advanced conclusions and facts in the field of experimental physiology of the nervous system and presented his own views, which were of great significance. On the basis of vast factual material, he submitted a question which was entirely new for that period—the dependency of bioelectrical phenomena of the tissues (nerves, muscles, glands) on the normal process of metabolism ("nutrition") of these tissues. On the basis of this general concept, he was one of the first in world literature to make the statement that the whole theory and practice of the effect of poisons and medicines on the nervous system must be based on the effect of these pharmocological agents on substances (albumins, fats and carbohydrates) and on the products of their transformation in the living nerve tissue which create the conditions for the generation of bioelectric currents in the nervous system. From this viewpoint he analyzes the character of the effects on the nervous system of a number of substances. Even now this analysis has not lost its significance; on the contrary, it has gained a particular meaning in the light of new facts and generalizations with regard to the chemism of nervous processes.

CHAPTER VIII

I. M. Sechenov's student years. Physiology at Moscow University during that period. The public interest in physiology during the 1850's and 60's. The Contemporary and its role in the publicizing of achievements in physiology. Criticism of Bervy's views.

In 1851, I. M. Sechenov submitted an application to Moscow University for admission to the medical school. By that time the 22-year-old Sechenov had graduated from the Mikhaylov Engineering School and was in the military service as a lieutenant in an engineering regiment in Kiev.

Here Sechenov mingled in a progressive circle of Granovskiy's followers, who, as Sechenov wrote in his Autobiographical Notes, "had a high regard for Moscow University" and for the noble medical profession. Under the influence of members of this circle[1] and because of the enormous public interest in problems of the natural sciences and physiology, Sechenov resigned from military service and entered Moscow University. Here Sechenov's teacher in physiology was Professor I. T. Glebov (1806-1884).

I. T. Glebov completed his secondary education at the same theological seminary in Ryazan that I. P. Pavlov attended later on. Glebov's dissertation, which touched on a number of vital problems of clinical physiology and pharmacology, was written in Latin and was published in Moscow in 1834. He worked a great deal in the best European laboratories and was a great admirer of the French physiologists Claude Bernard and Flourens. We have already mentioned that Glebov, while still a student, translated the two-volume textbook in physiology by F. Magendie, together with another student, Lunin. Glebov's services to his country are especially paramount in the organization of higher education and in the training of scientific workers in Russia.

I. M. Sechenov wrote in his Autobiographical Notes: "For me, personally, Glebov was one of the most interesting professors." Glebov lectured on comparative anatomy and physiology and presented facts and conclusions in comparative anatomy with such vividness that in his second year at school Sechenov "dreamed of a future career in

---

[1] For details, see my monograph on "Sechenov," edited by the USSR Academy of Sciences, 1945. (Koshtoyants)

99

comparative anatomy and not in physiology."[2] According to Sechenov, Glebov's presentation of his physiology course reflected his admiration for the scientific work of Flourens and communicated but little to his students of the brilliant achievements in physiology, in particular with regard to neuro-muscular physiology, that were so abundant in the forties and the fifties of the nineteenth century. The demonstrations of experiments were also poor at the lectures at which "there was a long line of pigeons whose brains were perforated with pins."[3*]

As an interesting detail we must note that according to Sechenov's reports he and his fellow-students "did not even learn about such a fact as cardiac arrest due to stimulation of the vagus nerve."[4] This experiment had already been known to physiologists for more than ten years. Thus it is not from the university course that Sechenov learned about the experimental inhibition of cardiac activity by stimulation of the vagus — the experiment that led him to the discovery of the phenomena of central inhibition and one that was to be his prime concern during his entire life.

N. A. Varnek (1823-1876) also lectured on physiology for 11 years (1849-1860).

Sechenov speaks warmly of Varnek's lectures in his Autobiographical Notes when reminiscing about his teachers at Moscow University. Varnek is noted for two original investigations which deal with the embryology of mollusks.

In spite of all the defects in the teaching of physiology at the University at that period, both Glebov and Varnek were able to arouse Sechenov's interest in physiology. Here is how he expresses it. "That same year I became convinced that I was not meant to be a medic and I began to dream about physiology. The enigmas of disease did not arouse the slightest interest in me since there was no key that would unlock their meaning; and as yet I could not develop a taste for studying these enigmas to differentiate between the essential and the irrelevant side issues—the main fascination of genuine lovers of medicine. On the other hand, that year I began to acquaint myself with physiology from the fascinating book by Bergmann and Lejkart, Anatomisch-Physiologische Uebersicht des Thierreichs (Anatomical-physiological Survey of the Animal Kingdom). Of all the books of my student years, I have kept this one to this day and consider it a marvelous piece of writing. At that time it fascinated me to such an extent that I interested the Vizar family in it and once delivered something like a lecture at their house on the gradual complication of the phenomena of life."[5]

---

[2] I. M. Sechenov. Autobiographical Notes. USSR Academy of Sciences, 1945, p. 53.

[3] Ibid.

*Translator's note: The prevalence of amphibians and birds in physiological experimentation and especially classroom demonstration must be explained in part by the absence of anesthetics and properly perfected anesthetic techniques.

[4] Ibid.

[5] Ibid., p. 64.

During his student years, Sechenov also became greatly interested in the problems of psychology, and this dual interest developed to such an extent that he actually became the founder of the new concept of psychophysiology.

During these same years, the lectures in pharmacology at the Medical Faculty of Moscow University were given by the Professor-Dean of the Medical Faculty, N. B. Anke (1803-1873),[6] whom Sechenov recalls in his Autobiographical Notes as the professor who headed the German party at the University. Anke had favored the appointment of a German classmate of Sechenov's, Einbrodt, to head the department of physiology at Moscow University in opposition to another group of professors, headed by Professor Inozemtsev, who wanted Sechenov to receive this appointment after completing his studies abroad. Sechenov spoke eloquently of this important milestone in his life and in the history of our science in his Autobiographical Notes. He writes: "Having completed the course and knowing many of my sins in the field of medicine, especially its practical aspects, it never occurred to me to take the examinations for my doctorate right away, but I was compelled to do so by our Dean Nikolay Bogdanovich Anke, who informed me that this was a faculty requirement. I believed him, but this was not true. Probably upon his insistence his two favorites, Yunge and Einbrodt—both German—also applied for their doctorate. Among the professors of medicine Glebov and Basov were Russophiles; they did not like the Germans to be given preferential treatment, and they were strict at the examinations. This is why Anke had to include at least one Russian applicant, hoping to soften the examiners. It is possible that they mellowed, but not entirely. Glebov did not pass Einbrodt, although the examinations were very simple and differed from the physicians' examinations (as it also happens at present) only in that the doctoral candidates had two additional questions to answer. Afterwards I heard that upon my return from abroad I could have been appointed professor of physiology to Moscow University instead of to St. Petersburg Medical Academy were it not for N. B. Anke. These are the circumstances: when Professor Glebov left the faculty, about a year after my departure abroad, Anke proposed Einbrodt to replace him with the stipulation that he be sent abroad at government expense for further study, while F. I. Inozemtsev had suggested I be given this appointment. Anke then stated that he knew from a reliable source that I was studying psychology and not physiology, and Inozemtsev's proposal was rejected."[7]

---

[6] Incidentally, one of the favorite expressions in the humor of L. N. Tolstoy, "Anke pie," is connected with the name of N. B. Anke. Tolstoy's son, S. L. Tolstoy, wrote: "For my father, Anke pie served as the emblem of a special ideology—thrift and family tradition, and, speaking in the modern language, the bourgeois tenor of life, conviction in the stability of the modern system." Anke was a friend of Doctor A. E. Bers, the father of S. A. [Mrs. Leo] Tolstoy; at that time he gave S. A. Tolstoy's mother a recipe for a pie which later became very much a part of the Tolstoys' family life, and "Anke pie" began to be heard from the lips of L. N. Tolstoy as a very definite image.

[7] I. M. Sechenov. Autobiographical Notes, p. 68.

The period of Sechenov's graduation from Moscow University, his decision to dedicate himself to physiology, and his studies in the physiological laboratories of Western Europe coincide with the enormous upheaval of interest in physiology in Russia.

Ye. V. Pelikan stimulated much activity, primarily in the teaching field, during that period in St. Petersburg. His public lectures played an exceptional role in the development of a broad interest in physiology among the Russian intelligentsia. Sechenov wrote about Ye. V. Pelikan in his Autobiographical Notes: "He was a very intelligent man, a well educated physician for his time (at that time he also lectured on certain fields of physiology), and we were great friends until his death." Ye. V. Pelikan was Sechenov's opponent when the latter defended his dissertation in 1860. Pelikan was the author of a series of pharmacological investigations and as early as 1857 had published a report on his investigation of the physiological and toxicological effect of curare. [8]

A series of articles about Pelikan's lectures at St. Petersburg Passage* that appeared in the popular newspapers and journals testify to the public's enormous interest in physiology. In 1859-60 the St. Petersburg Record [Sankt-Peterburgskiye Vedomosti] published articles under a definite enough title: "In defense of teaching physiology in Russia (in connection with the proposed public lectures of Ye. V. Pelikan at the Passage)." In early 1860 another journal, The Northern Bee [Severnaya Pchela], printed an article "The public course on experimental physiology in the Passage." In an article "Lectures in the Passage" (St. Petersburg Record, no. 6, 1860), Dr. Katolinskiy gives an enthusiastic report on Professor Pelikan's lectures on physiology and emphasizes their enormous social significance. "A bright thought illuminated our public life; a free message was born on the lectern; and the Professor's audience included all of our contemporary society rather than a narrow select circle." It is especially noteworthy that Pelikan's lectures on physiology were accompanied by demonstration of experiments.

Between 1856-61, D. I. Pisarev, the ardent proponent of science in our country, began to study physiological problems. In 1861 he published his remarkable article on "The process of life," dedicated to K. Focht's book Physiological Letters. This article abounds with the most advanced scientific ideas and is imbued with faith in the possibility of revealing the innermost secrets of organic life; it invites experimentation and accumulation of facts and in it we read Pisarev's unforgettable words "Words and illusions perish—facts remain." [9] Thus he concludes the formulation of his ideas concerning the analytical discernment of the essence of psychic phenomena. He wrote: "It is necessary to assume

---

[8] Ye. V. Pelikan. Bull. de la classe phys. -mathem. de l'Acad. des Sc., 1857, vol. XV, no. 357, Col. 321-27. See also: Bull. de l'Acad. des Sc. de St. Pet., 1868, vol. XII, p. 263, 259.
*A hall.
[9] Pisarev used these words to autograph one of his portraits reproduced in his complete works, published in 1897.

I. T. Glebov (1806–1884).

and to hope that in time the concept of psychic life, psychic phenomena will be resolved into its components parts. Their fate has been sealed; they shall follow the same path as the philosopher's stone, the elixir of life, the quadrature of the circle, pure thought and the power of life."[10]

Such propaganda—such words—were a call to scientific deeds. These are the words that inspired a number of talented young people, including I. P. Pavlov. Already at the peak of his life's path, I. P. Pavlov, as if transmitting the legacy of his teachers to a new generation, stated: "Facts are the air of the scientist; without them you shall never be able to attain any heights. Without them 'theories' are but empty labors."

This is when I. S. Turgenev published his famous novel Fathers and Sons (1858), in which, for the first time in world literature, there appears as the main hero a revolutionist-naturalist (Bazarov), who personifies the new generation of Russians who were courageously undertaking the dissection of nature to reveal its secrets and to free the people from their superstitions. Both Bazarov and Kirsanov, the hero of Chernishevskiy's novel What Is to Be Done?, are physicians-physiologists, new figures in the Russian society who played an exceptional role in the formation of the outlook of the Russian revolutionary intelligentsia, which had as its slogan "the struggle with reactionary elements and ignorance through scientific understanding of nature and society."

The reactionary Katkov, alarmed by the enthusiastic reception of Turgenev's new novel and of his hero, the physician-physiologist Bazarov, wrote about Bazarov in a letter to Annenkov: "Who knows what may become of such a type. Consider that this is only the beginning. If we praise him now, if we decorate him with the flowers of creativity, the struggle with him will be twice as difficult in the future." But no reactionary forces could stop the progress of this young branch of science, and physiology developed by leaps and bounds, attracting the most daring and gifted people, including 'the father of Russian physiology," I. M. Sechenov, who began his independent scientific activities in the field of physiology at this same time.

Thus the progressive element of the intelligentsia manifested an increased interest in the development of physiology in our country. The field of the natural science, whose subject consisted of the most exciting problems on the essence of life processes, including also the processes of consciousness, was the center of attention for naturalists and philosophers.

A sharply negative attitude towards physiology was assumed by the numerous representatives of the reactionary philosophical trend. The attitude of these opponents of the new physiology, which was impetuously developing towards the strict scientific method and the materialistic direction, was best expressed by the professor of physiology and pathology at Kazan' University, the Englishman Bervy, in his article "The

---

[10] D. I. Pisarev. Complete Works, St. Petersburg, 1894, vol. I, p. 322.

psychophysiological comparative view on the beginning and end of life,'' published in the Scientific Annals of Kazan' University [Uchenyye Zapiski Kazanskogo Universiteta] in 1858.

In this article Bervy wrote: ''From the moral world, materialism invades the sanctuary of science. The materialists, armed with scales, glassware and a knife, openly reveal to us the secrets of nature. . . . This direction, which is so dreadful for the common good, imposes on all of us the duty to do our utmost to reject the idea of materialism which reduces all phenomena of life to crude sensualism.''

Bervy also expounded his reactionary views at his lectures. Bervy's opposition to the new trends, both in the special field of physiology and, mainly, in the constantly growing antireactionary scientific ideology, was met with a strong rebuttal by Dobrolyubov. That same year (1858), in the bibliography section of The Contemporary, (no. 3), Dobrolyubov's extensive review of Bervy's article states: ''Such a direction in the natural sciences cuts into Mr. Bervy worse than a sharp knife. For the sake of the natural sciences he is indignant against our times, and after reading his brochure we can understand the cause of this meritorious professor's indignation, and we even sympathize with his sad plight, although unfortunately we are unable to alleviate his sorrow. Indeed, every page of Bervy's psychophysiological viewpoint proves that he studied natural sciences some time ago in the distant past when Schubert and Eschenmeier ruled in the field of anthropology, or possibly earlier, still in those prehistoric days even before Lavoisier. Our error would not be too great, it seems, if we were to relegate Mr. Bervy's education to the middle ages, judging from the fact that he substantiates his opinions with Latin quotations from Bacon, Seneca, Cicero and even (seemingly with the desire to justify his whole brochure) with the Latin proverb: Errare humanum est, which of course means: to err is human. The investigations of the newest naturalists are entirely unknown to Bervy. Most frequently his authority is Pliny (A.D. 23-79). He but rarely refers to Blumenbach and Bougainville, and of the new ones he knows only his 'scientific collaborator P. A. Pell, who had tangibly proved the deceptiveness of the conclusions which were intended to demonstrate the transformation of oats into rye' (p. 61).* Small wonder, then, that with such an education Bervy is extremely discontent with our times when the natural sciences have made such tremendous strides forward and have reconciled the philosophical interpretations of the forces of nature with the results of experimental investigations of matter. Nowadays the positive method has been adopted by the natural sciences, and all conclusions are based on experiments and factual knowledge, and not on visionary theories haphazardly formulated, nor on obscure guess-work with which ignorance and half knowledge were content in past days. The old authorities so greatly revered by Bervy are no longer recognized nowadays, and authorities in general are of no great significance in the matter of scientific investigations. Young people nowadays unhesitatingly brand these delusions as nonsense, and they even find fault with Liebig,

---

*Page number apparently refers to Bervy's book.

of whom Bervy, it seems, has not heard at all; they read Molleschot, Du Bois-Reymond and Focht and do not take even them at their word, and they attempt to verify their statements and even to supplement them with their own reasoning. When today's young people take up the study of natural sciences, they integrate it with the philosophy of nature where again, they do not heed Plato, Oken, nor even Schelling, but are guided by the more daring and realistic of Hegel's disciples. How can such a trend fail to anger Mr. Bervy, who in his philosophical pursuits stopped at Fichte, whom, however, he fails to understand, and whose theory (as Mr. Bervy himself confesses on p. 13*) 'appears to him at a sort of nebulous remoteness.' The progress in natural sciences destroys his medieval theories entirely and exposes him to ridicule not only in the eyes of the specialist who follows the progress of positive knowledge, but also in the eyes of any educated person born after Lavoisier and Fichte, and Mr. Bervy dislikes the trends of our times because they have outdated him.''

Dobrolyubov's biting and ridiculing criticism of Bervy had an enormous social effect, since it brought up questions concerning the progress of science and of scientific workers in our country. Towards the end of his detailed analysis of Bervy's philosophizing, Dobrolyubov states: "The readers must have begun to wonder long ago why we have bothered to quote these remarkable statements from Mr. Bervy's book when about five lines would have sufficed to arouse public ridicule. To explain our concern with Mr. Bervy, we shall submit one last quote, and it will show the readers that mirth alone is not enough—that the matter concerning Mr. Bervy is far from humorous. On page four he states: 'I present here to the world what I have annually taught my students,' and he adds, 'My students are young people, and as such they are receptive to all that is great and idealistic.' This is where we have the serious and tragic side of the situation. Let Bervy dream whatever he pleases, let him curse the modern development of natural sciences, let him doubt that he has a heart and lungs, and let him believe at the same time that a part is equal to the whole and that an animal wants to eat strictly in order to learn its own needs. But the harm is in the fact that he is teaching all this to his students, and in all probability he is teaching them something even worse; because, when a professor publishes his lectures he tries to polish them up.''

Is it worth our while to pity Professor Bervy, held fast in a swamp of medieval reactionary views, Dobrolyubov wonders? No, certainly not. We can and should pity those who had to attend this professor's lectures. "He does not deserve any sympathy,'' writes Dobrolyubov about Bervy, "if only because he is endowed with such unwarranted complacency in spite of his backwardness in science and his incredible transgressions against common sense. But these receptive young people under his guidance deserve the pity of any educated person, especially because they had to listen to him, since he was their professor.''

_____

*Also apparently a reference to Bervy's book.

But the students decided they did not want to listen to Professor Bervy any more. It is known from the history of Kazan' University that a letter signed by 71 students was addressed to Bervy expressing their categorical refusal to attend any further lectures and demanding that he immediately leave the faculty of physiology. A comparison of Dobrolyubov's article with the students' letter justifies the assumption that the students' demands were influenced by this article which had appeared in The Contemporary at a most opportune time. Of course Bervy had to leave Kazan' University that same year (1858), and he was replaced by the remarkable Russian scientist F. V. Ovsyannikov, who later on became an academician and founded the Kazan' Physiological School. We shall discuss his work and important activities in later chapters. Under the sponsorship of Kazan' University, Ovsyannikov had worked abroad at the most outstanding physiological laboratories of Europe, and this enabled him to pave the way for the high level of development of physiology at Kazan' University.

CHAPTER IX

Sechenov's first investigations. The Russian physiologists in the early period of Sechenov's career (Babukhin, Ovsyannikov, Yakubovich). The history of elections in the Academy of Sciences to the faculty of physiology.

The leading Russian physiologists of the second half of the nineteenth century, and especially I. M. Sechenov, were not imitators of Western European science, but they adopted the best traditions of classical experimental physiology of the 1840's to 1860's in Europe (Purkinje, J. Müller, Helmholtz, Cl. Bernard, Ludwig). They were able to make a critical appraisal of the current achievements of science, to assimilate and to enrich the methods and contents of the physiology of their times, and to lead Russian physiology along an independent path. Moreover, many of the outstanding works that have left their imprint on the history of physiology were performed at West European laboratories in collaboration with leading Russian physiologists.

These tendencies were most vividly reflected in Sechenov's early scientific activity in European laboratories.

After graduating from Moscow University (1856), Sechenov went to Germany with a specific subject for scientific investigation in mind. It concerned the influence of acute alcoholic poisoning on the organism of man, and later on this was the subject of his doctoral dissertation, "Data for the future physiology of alcoholic intoxication" (1860).

We know that Sechenov submitted this subject to Hoppe-Seyler, and the latter could only approve the young Russian physician's original scientific project. Much later Sechenov reminisced: "Hoppe-Seyler highly approved of my plan to study alcohol poisoning, which came to my mind as a matter of course due to the role of vodka in Russian life."

In this early period of his scientific activity, Sechenov displayed exceptional independence as an experimenter. For example, when he was investigating the effect of various substances on the neuromuscular system, he discovered that his data on the effect of potassium sulfocyanate on the nerves and muscles (1858) did not coincide with the data of the famous physiologist of the nineteenth century, Claude Bernard. Sechenov found a systematic error in Bernard's experiments which caused this contradiction.[1]

---

[1] Einiges über die Vergiftung mit Schwefelcyankalium. Virchow's Arch. f. path. Anat. u. Physiol., 1858, XIV.

In Helmholtz' laboratory, Sechenov made observations on the fluorescence of the eye which appeared more comprehensive and significant than the ones made at the same time by the Frenchman, Regnault.[2]

To illustrate the collaboration between Sechenov and Helmholtz, we shall quote briefly from Sechenov's Autobiographical Notes, where he narrates how he demonstrated the fluorescence of the eye of a pig which he obtained from the slaughter house. "When I showed Helmholtz this phenomenon, he placed my own eye in the light instead of the pig's and found that my crystalline lens was also fluorescent...."

Sechenov's work on the effect of acute alcoholic poisoning on human and animal organisms required a thorough study of the changes occurring in the blood and, particularly, the changes in the quantity and distribution of gases in the blood. The existing equipment, including the Meyer apparatus, turned out to be quite inadequate for the experimental analysis of the this complex question, and Sechenov designed his own instrument for the pumping out of gases from the blood, called the absorptiometer.[3]

Even though Sechenov came to Ludwig's laboratory just as a student, his absorptiometer opened up new horizons for his teacher's work, and, as soon as Ludwig learned how this new instrument worked, he had a duplicate made for his laboratory. The model of this instrument for the study of the gas content of blood became the basis for all future systematic investigations on this subject, and an array of new instruments of this type, labeled with the names of foreign scientists, are actually modeled on Sechenov's absorptiometer.

We learn of the appraisal by the greatest European physiologists of Sechenov's first brilliant successes as an experimenter from Ludwig's letters to Sechenov. Thus, in a letter dated August 29, 1859, Ludwig writes: "With your permission I should like to mention your observations in my textbook. Helmholtz wrote to Brücke ...that you have discovered a distinct fluorescence of the crystalline lens...." In a letter dated January 2, 1860, Ludwig writes to Sechenov: "I read your article on the fluorescence of the crystalline lens with great pleasure and your Parisian competitor's work does not measure up to it. I am very grateful to you for your concern about the gas instrument. When Dr. Schaefer finally starts to work, we shall certainly avail ourselves of your advice.... Just between us, although he is a good and skillful person and is quite learned, nevertheless his work lacks your flexibility and energy. Had you been here a lot would have been accomplished by now."*

---

[2] Ueber die Fluorescenz der durchsichtingen Augenmedien biem Menschen und einigen anderen Säugethieren. Gräfe's Arch. f. Ophtalm., 1859, Bd. V, Abt. 2.

[3] See Beitrag zur Pneumatologie des Blutes. Sitzgsber. der Wien. Acad. mat. naturwiss. 1859, XXXVI; also, Zeischr. f. rat. Medicine (3. R.) Bd., 1861, X.

*Translator's note: Following the Russian text, these excerpts from Ludwig's letters are an indirect translation of the German originals.

Thus, during his brief sojourn at Western European laboratories, Sechenov earned the reputation of an authority in physiology, thanks to independent and original formulation of problems, his talent, and his persistence as an experimenter.

His authoritative position grew and became permanent after he discovered the phenomena of central inhibition in 1862.

Babukhin, Ovsyannikov, and Yakubovich, Sechenov's contemporaries, must be included among the Russian scientists who greatly contributed to the creation of independent Russian physiological trends.

The outstanding histologist and founder of the Moscow Histological School, A. I. Babukhin (1835-1891), studied at Moscow University during the same years as Sechenov, and both started their scientific careers at the same time.

For a short time Babukhin was on the faculty of physiology at Moscow University. His interest in physiology dates back to the beginning of his scientific activities. It was not just by chance that Babukhin was appointed dissector in the department of physiology upon graduating from the University (in 1859); in 1860 he published his first scientific physiological treatise, "The tetanic contraction of the heart." [4] In the following year (1861), his article on the effect of certain poisons on cardiac function was published, and in 1862 Babukhin published his remarkable dissertation On the Relationship of the Vagus Nerve to the Heart. [5]

But Babukhin gained his greatest fame as a physiologist through his classic works on the study of the electrical organs of fish and on the bilateral distribution of excitation in the nerves. These investigations exercised a great influence in the development of world physiology of the neuromuscular system and of the general problems of electrophysiology. The bilateral conduction in the nerve fiber, which is the basis of modern concepts of the laws governing neural excitation, was most vividly demonstrated by Babukhin on the electrical organ of fish. Through his experiments he proved that stimulation of any small branch of the nerve leading to the electrical organ produces a discharge of the entire electrical organ. Consequently, the excitation arising from the stimulated nerve branch spreads, on the one hand, centripetally to the common nerve stem trunk and, on the other hand, centrifugally along the other nerve branches.

Babukhin first reported on the electrical organ of fish in 1869 at the Second Congress of Russian Natural Scientists and Physicians. [6] In this report, Babukhin formulated his classic concepts on the genetic link between the muscle tissue and a tissue of the electrical organ of fish.

---

[4] Moscow Medical Gazette, 1860, no. 26, 30, 31.
[5] Separate edition. Moscow, 1862, 120 pp. + 2 tables.
[6] "On the development and significance of the electrical apparatus in the torpedo." Proceedings of the Second Congress of Russian Natural Scientists and Physicians, 1869.

110

He did not stop at the morphological study of this remarkable organ by the method of fixed preparations, and in 1870 he travelled to Egypt to study by physiological methods the activity of the electrical organ in the sheath-fish of the Nile.

It was as a result of these physiological investigations that he was able to publish a series of articles on the function of electrical organs and on the nature of animal electricity during the years of 1876-1882.[7]

Babukhin's brilliant ideas, which were based on a wealth of factual material concerning the genetic link between the muscular elements and the tissues of the electrical organs of most fish, now find comprehensive electrophysiological and chemodynamic confirmation. It is only quite recently that data have been obtained indicative of the connection between skeletal muscles and the electrical organ of the skate in their relationship to acetylcholine and the role played in these two organs by guanidino-phosphoric compounds.[8]

A. I. Babukhin's importance was immense in the development of the experimental trend in biology and medicine and the education of physicians and naturalists at Moscow University. In 1887 one of Babukhin's students, Dr. N. P. Vinogradov, reported in the journal Moscow Calendar (under the editorship of Prugavin) that Babukhin "has done for Moscow what Sechenov did for St. Petersburg."

Sechenov described Babukhin's lectures thus: "Those who were fortunate enough to be among his first students vividly remember the impression made by Babukhin's appearance. He was endowed with a refined skeptical mind and an enormous analytical capacity; he was a product of his times, inspired by a passionate drive to search only for truth. He was direct and even crudely natural in his approach and instantly put an end to the flowery and shallow style of lecturing of some of his Moscow teachers, in order to appear before his listeners fully armed with the tools of the new European science that was ready to tackle any method or any investigation."

Other outstanding scientist-physicians and physiologists also became active at this time: N. M. Yakubovich, F. V. Ovsyannikov, S. P. Botkin, and others. These Russian scientists gained a high reputation in the best European laboratories as men devoted to science and as first-class experimenters.

---

[7] a) Uebersicht der neuen Untersuchungen über Entwickelung, Bau und Physiologische Verhältnisse der electrischen und pseudo-electrischen Organe. Reicherts Arch., 1876, S. 501-542.

b) Beobachtungen u. Versuche am Zitterwelse u. Mormyrus des Niles. 1877, pp. 250-274.

c) Notes on electricity. Abstracts from the latest investigations concerning the electrical organs of fish. Proceedings of the Physico-Medical Society of Moscow, 1882, no. 37.

[8] See, for instance, a note by E. Drigo, "Progress of contemporary biology," 1944, 17, p. 222.

N. M. Yakubovich (1817-1879) was a professor of histology and physiology at the Military Medical Academy beginning in 1857. His investigations centered on the histological structure of the central nervous system and aroused the keen interest of the greatest European physiologists and histologists, particularly in the Paris Academy of Sciences, which honored him with the Montyon Award. An article, "The microscopic investigations of the origin of nerves in the brain," was published in 1855-1856 by Yakubovich in collaboration with another leading Russian physiologist and histologist, F. V. Ovsyannikov.[9] Yakubovich's comparative histological investigations in the 1850's actually laid the foundation for the proper understanding of the relationships of the various parts of the nervous system and, more specifically, shed light on the origin of the sympathetic nervous system.

F. V. Ovsyannikov (1827-1906), one of the founders of an independent Russian school of physiologists at Kazan' and Petersburg Universities, was on the faculty of physiology at the Academy of Sciences for many years. In 1855 he completed the above mentioned work in collaboration with Yakubovich. In 1860 Ovsyannikov worked at Claude Bernard's laboratory and, at the invitation of this great French physiologist, he read a report on the finer structures of the nervous systems of salt water crayfish at the meeting of the Paris Academy of Sciences. At Petersburg University, where Ovsyannikov was on the faculty of physiology from 1864 to 1875, I. P. Pavlov was one of his students. As a versatile biologist, he worked in the field of histology as well as embryology and physiology. He published a series of interesting articles on the reflex regulation of respiratory movements and the vascular centers. In later chapters we shall discuss in greater detail Ovsyannikov's most important physiological investigations and his role in the development of physiology.

In 1862 Ovsyannikov's interesting article "On the luminosity of the larvae of the glow-worm" was published, and it is one of the first important investigations in the field of comparative physiology in Russia. During the same period (1865-1866), the zoologist Brandt published his important investigations in comparative physiology dealing with the physiology of the mollusk heart, crustacea, and insects in the Bulletin of the Academy of Sciences. These investigations paved the way for the comparative physiological approach in Russian science.[10]

Although the investigations of Babukhin, Yakubovich, and Ovsyannikov had a predominantly morphological (histological and microscopic) tendency, they also made a most valuable contribution to physiology. In this period, their names, together with Sechenov's, personified Russian physiology. They were also well known abroad as outstanding Russian

---

[9] Mikroskopische Untersuchungen über die Nervenursprünge im Gehirn. Bull. Ph.-M., 1855, vol. XIV, no. 11, pp. 173-174.

[10] However, it must be noted that already in 1816 the Academician P. Zagorskiy presented a communication in the field of comparative physiology, "A study of the air contained in the swimming bladder of fish," in the Supplement of the Technological Journal (vol. I, pt. 2, p. 46), which was published by the Academy of Sciences.

N. M. Yakubovich (1817–1879).

physiologists. In the first half of the 1860's, other outstanding pysiologists appeared in our country: Tsion, Shchelkov, Bakst, Danilevskiy, and others.

A noteworthy event took place in the late 1850's, i.e., in the period when a remarkable group of Russian physiologists was formed—the elections for appointments to the faculty of physiology and anatomy at the Academy of Sciences.

After Academician P. A. Zagorskiy died in 1846, the department of anatomy and physiology at the Academy of Sciences was headed by the famous zoologist K. E. Von Baer (1792-1876). In the late 1850's, Baer had decided to retire, and he began to look for a suitable successor. While he was abroad he interviewed foreign scientists, the German scientist Kühne among others.[11] This provoked a strong reaction among Russian scientists and high social circles. This reaction is most vividly reflected in a letter from N. M. Yakubovich to the president of the Academy of Sciences and Minister of Public Education, Ye. P. Kovalevskiy (this letter was first published in our monograph Sechenov). It reads, in part, as follows:

> Academician Baer has been looking for a worthy successor abroad, but not among the Russians who are so diligently working in every corner of Europe; he did not even inquire about them, but explored the possibilities among his fellow-foreigners. On behalf of us, the Russians, I feel the offense and insult of such an attitude deeply, for we are just as honest, as successful and as diligent as Dr. Kühne. I hope that the St. Petersburg Academy of Sciences is a Russian academy and that a Russian has an equal right to an appointment ...."

Further on, Yakubovich petitions for the right to have his candidacy voted upon in the Academy of Sciences and adds:

> "More than one Russian heart will respond if this request is granted. It will reassure our young people who are working at home and abroad by the sweat of their brow; it will kindle in us the hope of a just reward for our noble endeavors; and finally, it will satisfy and revive our national dignity. In this regard I take the liberty of mentioning to Your Excellency Mr. Sechenov and Mr. Botkin; both are outstanding and most deserving of your special consideration; the former is a physiologist and the latter a clinician."

One cannot read the next lines of this remarkable letter by Yakubovich without a flurry of emotion. They also reflect the great significance of Yakubovich's own work. He wrote to the minister:

> "If I were to remain silent in this matter, I feel it would be a crime against my own conscience and my country.... I frankly confess that my constant and greatest hope has been to earn the right to a position of honor upon my return to Russia; that of Active

---

[11] Subsequently professor of physiology in Heidelberg.

114

Academician of the St. Petersburg Academy of Sciences, in addition to my position as professor of the Medical-Surgical Academy. These two most compatible positions would provide the necessities of life as well as the opportunity for scientific work and scientific influence. This desire has been my only ambitious dream, my only pride; and I trust it is both pardonable and justifiable, since it is inspired by a purely scientific ambition, by the gigantic task I have undertaken, and, finally, by noble competition of a Russian scientist with the top scientists of Europe in the precise and factual solution and explanation of one of the most difficult problems of the natural sciences and in the complicated exploration of the structure of the nervous system of animals in general, and man in particular. I have devoted eight years of my life to this work, and I am still engaged in it. To what extent I have succeeded in my investigations is not for me to say; this right belongs to others. But I hope that the reactions of the top ranking German scientists and their great interest in me, especially the immortal Johannes Müller, Humboldt, Virchow, Reichert and others, and, finally, the first Montyon Award of the Paris Academy of Sciences and the report of the best of European physiologists and experimenters, Claude Bernard, are ample testimony to the fact that if I have still not untied the Gordian knot, my efforts nevertheless have earned universal respect and attention; and this has given me the courage to feel I have the right to address Your Excellency. And on the basis of this right, which was acquired by honest scientific work before all Europe, I dare most humbly to beg that Your Excellency defer temporarily the appointment of Dr. Kühne as Academician Physiologist in our Academy of Sciences and to grant me the opportunity to compete publicly for this appointment before the St. Petersburg Academy of Sciences upon my return to St. Petersburg, i.e., in September, 1860. I should like to compete by demonstrating my discoveries, which represent the microscopic structure of the nervous system, as well as my preparations, i.e., the results of precise observations taken from nature, which supply a multitude of reliable facts which are properly mine, and which are in direct contradiction to currently held views. These facts are the result of 20 years' scientific work, of precise preliminary studies of comparative anatomy and of the history of development, of positive physiological knowledge in general, and my eight year sojourn at Dorpat University, of which Russia can be proud, as it is a university which is on a level with the foremost universities of Europe. I beg Your Excellency's magnanimous indulgence, and dare add that I am not asking for your eminent patronage and influence in my appointment as Academician. I am only asking for the opportunity to compete in an open and lawful and honest contest before the Academy and to defend the honor and name of a Russian scientist, as well as his right to apply for the position of Academician of the Academy of Sciences, thereby justifying my audacity in writing this letter."[12]

[12] Archives of USSR Academy of Sciences, fund 2, register 1 (1857), no. 10, pp. 16-20.

This striking letter, as well as the favorable comments on Yakubovich's work that he mentions in the letter, are preserved in the archives of the Academy of Sciences. A detailed and lengthy commendation in connection with the first Montyon Award prize by the Paris Academy of Sciences was signed by the greatest physiologist-experimenter of that period, Claude Bernard, and by other outstanding French scientists, Milne-Edwards, Flourens, and others.[13] The letter of commendation of the famous physiologist Johannes Müller is of particular interest, and we quote it here in its entirety.[14] J. Müller wrote to N. M. Yakubovich (on July 19, 1857) as follows.

"My dear colleague!

"I thank you very much for sending me your publications on the finer structure of the brain and spinal cord and for giving me the opportunity to acquaint myself with your vast treasure of microscopic preparations and excellent drawings.

"Although many excellent investigators have displayed their ability in this field before, it is, however, thanks to your persistence and thoroughness in this very difficult, yet fruitful, problem that you have succeeded in obtaining substantial and original results with regard to the general understanding of the fine distribution of the nervous system, i.e., of the nerve centers; this has been of prime interest to physiologists, and in the future they will be able to make use of your data as a basis for the explanation of the relationships between physiological phenomena.

"First of all, with regard to the exceptional wealth of microscopic material that you have collected, I do not mind confessing that your sections of chromous oxide preparations excel anything I have seen thus far.

"When making microscopic sketches it is impossible to reconstruct from a view of the separate sections the general fine topography of the nerve centers, and in order to draw any conclusions it is necessary to make sketches of a large number of sections. Nevertheless, you resolved to make an analysis, through your drawings of the sections of the spinal cord, of all your sections, and consequently of the general results from several thousand preparations after which these drawings simultaneously conveyed both the whole and the nature of the models or diagram.

"Moreover, these drawings, which are both copies from nature and an expression of the results of repeated analysis, are executed with incomparable meticulousness and elegance which arouse the admiration of anyone contemplating such work. Even though not all of the drawings of this microscopic topography of the spinal cord and the brain have been completed, it is highly desirable that the

---

[13]Comptes rendus des séances de l'Académie des Sciences, séance du 14 mars, 1859, vol. XLVII.
[14]I wish to express my gratitude to the director of the Archives, USSR Academy of Sciences, Knyazev, for putting at my disposal the data from the N. Yakubovich Archives. J. Müller's letter has been published here for the first time.

rest should be executed in a similar spirit and style. I am pleased my opinion of your work concurs with that of such gentlemen as the State Counselor, Professor Reichert, in Breslau, in whose Physiological Institute you performed your work for nine months. What you were able to achieve with your personal means was possible thanks to your self sacrifice as manifested by your rare love for the subject. However, it is to be desired in the interest of science that such superior work be supported to the degree its high quality deserves. Considerable funds and experts are required for the execution of the drawings and their engraving. For this, the interest of prominent people connected with science must be gained; we must wait for them to defend the unusual and highly valuable scientific problems and noble ambitions, and they should be willing to grant this problem the important place it deserves."

The problem of a Russian rather than foreign replacement for the department of physiology at the Academy of Sciences after Baer's retirement extended beyond the walls of the Academy. Articles on this subject appeared in the leading Russian newspapers and magazines. We quote here in full an article printed in the Notes of the Fatherland under the heading "Concerning the forthcoming elections in the Academy of Sciences."

"K. E. Baer, one of the outstanding members of our Academy of Sciences, retired recently. His age and ill health prevented him from continuing his activity which had long since gained for him one of the highest places among European scientists. Everything he wrote showed him to be both a specialist-scientist and a deep thinker. One could disagree with him, but even in disagreement one had to give credit to his great mind and extensive knowledge. During his nearly 13 years of work in Russia this honored Academician was not only an armchair scientist; he could also usefully apply his knowledge to the important vital problems of our country. His study of the various regions of Russia, correlating their natural science with the economic resources, made Baer's work so important for our country that one may be certain of Russia's deep gratitude for his academic activities.

"Who then shall replace this esteemed academician? Whom will the members choose? Whom will they find worthy of taking over the heritage of one of the most famous European physiologists? These questions are being raised in various quarters, and they prove that our public, which years ago was so indifferent to academic elections, is beginning to be aware of its moral link with this highest Russian scientific institution. In recent times some of our literature has, perhaps, been carried away by nationalistic feelings and has expressed attitudes that were not quite favorable to the Academy of Sciences, and it is therefore not surprising that certain people are given to somewhat unfavorable opinions concerning the forthcoming elections. More than once our Academy has shown its ability to appraise the scientific achievements of both foreigners and Russians, and we are convinced that the Academic appointments reflect the development of science among Russians, rather than nationalistic tendencies. With equal merits in the scientific accomplishments of the candidates, the Academy would rather elect a Russian than a foreigner.

Фотокопия письма К. Людвига к И. М. Сеченову
(продолжение см. на стр. 207)

Photostat of a letter from K. Ludwig
to I. M. Sechenov (continued)

However, it is guided solely by the scientific accomplishments and makes its selection in the interest of science. Therefore, although we do not have direct information as to the intentions of our academicians, we are nevertheless convinced that the rumors of the possible selection of a well respected chemist from Dorpat as successor to such a famous physiologist as K. E. Baer are without foundation. If the scientist in question has done some investigations in physiology, they were always of a chemical nature, and none of the naturalists consider him a physiologist.

"This rumor is the more unfounded since precisely in the field of physiology we have several men whose scientific importance has been recognized in Europe. Far be it from us to attempt a comparative evaluation of the scientific accomplishments of these men; we only listen to the discussions among the people and wish to communicate to our readers the name which has been most frequently mentioned by those who have an unbiased attitude towards our Academy of Sciences—by those who refuse to believe that nationalistic hostility can influence the election of scientists. These people mention more and more persistently the name of I. M. Sechenov as the most probable candidate for Baer's place, and we must admit that Sechenov, by virtue of his scientific accomplishments, fully deserves public appreciation. The European physiologists speak with deep respect of his works and place them among the most important contemporary accomplishments. Just recently one of his discoveries on the physiology of the nerves immediately aroused the most animated discussions on the implications as to future achievements. We are unable, nor do we desire, to go into details, but we only wish to point out that the name of I. M. Sechenov is not only one of the best known names among our scientists but also one that enjoys the highest respect in Europe. We repeat that some of the selections made by the Academy of Sciences prove beyond a doubt that it would readily accept a Russian into its midst if his scientific accomplishments warrant his being considered, and we are therefore convinced that a foreign candidate could have preference over I. M. Sechenov only if he occupied one of the highest positions among European physiologists. It probably would never occur to the Academy to search for a successor to K. E. Baer outside the field of physiology, and with qualifications such as Sechenov's it has no reason whatsoever to select a foreigner. There could hardly be a question of selecting a scientist of lesser stature than the candidate mentioned."

The public interest aroused in this matter brought results. In 1860 the Academy of Sciences published "an announcement from the Imperial Academy of Sciences to Russian scientists who desire to occupy in this Academy the position of associate member in physiology and anatomy," to the effect that: "A competition is being held to fill the vacant position of associate in physiology, primarily in the physico–chemical field not excluding, however, the field of anatomy. Therefore, Russian scientists who feel themselves capable of occupying such a position are invited to submit to the Academy, within six months from the date of this announcement, reprints or manuscript copies of their scientific composition as proof of their qualifications."

Sechenov was among those who responded to this interesting announcement. On December 1, 1860, Sechenov made an application in which he asked "to be granted the honor of being included among the competitors for the designated position." However, on December 22, 1860, Sechenov sent a second letter to the Academy of Sciences which said: "Completely unexpected family circumstances compel me to think that in the near future I shall have to seek a significant increase in my income. Under these circumstances it would be impossible for me to fulfill conscientiously the obligations which rest on every member of the Academy of Sciences, in the event I should be honored by an appointment. I therefore respectfully request that the conference of the Academy exclude my name from the list of competitors for the position of associate in the department of physiology."[15]

Sechenov's rather sparse recollections in his Autobiographical Notes and the archive material permit us to assume that Sechenov's refusal to be a candidate for the position at the Academy was connected with his reluctance to be involved in the intrigue which attended the 1860 elections. Sechenov was elected corresponding member of the Academy of Sciences much later, in 1869.[16]

In the early 1860's Yakubovich and Ovsyannikov were elected associates of the Academy of Sciences. Ovsyannikov was elected extraordinary Academician, and, in 1864, he was appointed ordinary Academician on the faculty of physiology. For more than 30 years he was the representative of physiology at the Academy of Sciences. As we shall see later on, Ovsyannikov made many valuable contributions in the field of physiology, but we must mention here the versatility of his interests and work. We know that he was a first rate histologist and worked with N. M. Yakubovich on the histology of the nervous system. In collaboration with Kovalevskiy and Wagner, he published a number of works on embryology. Finally, he did some very valuable investigations in the field of artificial breeding of fish, an endeavor which was greatly appreciated both in Russia and abroad. In 1864 Ovsyannikov raised the question of creating a physiological laboratory at the Academy of Sciences, and it was first organized at the anatomical museum of the Academy and subsequently, in 1879, obtained its own budget and building.[17]

---

[15]Archives, USSR Academy of Sciences, fund 2, register 1 (1868), no. 17, pp. 1-4. Quoted from T. A. Knyazev's and M. F. Knyazeva's work. Journ. Inst. Hist. of Science and Technology, series I, issue 7, p. 416.

[16]That same year Sechenov was elected honorary member of St. Petersburg University.

[17]The first physiological laboratory of the Academy of Sciences was located on Mendeleyev Row in a semibasement. Several generations of Russian physiologists worked in it. Here the Russian physiologist Kulyabko saw for the first time the beat of a resuscitated human heart. This is where I. P. Pavlov, after Ovsyannikov's death, equipped his academic laboratory (from December 1, 1907). In 1924 he moved from this building, after it had been damaged by a flood, to the new building of the physiological institute of the Academy of Sciences, which is still standing. However, the history of this first physiological laboratory of the Academy does not end in 1924. In 1939 the physiologists of the Academy of Sciences, under the direction of A. A. Ukhtomskiy, began to work in this same building. Ukhtomskiy equipped his electrophysiological laboratory in it. He was

F. V. Ovsyannikov (1827–1906).

By the end of 1858, Sechenov had actually completed the scientific investigations he had begun abroad, and early that year he had begun to consider his future plans for a scientific and pedagogical career in Russia. During this period of Sechenov's residence abroad, a friendship developed between him and the famous painter A. Ivanov, whom he had met in 1856 in Berlin, and in the following year they saw each other frequently in Rome. In the Pushkin House of the Academy of Sciences, Sechenov's letters to Ivanov are preserved; they are of interest primarily as a characterization of that period. In a letter of January 18, 1858, Sechenov wrote to the artist: "At present I am very busy. Professor Matyushenkov, whom you know, wrote me recently that I am being considered for an appointment in Moscow, but to get it, I must defend my dissertation. And I am working on it, i.e., the dissertation, right now."[18]

However, his efforts failed. Apparently due to the strong faction of German professors at Moscow University, Einbrodt was appointed to the faculty of physiology. We find an explanation for this turn of events with regard to Sechenov's appointment in his Autobiographical Notes. He writes: "When Professor Glebov left the faculty, about a year after my departure abroad, Anke proposed Einbrodt to replace him with the stipulation that he be sent abroad at government expense for further study, while F. I. Inozemtsev had suggested I be given this appointment. Anke then stated that he knew from a reliable source that I was studying psychology and not physiology, and Inozemtsev's proposal was rejected."[19]

Due to Einbrodt's[20] appointment to the faculty of physiology at Moscow University, Sechenov actually remained without any plans for further scientific work at home. In this connection he wrote to Ivanov in a letter dated November 11, 1858: "... I received the news from Botkin that the appointment that I hoped for was given to a classmate of mine at the University. At first I considered practicing medicine, in order to support myself and Giulia, but the idea was so disgusting to me that I turned my back on worries about the future and remained faithful to physiology...."[21]

Soon, however, an opportunity appeared at the Medical Surgical Academy. A. P. Zagorskiy had retired, and N. M. Yakubovich already had been somehow able to convey to his coworkers the historical tradition of his laboratory on Mendeleyev Row (no. 1)—a relic of Russian physiology. The history of the physiological laboratory of the Academy of Sciences is found in: Historical Data on the Academic Institutions for 1889-1914, pt. II, pp. 211-245. Petrograd, 1917.

---

[18]Fund 365 (Botkin's fund), register 2, no. 51.
[19]I. M. Sechenov. Autobiographical Notes, USSR Academy of Sciences, 1945, p. 68.
[20]Einbrodt was born in Moscow and was the son of a pharmacist who worked in a pharmacy established by a masonic group.
[21]Fund 365. The name of the Italian, Giulia (Julia in one of his letters) is encountered in all five of Sechenov's letters to the painter Ivanov. Apparently it is the Señora Maria, "young, slender, with the features of a Del Sarto madonna," to whom Sechenov devoted several pages in his Autobiographical Notes. See: Kh. S. Koshtoyants. Sechenov. USSR Academy of Sciences, 1945, pp. 41-43.

offered a professorship to teach physiology. The growing demands for courses in anatomy, physiology, and histology at the Academy, as well as the need for expansion in the field of experimental medicine consistent with the achievements in contemporary physiology, increased the urgency of hiring someone whose training was on a level with the newest physiological attainments. Professor Glebov, Director of the Medical Academy, selected Sechenov, who had been a student of his at Moscow University, and he undertook the necessary steps. We learned of Glebov's efforts on behalf of Sechenov from a letter written by Ludwig to Sechenov, who was then in Heidelberg, dated May 4, 1859. Referring to his meeting with Botkin, Ludwig informs Sechenov: "... he told me that Glebov, an important official in the Ministry in Petersburg, had written him that you should inform him (Glebov) in writing as to where and to what extent you have studied physiology. With such an official document in hand he might be able to intercede for you."[22] Apparently having written to Glebov and having received a positive answer, Sechenov arrived in St. Petersburg on February 1, 1860. During the following two months Glebov assisted him in the defense of his dissertation and in its publication in the Military-Medical Journal. Sechenov was confirmed at first as an associate at the Academy; he and Professor Yakubovich shared the teaching duties, and soon Sechenov and his lectures became the center of physiology, the significance of which spread far beyond the confines of the Medical-Surgical Academy, extending all over Russia.

One of his first courses was devoted to lectures on animal electricity. These lectures, accompanied by excellently executed electro-physiological experiments, were very impressive in their novelty and depth. Soon Sechenov published these lectures, first in the Military-Medical Journal and subsequently as a separate monograph.[23] This work attracted the attention of scientific circles, and the Academy of Sciences awarded him the Demidov Prize for it. When this award was presented, a commendation was delivered by Ovsyannikov.

From the start of his tenure at the Medical-Surgical Academy, Sechenov began to enlist students and young doctors to participate in scientific research. He thus laid the foundation for the Russian physiological school of the second half of the nineteenth century.

Sechenov's appointment to the faculty marks the beginning of a new era in the department of physiology at the Medical-Surgical Academy. This is the time (1860) when the foundation was laid, in the modest physiological laboratory of the Medical-Surgical Academy, which led Russian physiology to one of the highest positions in world physiology. During its entire existence, the department carefully preserved the memory of its reformer and his tradition. Nearly half a century after Sechenov's separation from the Medical-Surgical Academy, I. P. Pavlov, Sechenov's successor, began to search for a suitable portrait of Sechenov for the department. With this in mind, Pavlov wrote to a former student

[22]I. M. Sechenov. Selected Works. Pub. VIEM, 1935, p. XI.
[23]I. M. Sechenov. On Animal Electricity. St. Petersburg, 1862.

of Sechenov's, Professor M. N. Shaternikov. Here is the full text of this letter, dated May 9, 1916. Pavlov writes:

"Esteemed Mikhail Nikolayevich:
"It goes without saying that I am exceedingly happy to receive a portrait of Ivan Mikhaylovich (Sechenov) in the midst of his students at the Academy. Who, if not Sechenov, who laid the foundation of Russian physiology, who started it at the Academy, and who, through his scientific and educational activities, left an indelible impression in the minds of his disciples, should occupy the place of honor on the walls of the present physiological laboratory of the Academy. This portrait will be the Academy's best and dearest ornament. Will you kindly give my regards to Maria Aleksandrovna, whom to my deep regret I do not have the honor of knowing personally, and also the sincere gratitude of the entire laboratory for her gift.
"Many thanks for sending me the splendid biography of Ivan Mikhaylovich. With best wishes. I. Pavlov."[24]

In 1863, three years after Sechenov had begun working at the Medical-Surgical Academy, a new University regulation called for the creation of a new department of human anatomy and animal physiology; these fields had previously been included in the department of zoology, and this laid the foundation for the development of experimental physiology at the University. In 1866 the St. Petersburg University first made a specific allocation of funds for the establishment and maintenance of a physiological laboratory (1,000 rubles a year). Academician F. V. Ovsyannikov was appointed to organize and direct the laboratory, and he remained as a teacher at the University for the next 20 years. During 1866-1868 Ovsyannikov, who was fully aware of the complexity and diversity of the task of physiological training, invited two men who were already well known for their brilliant accomplishments in physiology as teachers of specific areas of physiology. These men were I. F. Tsion and N. N. Bakst.

Tsion's name was well known because of his discovery of the depressor nerve and his description of a new reflex form of regulation of the cardiovascular system, while Bakst gained recognition through his precise investigations in neurophysiology in collaboration with Helmholtz. Tsion's achievements will be discussed in another chapter. Here we shall comment briefly on Bakst's investigations.

Bakst graduated from Petersburg University in 1862 and was sent abroad to prepare for a professorship in physiology. His first work was performed in Helmholtz's laboratory and was published in German, in 1867.[25] This article presented the first determinations of the speed of distribution of excitation in human motor nerves. He subsequently spent much time on this investigation, and he achieved a high experimental skill.

---

[24]This is taken from the copy of the Moscow division of the Academy of Sciences; Professor O. P. Molchanova has the original.
[25]Monatsberichte der Akademie der Wissensch., zu Berlin, 1867.

124

He also devoted much attention to the physiology of the sense organs. In 1867 his translation from English language of V. Odling's book Animal Chemistry was published.

Ovsyannikov, Tsion, and Bakst not only raised the level of the teaching of physiology at the University to unprecedented heights, but they also organized scientific research work in the laboratory, and in the early 1870's it began to attract the most gifted students. I. P. Pavlov also came as a student and entered Petersburg University in 1870.

The 1850's and 1860's mark the beginning of an upsurge in the natural sciences in Russia. It was during this period that our scientists achieved world recognition in all fields of natural science, especially in chemistry and physiology, through their basic work, and it was then that they created independent scientific schools, primarily as an outgrowth of university laboratories. Suffice it to mention the names of such Russian naturalists of that period as Zinin, Butlerov, Beketov, Mendeleyev, Sokolov, Sechenov, and Borodin. They all worked independently, but also attracted a number of talented young people, thus creating independent scientific schools and establishing traditions that have been preserved to this day.

The development of the sciences, and natural sciences in particular, at the Russian universities was contrary to designs of the tsarist tyranny, and both the students and leading university professors were subjected to terrible constraints. It is well known that precisely during these years there were numerous instances of student rioting at the two main Russian universities, Moscow and Petersburg. The historians of the Russian universities have written extensively on this special topic.

Even though they were in power and had material wealth, the parasitic clique of tsarist officials and subordinates was unable to curb the people's enormous drive toward creative knowledge and the mastery over the secrets of nature. Also, with every passing year, more and more Russian youths aspired to enter the universities for the sake of knowledge and science, and they listened to the voice of the new masters of the mind, the scientists, among whom the most powerful and most captivating voice belonged to Ivan Mikhaylovich Sechenov.

CHAPTER X

The history of I. M. Sechenov's discovery of the phenomena
of central inhibition.

In the history of world physiology I. M. Sechenov's name is inseparably linked with the discovery of one of the most remarkable characteristics of the function of central nervous system—central inhibition. To him belongs the exclusive credit in world science of the discovery of brain centers which depress spinal reflexes and also of demonstrating the broad significance of these centers in the reflex coordination of motor acts. Moreover, it is well known that it was precisely on the basis of these experiments and of the new philosophical outlook that Sechenov wrote his famous treatise Reflexes of the Brain.

In 1862, while working in Paris in Claude Bernard's laboratory, Sechenov demonstrated that by sectional separation of the brain from the spinal cord it is possible to determine the specific region of the brain which will govern depression of spinal reflexes when the specific transected surface is stimulated. The strongest and longest depression of reflexes (as compared with a similar effect from other regions) is elicited when the optic lobes of the brain are bisected. Stimulation of the transverse section of the optic lobe by a crystal of table salt also elicits a strong depression of the reflexes. Control experiments have demonstrated that an application of table salt to a transverse section of the spinal cord will not elicit such a depression of reflexes. On the basis of numerous experiments, Sechenov arrived at the important conclusion which reveals the essence of his discovery: "Thus these experiments have established the presence of nerve mechanisms in the optic lobes of the frog which, when stimulated, depress reflexes, and the absence of such depressive mechanisms in the spinal cord."

The discovery of the Weber brothers demonstrated the phenomenon of peripheral neural inhibition of organic functions, while Sechenov discovered the very important phenomenon of central inhibition; Sechenov discovered a specific physiological function of the brain. Sechenov's basic theory of central inhibition, although subjected to numerous attacks and experimental verifications by many scientists over a number of decades, remains unshakable to this day.

Sechenov's work was published in 1863 in the Proceedings of the Paris Academy of Sciences, with an introduction by Claude Bernard ("Note sur les moderateurs des mouvements réflexes dans le cerveau de la grenouille," présentée par M. Bernard).* This fact is of particular interest, since, in the detailed biography of Claude Bernard recently published in the U.S.A., the author of the book (Olmsted) attempts to refute Sechenov's priority in this important physiological discovery in favor of Claude Bernard himself.

In 1863 Sechenov published this work in Russia,[1] and, beginning with 1865, his articles on the analysis of the phenomenon he had discovered were published regularly in the Bulletin of the Petersburg Academy.[2]

As I. P. Pavlov indicated in one of his speeches dedicated to Sechenov, his article on reflex-inhibitive centers "and the fact described in this article must be considered the first victory of Russian thought in the field of physiology, the first independent and original work which immediately made an important contribution in physiology."[3]

The history of this discovery is most informative. There is no doubt that two facts were known before Sechenov: first, that the nature of reflex reactions is changed in decapitated frogs, and, second, that in the brain there are special areas that are functionally related to underlying areas of the central nervous system (the spinal cord) and that have an inhibitory influence (for instance, those described by Weber). Moreover, at that time some physiologists were already aware of the fact that the thalami optici have a depressing action. It is curious to note that there are such indications in Russian physiological literature, in an article by the Kazan' professor A. A. Sokolovskiy, published in 1858, in the Annals of Kazan' University, "On the effect of various substances on the nervous system as an application of Du Bois-Reymond's theory on the quieting and excitation of nerves." Discussing in his article the various forms of inhibition of nervous activity, external as well as internal, Sokolovskiy writes: "And finally let us take into account the inhibitory influences (Hemmung) of the ganglia of the brain (corpora striata et thalami optici)

---

*A note on moderators of reflex movements in the frog's brain."
[1] "Investigations of the centers which inhibit reflex movement in the frog's brain." See Medical Herald, 1863, nos. 1, 2, and 3. "A supplement to the theory of nerve centers which inhibit reflex movements." See Medical Herald, 1863, nos. 34, 35.
[2] Neue Versuche über die Hemmungsmechanismen im Gehirn des Frosches, als Erwiderung auf die im Laborat. des Hrn. M. Schiff ausgeführten Untersuchungen—Bull. de l'Acad. des Sc. (series 3), 1865, vol. VIII, January, cols. 145-162. This work was read before the Academy on November 17, 1864; Notiz über die erregende Wirkung des Blutes auf die cerebrospinalen Nervencentra des Frosches. Bull. de l'Acad. des Sciences (series 3), 1865, vol. VIII, June, cols. 380-384. These two articles, which were published in the Annals of our Academy and which were very important, were omitted from the "List of Sechenov's works" in the first edition of his Autobiographical Notes (Moscow, 1907).
[3] Speech at the Society of Russian Physicians in Petersburg on March 15, 1914. See I. P. Pavlov, Twenty Years of Experience in the Objective Study of Higher Nervous Activity (Behavior) of Animals, 5th edition, 1932, p. 169.

on the spinal cord via the intermediate nerves between the ganglia of the brain and the cells of the spinal cord (rami communicates), and the similar influence of the medulla oblongata through the vagus nerves on the cardiac plexi, and the influence of the splanchnic nerve (Pflüger) on the solar plexi. . . ."

We see then from this excerpt that a direct and clear reference to the thalami optici as an inhibitory center was made four years prior to the publication of Sechenov's observations concerning this problem.[4]

However, the basis for Sokolovskiy's important conclusions of 1858 remains obscure. Indeed, in the last chapter of Pflüger's monograph on the inhibitory nerves of the intestines (1857), to which Sokolovskiy makes reference, the question of inhibitory centers is raised, but the problem of the topography of such centers and of the mechanism of their function is not solved. There remains one supposition, that Sokolovskiy's data may be traced to Sechenov's teacher, Professor Carl Ludwig, who already knew that the thalami optici were nerve centers exercising inhibitory influence. But Ludwig apparently did not attach any great significance to this fact. Only this can explain the correspondence between Ludwig and Sechenov concerning the latter's discovery of the inhibitory influence of stimulation of the thalami optici on the spinal reflexes. Two letters from Ludwig to Sechenov speak of this eloquently, and we present here some excerpts.[5]

In a letter dated November 25, 1862, Ludwig wrote:

"Dear Sechenov, For days I have intended to write to you and to thank you for informing me of your results, but somehow there was always something in the way. Your data are all the more interesting to me since for years I was occupied with the same problem, and at the end of last summer I undertook a systematic study of the same with Mr. Tomsa. I shall not interrupt this work now, especially since we (Tomsa and I) have arrived at the same conclusion as you did, but from a completely different angle. I know which region must be damaged in order to obtain hypersthesia, and I repeatedly demonstrated this phenomenon last summer. However, as you know, I place but little value on precedence; I am content in the knowledge that a correct solution of some problem or other has been formed. Therefore I do not intend to hurry with the publication of my (or rather our) results. At any rate, I do not intend to publish anything on this subject in the near future."

---

[4] This most interesting detail in the history of physiological views in Russia was pointed out to me by L. Vasil'yev, a professor of physiology at Leningrad University.

[5] Ludwig's letters to Sechenov, which are of enormous interest in the history of physiology, were published in part in Sechenov's excellent biography written by his disciple, M. N. Shaternikov (see Sechenov, Selected Works. Moscow, 1935).

In a letter dated November 29, 1862 Ludwig again returns to the problem which so intensely worried Sechenov:

"I am afraid that when you receive my letter informing you that we too are studying the spinal cord you will worry even more, and I hasten to put your mind at ease. Tomsa and I are too far advanced in our work to give up further exploration of this problem. But I repeat, although I have known for a long time which area, when injured, leads to hypersthesia, I am in no way anxious to publish my data. If you see Kühne, he can tell you that already two years ago I suggested that he explore the inhibitory phenomena in the spinal cord and even gave him a working outline."

These data show that Sechenov persisted in his work along an independent path; he thus obtained an array of entirely new facts and had a general-physiological approach to the phenomenon of central inhibition. When his work appeared in print in 1862-1863, in the German, French, and Russian languages, Sechenov gained broad recognition as the first physiologist to have formulated and submitted to thorough experimental analysis the problem of central inhibition in the nervous system. In this connection, the first lines of a letter from Ludwig to Sechenov after he had received a reprint of Sechenov's article are of great interest. On November 15, 1862, Ludwig wrote:

"Dear Sechenov, I was overjoyed to hear about the publication of your article, and even greater was my pleasure when I actually received a copy of this valuable work. Reading it reminded me of the beautiful experiments you had demonstrated to me, and thanks to your advice I succeeded in reproducing them at one of my recent lectures. It would be superfluous to advise you to continue to work on this subject; it will reward you with yet more discoveries. . ."

Thus the possibility is by no means excluded that the inhibitory influences of the "Sechenov center" were known to other physiologists prior to Sechenov's investigations. But the indisputable fact remains that Sechenov independently discovered the inhibitory influence of stimulation of the thalami optici, and, most important, that he proved the reflex nature of the processes of central inhibition and submitted a detailed physiological analysis of this significant phenomenon, which no one had done before. This may explain the attitude towards Sechenov's work of the two most outstanding physiologists of that period, i.e., K. Ludwig and Claude Bernard. As we have seen, Claude Bernard presented Sechenov's work for publication in the Proceedings of the Paris Academy of Sciences, while Carl Ludwig requested Sechenov's permission to demonstrate his experiments at his lectures.

In evaluating Sechenov's role in the exploration of the problem of central inhibition, one must bear in mind first of all that Sechenov did not stop at the discovery of a locus in the midbrain whose stimulation depresses spinal reflexes (he had done this in Paris in 1862); he also worked out experimentally and in detail the means and methods for accomplishing acts of central inhibition and thereby opened a new page in the physiological concepts of the nature of reflex acts. Sechenov and his students proved that in addition to inhibitory centers there also exist excitatory centers, and he demonstrated clearly that the depressing mechanisms exist both in the brain and in the spinal cord.

While investigating the conditions under which inhibitory phenomena in both the motor reflexes and the rhythmic work of the lymph heart appear, Sechenov discovered a number of most important phenomena indicative of interrelationships between the central and peripheral portions of the nervous system. These investigations were carried out mainly in 1867-1868, while Sechenov was in Graz (Austria), and his letters home during that period vividly unfold the essence of Sechenov's investigations as he appraised them. Thus in a letter dated October 12, 1867, Sechenov wrote to M. A. Sechenova-Bokova:[6]

"Imagine, for instance, the following situation: one lateral side of the spinal cord of the frog is transected, and afterwards a transection is made of the brain in the area the stimulation of which elicits inhibition of reflexes. Some two minutes after transection of the brain we can place the frog right before us on the table and observe to our heart's content, even for 24 hours, the pulsation of the lymph hearts on both sides. Now place some salt on the transverse section. The frog does not move; one of the hearts—on the transected side—continues to pulsate while the other stops. The salt remains. The stimulus strengthens, the frog begins to crawl or jump (compulsive movements); but in about two minutes it quiets down (while the salt is still in place). Just as before, one lymph heart has stopped, the other is pulsating. During this time it is possible to pinch the leg on the side of the inactive heart and even shear it with scissors, and the frog will not react, while the leg on the opposite side reacts violently even to mild pinching. Now remove the salt from the wound and leave the frog alone for about 10 minutes. The depression of the spinal cord gradually passes and stimulation of the previously insensitive leg begins to produce a weak reaction. At this moment pinching the skin evokes one, two, three contractions of the stopped lymph heart. Is it not obvious that so long as stimulation of the brain acts on the excitability of the spinal cord in a strongly depressing manner it is impossible to stimulate either the reflex apparatus or the motor mechanism of the lymph hearts from the periphery; but as soon as this effect begins to weaken, both are possible. Do you understand then, my darling child, that these experiments are no less important than those which I performed in Paris, and by their elegance they surpass everything I knew until now in physiology (as far as the nervous system is concerned)."

_____

[6] This letter and those that follow are being published here for the first time; the originals are in the possession of Professor (Mme.) O. P. Molchanova.

I. M. Sechenov in the laboratory at the Medical Surgical
Academy (early 1860's).

These last lines hardly sound as though Sechenov overrates his works. Indeed, these experiments revealed for the first time, under experimental conditions, the interrelationships between the central nervous apparatuses which regulate the neural reflex processes and those centripetal impulses which, under normal conditions of animal life, are the source of coordinated reflex acts.

Sechenov's next two letters, of the same period, speak with special distinctness of his achievements in this direction. In the first of them, dated January 30, 1868, Sechenov wrote:

"I am able to stop a frog's walking movements by stimulating a nerve. The procedure is very simple: the frog's brain is transected just behind the optic lobes, and the frog begins to make so-called compulsive walking movements, i.e., it constantly crawls; if this frog's sciatic nerves are stimulated with table salt it remains immobile during the entire period of stimulation, i.e., for five minutes or longer; but as soon as the stimulated portion of the nerve is cut off, the frog will begin to crawl again. This fact is important in three respects: 1) it demonstrates inhibition of a new form of movements; 2) it proves that inhibitory mechanisms enter into centers governing walking movements; 3) it explains the apparently paradoxical fact (which I had already mentioned to you in Graz) that in the frog with ligated optical thalami, stimulation of the sciatic nerve with alternating current or caustic alkali elicits a pain reaction, while stimulation with NaCl almost never has this effect. This can now be readily explained. Any stimulation of the sciatic nerve in general triggers two distinct central mechanisms: the apparatus that produces pain and its aftermath, and the mechanism that inhibits movements; if upon such stimulation the former is more strongly stimulated at a given moment, the results will be movement, and vice versa. In order to verify this idea I performed the following experiment: the thalami optici of the frog were transected and the sciatic nerve was exposed; if the latter is immediately stimulated with induction currents of moderate or great intensity the frog will sense the stimulus and jump; but if we begin with very weak stimulation of the nerve and then gradually increase the current, the frog will remain immobile even with very strong currents. In other words, with a gradual increase of an initially weak stimulus the mechanisms which paralyze movement will be stimulated more rapidly than the mechanisms which produce the same movements."

"What do you say about this my bright little bird? The dreams which I had when I wrote the Reflexes of the Brain have materialized."

This was indeed a brilliant solution of problems in the field of the physiology of the central nervous system which Sechenov outlined in the concluding pages of his brilliant monograph, Reflexes of the Brain, where he had pointed out with remarkable foresight the missing links in experimental analysis, indispensable for the reconstruction of the true picture of the mechanism of reflex regulation of motor acts. His second letter, dated February 29, 1868, is especially interesting in this respect. In this letter, also unpublished until now, Sechenov describes his "experiment of the white lady." This was the name he had given to the experiment, since on that day Sechenov had attended a performance of the opera "The White Lady" (by Boieldieu) in Graz, and so, in a letter to Sechenova-Bokova, he jestingly calls his experiment "the experiment of the white lady":

"Here it is. If we cut away the cerebral hemispheres of the frog it will sit, as you know, quite still. In such a frog, the sciatic nerve is exposed, and the thigh is cut out from the popliteal space as high as possible. If the sciatic nerve is then stimulated with weak or moderate induction currents the frog immediately runs away, i.e., it makes a jump; but if we instantly stimulate the nerve with strong currents the frog remains in its place and starts running only after the effect of the current ceases. One could not think of a simpler and clearer experiment on reflex inhibition of the walking movement. I expect that the experiment of the white lady will please even you, my strict beauty. But this is only half the story; this very day some facts have been discovered that for the present I am able to explain to myself only as due to the presence of inhibitory mechanisms in the spinal cord. However, in order that you may understand me, I must tell you first why in general one must assume that there are inhibitory apparatuses also in the spinal cord. You know about the inhibitory apparatus of the heart: the centers of the vagus nerve in the medulla oblongata, then in the fibers of the vagus and then the endings of the vagus in the venous sac (in the frog) of the heart have an inhibitory effect on the motor elements of the heart. An inhibitor of re-flexes must have the same pattern, and therefore the middle portions of the brain (the direct stimulation of which depresses the reflexes) must correspond to the vagal centers; from here some conductors that correspond to vagal fibers must descend along the spinal cord, and these conductors cannot end directly in the reflex mechanism—otherwise when they are stimulated they would produce a movement—but rather they must terminate in inhibitory mechanisms that are linked with the reflex mechanisms. Fortunately, both end apparatuses are separated from one another, and therefore they may be stimulated individually; but until now this could not be shown in the spinal cord. Now here is what I have discovered: the animal is decapitated (right below the fourth ventricle), and the sciatic nerves are exposed. If they are stim-ulated with currents of weak or moderate intensity, then instantly after stimulation is begun reflex movements of varying intensity are elicited; (it would take quite a bit of time to describe it) but they are always present. If however the nerve is stimulated immediately with the intensity that produced the phenomenon of the white lady, the result would be that at the beginning of the stimulation there is rest and only after a certain length of time do the reflexes appear. I think that this rest indicates the existence

133

at that moment of a predominance of the inhibitory over the motor mechanisms. One thing is certain, this rest cannot be the result of overstimulation, because by the very essence of this concept there must be stimulation before there can be overstimulation.''

''So as you see my darling child there is no need for you to worry about my work. Independently of the fact that it solves the problem of reflex inhibition of reflexes and of the act of walking, the work contains the elements for the analysis of the alternating phenomena of spinal activity (i.e., the alternating movements of flexion and extension of limbs upon stimulation of the skin); it proves in the most positive fashion that inhibition of reflexes, standstill of the lymph hearts and of the blood heart upon stimulation of the mid-portions of the brain are the result of stimulation of specific nerve centers. Finally in this work entirely new problems shall be discussed on the relationship of the walking apparatus to reflex mechanisms. I only fear that this project will take a long time since 'the deeper you go into the forest, the more the timber.' But it really matters little if I clip off some two weeks from other work to do this one. You understand my golden darling that within these problems rests my soul.''

''The experiment of the white lady'' fascinated Sechenov; it prompted him towards a number of important findings, including the existence of inhibitory centers in the spinal cord. Primarily, however, these experiments led him to the basic physiological problems of regulation of coordinated movements. He demonstrated his experiment to many foreign and Russian physiologists. I. I. Mechnikov, who visited Sechenov in Graz in 1868, was fascinated by the experiment. It was precisely during this visit that Mechnikov became inspired to dedicate himself to physiology. We learn of this from Sechenov's letter to Sechenova-Bokova dated March 17, 1868. He writes:

''Mechnikov left here yesterday morning. He intends to work in my laboratory beginning next September and in general is beginning to dream of becoming a physiologist. I of course am encouraging him in every way, since he is a very talented gentleman.''

In his description and interpretation of ''the experiment of the white lady,'' aside from the most important conclusions with regard to the mechanisms of coordination, Sechenov's comparison of the phenomena of central inhibition of cerebro-spinal reflexes with the mechanisms inhibiting cardiac activity is particularly striking. It is interesting that Sechenov was led to the exploration of the inhibition of spinal reflexes by the central regions of the nervous system on the basis of the Weber brothers' discovery of the inhibitory influence of the vagus on the heart. It is known that the beginning of Sechenov's first report on his discovery of inhibitory phenomena of spinal reflexes refers to the Weber brothers' findings. The juxtaposition of the facts indicative of the relationship between the cerebro-spinal nervous elements in the phenomena of inhibition of spinal reflexes with the facts of central and local regulation of cardiac inhibition under the influence of the vagus nerve on the one hand sharpened Sechenov's interest in the mechanism of inhibition of cardiac activity and, on the other hand, made it necessary to ascertain the anatomo-physiological pathways leading the inhibitory influence of the center to the spinal cord.

The above letters, which reveal Sechenov's creative plans during the period of his work on "the experiments of the white lady" and inform us of Mechnikov's visit to him at precisely that time, clarify the background of Sechenov's and Mechnikov's two joint projects on the nature of the effect of the vagus nerve on the heart. Sechenov constantly returned to this subject in his major monographs on the physiology of the nervous system, thereby emphasizing the identity of the means of accomplishing inhibitory influences from the centers upon the periphery. Here again the analogy between the spinal synapses and the intracardial ganglia along the pathways of central inhibitory influence has not lost its significance up to our time.

Sechenov persistently searched for the pathways along which the inhibitory influence from an established center was effected. However, for a long time this problem was considered unsolved. Only now, through the joint efforts of Academician L. A. Orbeli and his closest assistant, Professor A. V. Tonkikh, has it been proved that the marginal sympathetic trunk is precisely this pathway. In the history of development of this problem, it is of particular interest that Sechenov himself studied it, and, as may be seen from his unpublished letters, he knew that the sympathetic nervous system was the pathway along which the inhibitory influences of the mid-portions of the brain were distributed. Thus in a letter from Graz to Sechenova-Bokova dated October 19, 1867, we read:

"I have begun the investigation from another viewpoint, to determine the nature of the motor impulses, and already have several splendid facts: first, I can stop the lymph hearts for one to three hours and longer by transecting all of the posterior roots of the frog's spinal cord; second, I have found several ways to make the hearts pulsate again—by transection of the brain at the upper border of the medulla oblongata, or by transection of any point of the spinal cord or, finally, by extirpation of the abdominal chain of the sympathetic nerve. All these facts are explained in the following manner: in the normal frog there is tonic excitation within the realm of the sympathetic nerve that stops the heart in diastole (Goltz found, two or three years ago, that stimulation of the intestines evoked a diastolic arrest of the heart); but as long as the posterior cerebrospinal roots are intact, any excitation of them overcomes this influence, and the hearts pulsate with every movement of the animal; however, as soon as the cutaneous influences are eliminated, the effect of reflex inhibition has the opportunity to manifest itself fully, and, conversely, it is eliminated when the sympathetic nerve is destroyed."

The novelty, the fascinating prospects, and daring generalizations in the field of investigation of reflex mechanisms attracted to Sechenov a number of gifted and dedicated young people. Among the first of Sechenov's students was I. G. Berezin (1837-1866), who graduated from the Military-Medical Academy the year of publication of the Reflexes of the Brain (1863), and whom Sechenov interested in experimental work while he was still a student. In 1866 Berezin published his doctoral dissertation on the subject Reflexes Elicited by Thermal Influences on the Skin of the Frog (St. Petersburg, 1866), an article in a Russian journal (Medical Herald, no. 6), and a German one as well on the subject "Experimental proofs of dissimilarity between the reflex nerve fibers and the conscious sensory nerve fibers in the frog." These two works laid the foundation for a study of strictly scientific functional differentiation of the sensory elements of the nervous system; this was significant, both for an analysis of the complex problem formulated by Sechenov on the signalling pathways from the sensory regions of the brain and spinal cord and also for the more general problems on the physiology of the sensory nerves and nerve endings. Berezin's work made a tremendous impression on his contemporaries. His data and findings were included in international reference books (such as Hermann's Handbuch). Sechenov valued his young and promising student very highly, but that same year (1866) Berezin died of cholera at the age of 29.[7]

To appraise Berezin's role in the development of the physiology of nervous processes, it is of interest to present here an excerpt from Sechenov's Physiology of the Nervous System, published that same year, 1866.

"When the printing of this chapter was nearly completed, Mr. Berezin, an assistant at the physiological laboratory of the local Medical-Surgical Academy, made a highly important discovery which changed the existing view concerning the inter-relationship of the reflex and sensory fibers of the skin, a view which I have developed in paragraph 72.

"By transecting single, pairs, or groups of three spinal roots supplying the hind extremity of the frog, he found that by preserving only the superior roots the conscious sensitivity in the skin of the hind leg remains, although dulled in the normal animal, even with relatively weak pain stimulation (acid) of the skin; in other words, the latter evokes reflexes both in the hind leg and in the front part of the body even when the lateral half of the spinal cord is also transected on the side of the transected roots, or when a portion of the posterior half of the cord is cut out in the region of the fourth vertebra. If, however, with only one of the upper roots remaining intact we decapitate the animal (the spinal cord remaining intact), even the strongest stimulation of the skin (with concentrated sulphuric acid) will not elicit the slightest body movement.

"This experiment proves in a most positive manner the dissimilarity between the sensory and the reflex fibers of the skin in the hind leg of the frog.

---

[7] An article by V. D. Lashkevich about I. G. Berezin was published in the journal Medical Herald, 1866, no. 42.

"Berezin's next experiment is no less important. If in a frog only one upper root is left intact, cutting out of the hemispheres appears sufficient for the abolition of the reflex body movements.

"From this fact it follows that in the reflexes of the frog's brain a movement may appear as a consequence of a conscious pain sensation. Indeed, no one assumes that there are reflex-like apparatuses in the cerebral hemispheres; on the other hand, as a rule the mechanisms which produce conscious sensations are attributed to the hemispheres.

"The fibers going from the skin of the hind legs to the brain along the middle and lower roots are linked with the coordinating centers; for this reason, when all the roots are intact, the brain reflex may be elicited even after removal of the hemipsheres.

"Finally, Berezin's discovery discards the idea expressed in paragraph 73 on the relationship of the coordinating centers to the cells of the posterior horns. In that paragraph the assumption was made that the points in the brain where the sensory fibers converge serve as collective centers with regard to the cells of the spinal cord. Obviously now this idea is discarded, since the sensory fibers in their entire length are separated from the reflex [efferent] fibers. However, for the motor half of the entire dermo-muscular apparatus, the concept of coordinating mechanisms as collective centers with regard to the cells of the anterior half of the spinal cord still holds true."

V. V. Pashutin (1845-1901), the subsequent founder of the Russian school of pathology, began his scientific career in Sechenov's laboratory, together with Berezin. Pashutin also began his experimental work as a student under I. M. Sechenov's guidance. It was undoubtedly on account of Sechenov's great interest in the inhibitory effect of the vagus nerve, and also under the influence of Pflüger's work published in 1857 on the inhibitory influence of the vagus nerve on intestinal movement, which was of interest to Sechenov, that Pashutin performed experiments in this direction on cats and published the results of his work in 1865. The same year an article on the work done by Sechenov in collaboration with Pashutin was published simultaneously in Russian and in German; their article, entitled "New experiments on the brain and spinal cord of the frog," was of great significance in the development of Sechenov's viewpoints.

Like Berezin, Pashutin, at Sechenov's suggestion, made an experimental analysis of the important problem of functional differentiation between the pain and tactile sensitivity of the frog's skin.

Under the influence of facts obtained by his young assistants, Berezin and Pashutin, Sechenov made some important corrections in the second edition of his book Reflexes of the Brain.

This touched upon the important problem of processes that intensify the reflexes in addition to the processes discovered by Sechenov that inhibit reflexes. Thus Sechenov, in the second edition of his Reflexes of the Brain, in 1866, wrote:

137

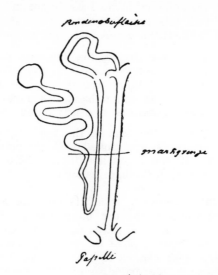

[handwritten facsimile of the end of a letter, in German cursive]

Фотокопия конца письма К. Людвига к И. М. Сеченову

Photostat of the end of K. Ludwig's letter to I. M. Sechenov.

"And where are the practical experiments on the mechanism which intensifies the reflexes akin to those performed on the mechanisms that inhibit them? Such experiments already exist, and I am all the more glad to report them since they are very simple, clear, and convincing for any one who does not inject prejudice into the solution of our problem. Mr. Berezin, an assistant in the physiological laboratory of this Academy, has found that if, after a frog is kept at room temperature (i.e., 17-18°C) for several hours, its hind legs are immersed in ice water, it will very soon pull them out. This means that the frog feels the cold, that it is unpleasant to it, and it begins to move for the purpose of avoiding the unpleasant sensation; and it must be noted that this movement is always very violent, as if the frog were frightened. However, if the cerebral hemispheres are removed and the procedure of immersing the frog's legs is repeated, the animal remains completely still. However, the situation is changed if more of the skin's surface is cooled; if, for example, the entire lower half of the body is submerged in the ice water—the frog will move its legs. Is it not obvious that in eliciting movement by cooling the skin the hemispheres act similarly as the cooled area is enlarged? It is well known that the latter condition in general intensifies the cooling effect (the feeling of cold becomes unbearable); consequently the hemispheres also act in an intensifying manner with respect to the cooling effect, i.e., with respect to movement. Another experiment proving the presence in the frog's brain of mechanisms which intensify involuntary movements is credited to the student Pashutin. He has found that the movements of the frog caused by touching its skin are greatly intensified if the middle section of the brain is stimulated with electrical current. The frog reacts similarly to a man who has been unexpectedly touched: its entire body flinches at the contact; however, when the brain is not stimulated, it very often remains quite still."[8]

Sechenov concludes his first report of his discovery of a special center having an inhibitory influence on reflex acts by pointing out that these phenomena, although they were observed in frogs, must have a generalized significance in the physiology of the central nervous system of all animals. That Sechenov attributed a universal significance to his discovery by experiments on frogs is evident by the fact that these very experiments supply the foundation of his remarkable monograph Reflexes of the Brain. L. N. Simonov, one of his disciples, provided the first experimental proof of the broader significance of the phenomenon discovered by Sechenov.

In 1866 Simonov published an article in which he demonstrated the presence of mechanisms inhibiting the reflex processes in mammals as well. The article appeared in the Military-Medical Journal (1866, pt. 97, v. II, pp. 1-31, 67-92) under the title "Experimental proof of the existence of central inhibition of reflexes in mammals." That same year Simonov published this article abroad.[9] This brilliant work

---

[8] I. M. Sechenov. Reflexes of the Brain. USSR Academy of Sciences, 1942, pp. 53-54.
[9] Simonoff. Die Hemmungsmechanismen d. Säugethiere experimentell bewiesen. Arch. f. Anat. u. Physiol., 1866, p. 545.

was Dr. Simonov's only scientific investigation. In later years he devoted himself to problems in the theory and practice of medicine. It is of interest to mention the publication of Brown-Sequard's lectures on physiology and pathology of the nervous system (1867) in a Russian translation by Simonov.

Obviously, Sechenov valued Simonov's investigations highly, and his work was submitted for the Baer prize when it was first awarded in 1867. It is important to mention that at the same time Sechenov submitted his own book, Physiology of the Nervous System, published in 1866, for the same award. The first Baer award was given to two most outstanding Russian zoologists, I. I. Mechnikov and A. O. Kovalevskiy, since works in zoology and embryology had a preferred status in the competition, Baer himself having been an innovator precisely in zoology and embryology. A reviewer of Sechenov's and Simonov's works, the member of the award committee physiologist F. V. Ovsyannikov, gave high praise to Sechenov's and Simonov's works, but he commented that Sechenov's book, Physiology of the Nervous System, was in the nature of a textbook.[10] This of course was not so: Sechenov's book from beginning to end represented a new message in the field of nerve physiology. With all due respect to the objectivity of the decision of the award committee which awarded the first Baer prize—established in memory of a great embryologist—to the embryologists Mechnikov and Kovalevskiy, we are unable to agree with its appraisal of Sechenov's book.

During the course of almost three decades, a number of Russian and foreign physiologists, including Schiff, Tsion, A. A. Gertsen, Meltzer, and others critically scrutinized Sechenov's views and facts concerning "Sechenov inhibition." One of the first to appear with the critique of Sechenov's work was A. A. Gertsen (1864).[11] Later, the Petersburg physiologist I. Tsion brought forward his own theory on the nature of the phenomenon of central inhibition. This article appeared in a volume dedicated to Carl Ludwig.[12] We have mentioned before Ludwig's sympathy for the works of his favorite disciple, Sechenov.

Sechenov refuted all objections with exceptional conviction. In the course of further study of the processes of inhibition in the central nervous system, Sechenov's original conclusions underwent significant changes, but the core of this theory, i.e., the viewpoint that central inhibition is the basis of coordination of reflex activity, and that it is the process that precedes increased excitability of the corresponding neural elements (what later on was described by the English investigators as induction), has remained a major contribution to

---

[10]See Ovsyannikov's review. Annals of the Academy of Sciences, 1867, vol. XI, pp. 148-149.

[11] A. A. Gertsen. Expériences sur les Centres Modérateurs. Turin, 1864.

[12] I. Tsion. Zur Hemmungstheorie d. reflectorisch. Erregungen. Beiträge zur Anat. u. Physiol. als Festgabe Carl Ludwig gewid. v. s. Schülern. I. H., p. 96, 1875.

140

physiology.[13] With this work, Sechenov also laid the foundation for the understanding of the reflex inhibition of the activity of the vegetative organs (in particular organs of blood and lymph circulation), as well as for the understanding of the physiological bases of antagonistic influences which assure the performance of complex coordinated acts.

As we shall see in subsequent chapters, these views originally formulated by Sechenov were elaborated by his most outstanding disciple, N. Ye. Vedenskiy, while credit for the discovery of reflex inhibition in the vegetative organs (in the lymph hearts) belongs to the first Russian woman-physiologist, P. V. Suslova, whose work on the physiology of nervous regulation of the lymph hearts (Beiträge zur Physiologie der Lympherzen, Zürich, 1867) gained wide recognition.

Sechenov's experimental investigations concerning the nature and significance of the phenomenon of inhibition of reflex acts, discovered by him, and his attraction from the time of his student years to the basic problems of psychology led him to produce his immortal work Reflexes of the Brain, which originated the glorious traditions of Russian neurophysiology.

We have presented here the basic data and facts dealing with Sechenov's discovery of the phenomena of central inhibition and of the early years of Sechenov's and his students' investigations of important physiological problems of those times.

By Pavlov's definition Sechenov emerged as the originator of a new direction in the exploration of the physiology of the central nervous system, and he aroused a general interest in its phenomena of inhibition. Sechenov's investigations in this direction have a historical and logical connection with the investigations in the field of inhibition in the central nervous system subsequently conducted by Pavlov and his disciples in the twentieth century. Pavlov's concepts on the various forms of inhibition in the brain constituted a most important part in the theory of the conditioned reflexes, and the Pavlovian theory of protective inhibition led to the use of sleep therapy, which has had such beneficial results in the hands of experienced psychiatrists in the treatment of schizophrenia, for instance. The same theory of protective inhibition was applied by Pavlov's disciples with great success during the Second World War in the treatment of traumatic shock, burns, trophic skin disease, etc.

Such are the lessons handed down to us by this page in the history of science. Who could have anticipated such possibilities from an experiment on a frog of such extremely simple design and technique! Who could have imagined that theoretical conclusions and practical procedures of such major significance would result from a simple attempt to measure the time that it takes for a frog to withdraw its leg from a beaker filled with an acid solution.

---

[13] The problem of development of the Sechenov theory of inhibition is excellently presented in an article by M. A. Pankratov. Proceedings of the Lesgaft Scientific Institute [Izv. Nauchn. inst. im. Lesgafta], 1940, vol. XXII, p. 207.

CHAPTER XI

The scientific views of N. G. Chernyshevkiy. Sechenov and Chernyshevskiy. The Contemporary, and the history of publication of Reflexes of the Brain.

In the 1850's and 1860's, The Contemporary, published by N. G. Chernyshevskiy, devoted considerable space to the natural sciences, and in particular to physiology. Chernyshevskiy's philosophical works, and especially his article "The anthropological principle in philosophy," laid the foundation for a materialistic approach to the most difficult branches of the natural sciences. Chernyshevskiy appealed for world understanding and courageously publicized the postulate that the organization of the body is the cause and source of psychic phenomena. His philosophical work proclaimed the unity of theory and practice. In all his works and by his own example Chernyshevskiy demonstrated that the scientist should first of all be a citizen. In this respect he appears as the preceptor of the new generation of Russian scientists deeply dedicated to their people.

Chernyshevskiy's article "The anthropological principle in philosophy" is an important milestone in the development of theoretical science in Russia. It was written in the late 1850's and appeared in print in 1860. In this work he expounds with remarkable consistency the idea of the unity of all phenomena of nature, along with the qualitative characteristics of these phenomena at the various states of development. As a follower of Feuerbach, Chernyshevskiy materialistically solves a central philosophical problem, i.e., the problem of the soul and body, and boldly formulates that man and his consciousness are links in the general chain of phenomena of nature, subject to investigation by the scientific method.

"The unity of the laws of nature," writes Chernyshevskiy, "was understood long ago by men of genius; but only in recent decades has our knowledge reached such dimensions that it can prove the accuracy of this interpretation of phenomena of nature in a scientific manner."[1] Here Chernyshevskiy has in mind mainly the material chemical unity of nature: "Chemistry represents almost the greatest glory of our century."[2]

Chernyshevskiy scrutinizes concretely and in detail the problems of chemical unity of inorganic and organic nature, and with the foresight of genius demonstrates both the similarities and the differences among

---

[1] N. G. Chernyshevskiy. Collected Philosophical Works. OGIZ, 1938, p. 70.
[2] Ibid, p. 69.

chemical phenomena at various stages of life. He brings forward numerous examples showing how quantitative regrouping of chemical elements leads to qualitative changes in the properties of a newly formed chemical substance (water, diamond). He compares the combination of iron and oxygen in the inorganic world (rust) with the same combination in the red blood corpuscle (hemoglobin) and arrives at a most important theoretical conclusion.

"Thus, for instance, iron rust consists of a combination of iron with oxygen in such a simple and constant proportion that it is necessary to use an unusually high temperature or unusually strong reagents in order to produce a change in its substance. But in the blood corpuscle oxidized iron forms only one of the elements of a most complex chemical combination with the admixture of various other substances, for instance, water, and is incapable of maintaining its composition for any length of time; one may say that a blood corpuscle does not exist in a constant form as does rust, but changes incessantly, acquiring new particles and losing others."

In describing the general character of complex organic chemical compounds which participate in the life processes, Chernyshevskiy writes: "They have a very strong tendency to exist through the constant processes of appearing, growing, renewing themselves and, finally, of destruction under ordinary circumstances so that the existence of an object consisting of such combinations presents a constant renewal of its components and must be conceived as a perpetual chemical process."[3]

"Physiology and medicine find," writes Chernyshevskiy, "that the human organism is a most complex chemical combination which undergoes a complex chemical process called life. This process is so complex and its understanding is so important to us that the branch of chemistry concerned with these investigations was accorded, because of its importance, the status of a separate science with a special name—physiology."

From these considerations Chernyshevskiy comes to the following conclusions. 1) . . .physiology is but a modification of chemistry, and its subject is the modification of objects examined by chemistry. . . ." 2) "Medical phenomena enter into the system of physiological phenomena, and the whole system of physiological phenomena in turn enters into the still broader system of chemical phenomena."[4]

In his detailed analysis of the subject and achievements of physiology, Chernyshevskiy especially emphasizes the necessity for the comprehensive study of physiological phenomena. ". . .physiology seemingly considers the specific subjects of respiration, nutrition, circulation, growth, aging, and death. But here again one has to remember that these different stages and aspects of the life process are subdivided solely for the purpose of facilitating theoretical analysis, while in reality they compose a single indivisible whole."[5]

---

[3] Ibid., p. 65.
[4] Ibid., p. 90.
[5] Ibid., p. 91.

143

In approaching the solution of the central problem of his philosophical article, i.e., man's place in nature and the nature of human consciousness, Chernyshevskiy defines the science of man, i.e., anthropology, as "the science that always bears in mind, in considering any component of the life process, that the entire process and each of its components occur in the human organism, that this organism serves as material that generates the phenomena under consideration, that the properties of these phenomena are determined by the property of the material, and that the laws governing these phenomena are but special individual instances of the effect of the laws of nature."[6]

This profound scientific approach to the understanding of the nature of man and his consciousness diverges sharply from the vulgar-mechanistic notions of the German philosopher-mechanists of the nineteenth century, such as Buchner, Focht and Moleschott, popular at that time in Germany and Russia. Chernyshevskiy, who stood firmly on the position of dialectic materialism, insisted on the material nature of the phenomena of consciousness and their interrelationships with physiological processes and considered these phenomena first of all by their historical development.

And we see that in his work Chernyshevskiy pays a great deal of attention to the important problem of the manner of expression of sensations and emotions in various animals. The basic task confronting Chernyshevskiy consisted of proving that the phenomena of human consciousness are connected historically with the so-called psychic phenomena of the animal kingdom, and that only with a break in this historical succession can the phenomena of human consciousness be conceived by the idealists as some kind of miracle standing in some way isolated in the world of phenomena.

Indeed, these pages of Chernyshevskiy's work, published in 1860, appear as forerunners of the postulates presented in Darwin's classical writing, and especially in his work The Expression of the Emotions in Man and Animals. In comparing these Darwinian writings with the views already presented by A. I. Gertsen in the 1840's, we notice that the idea of evolution of the human psyche was cultivated for decades by Russian philosophers.

Among the books N. G. Chernyshevskiy took with him when he was in the Petropavlovsk fortress (1862-1864) were several highly important scientific works. It is known that in Alekseyev ravelin he had: Charles Darwin's The Origin of Species, Huxley's Man's Place in Nature, Lyell's Geological Proofs of the Antiquity of Man with some Remarks on the Theory of the Origin of Species, and Physiological Letters by Focht.[7] His copy of the latter book with the inscription "From the ravelin" is preserved in the Moscow Museum of Literature Museum, and on the title page there is a penciled notation in Chernyshevskiy's handwriting,

---

[6] Ibid., p. 96.
[7] N. M. Chernyshevskaya-Bystrova (Mme.). Chronicles of N. G. Chernyshevskiy's Life and Work. Academia, 1933, p. 119.

"More precise knowledge results in increasing might, greater wealth and higher virtue."[8]

Chernyshevskiy's book The Anthropological Principle in Philosophy played an exceptional role in the history of the Russian social movement; it consistently and sharply expounded the proposition that is is impossible to have a genuine materialistic viewpoint without the development of the natural sciences. At the same time, by propagandizing the Feuerbachian ideas, Chernyshevskiy pointed out the means of overcoming the narrow-mindedness of the German vulgar-materialists, Buchner, Focht, and Moleschott, whose ideas were widely circulated in Russia.

The burning controversies with regard to physiology became expecially acute with the appearance in the Russian language of G. H. Lewes' (1817-1878) Physiology of Common Life (1861), which was translated by Borzenkov and Rachinskiy (the latter also translated Darwin's Origin of Species). Lewes' Physiology of Common Life enjoyed an enormous success in Russia.

The journal The Contemporary, which did not falter in its defense of advanced scientific ideas, appraised this book highly, suggested that it might play an important role in the formation of a materialistic ideology, and propagandized it in every way.

In this propaganda M. A. Antonovich came to the fore. In the second number of The Contemporary for 1862 he published a review of Lewes' The Physiology of Common Life under the title "Contemporary physiology and philosophy." A high evaluation was given to the materialistic conclusions of experimental physiology in the most difficult areas of this science, while, at the same time, the article was directed against the reactionary journal, the Russian Herald, which had responded to the appearance of Lewes' book in its own way.

Under the title "The language of physiologists and psychologists," there appeared in the Russian Herald (1861-1862) a series of articles signed by the rather well-known professor of theology, Yurkevich, who was already known for his criticism of the scientific conclusions of Chernyshevskiy's work The Anthropological Principle in Philosophy. In these articles Yurkevich disputed the materialistic concept of life processes and the significance of physiology for the analysis of complex processes occurring in the organism, especially of the processes of higher nervous activity. Making use of all kinds of verbal devices, of biased juxtaposition and of various ideas taken out of context and separate from the general intent of the book, Yurkevich endeavored to prove that even the physiologist Lewes came to the conclusion that nonmaterialistic life and psychic mystery are inaccessible to the methods of physiology. This was in accordance with his own preaching, as well as that of other reactionaries. He also used every opportunity to criticize Chernyshevskiy's scientific views.

---

[8] Publications of the Museum of Literature. See Pravda, 1935, no. 82.

Thus one can readily understand the unique structure of the critical article concerning Lewes' book written for The Contemporary by Antonovich. His article represents both a defense of Chernyshevskiy's progressive, novel scientific and philosophical ideas and an attack on Yurkevich's reactionary theological views. The article speaks with high praise of Lewes' book and at the same time advances a number of exciting philosophical-materialistic problems which have a direct relationship to physiology. The final lines of Antonovich's article are of special interest in the history of physiology. A year before the appearance of the Reflexes of the Brain, Antonovich wrote in the pages of The Contemporary:

"Let us take an example: for a long time sensations were in the realm of metaphysicians and psychologists, but they did not accomplish anything with them and only instilled a superstitious fear of their mysteriousness. When the 'philosophical physiologist' attacks the problem of sensation, he too understands its mysteriousness and knows that he is unable to observe it directly with any of his five senses, just as he is unable to observe the actual mechanism of muscular contraction which causes movement; but he is able to observe those activities and phenomena which are revealed by way of sensation. Suppose he pricks the leg of a frog and observes whether the latter has sensed the prick or not; if the frog retracts the leg it means that it sensed the prick, it feels pain, a sensation is present. In another animal he removes the brain, examines its structure, begins to perform various experiments on the animal and then draws from them some conclusions with regard to sensation. To be sure, he has not penetrated the mystery just as the metaphysician and psychologist will fail to do; but, as Lewes expresses it, the realm of mysteriousness is transformed into a realm of mysteries governed by laws; he knows many facts concerning sensation, he learns to recognize the laws of sensation and the store of his knowledge increases, which is of course of utmost importance. The improper attitude toward mysteriousness is to be afraid of it, to despair and to embark on fabrications and fantasies; psychologists, too, have the right to study sensation and its more complex effect; one just has to ask of them that they observe what actually occurs without fear of mysteriousness and refrain from deliberate fabrications of various suspicious and nonexistent agents."

Although not written by a specialist-physiologist, these concluding words of the article in the journal The Contemporary touch upon the most burning problems of physiology of that period, as well as upon the problems which, during the course of succeeding decades, began to occupy the center of discussions between physiologists and psychologists.

The discussions presented above are historically and logically linked with the history of interrelationships of the editors of The Contemporary with I. M. Sechenov and the publication of his remarkable work Reflexes of the Brain, which, in turn, is the most brilliant expression of the close bond between The Contemporary as an organ of militant revolutionary democracy and the progressive natural scientists.

To this period belongs also the establishment of personal contact between N. G. Chernyshevskiy and Sechenov. Unfortunately, this event has

146

been little studied. On the basis of existing documents it may be determined that Sechenov and Chernyshevskiy met in 1859-1860 through Dr. Peter Ivanovich Bokov, whose name is so closely linked with the history of I. M. Sechenov's personal life.

P. I. Bokov, a physician by profession who joined the radical revolutionary circles of the 1860's, served as the prototype of Lopukhov in Chernyshevskiy's What is to be Done?

Among the first women to acquire a university education was Maria Aleksandrovna Obrucheva-Bokova, Dr. P. I. Bokov's wife. Sechenov made Bokov's acquaintance through her when she was attending his lectures at the Medical-Surgical Academy. An undated calling card of Bokov's with the inscription "P. I. Bokov and I. M. Sechenov invite Chernyshevskiy and Aleksandr Nikolayevich (Pypin, a cousin of Chernyshevskiy) on the occasion of Maria Aleksandrovna (Bokova) having successfully passed her examinations" must be attributed to 1861-1862, since Chernyshevskiy was arrested July 7, 1862.

Concerning the personal relationships between Chernyshevskiy and Sechenov, we have eloquent reminiscences of N. A. Pypin, Chernyshevskiy's closest relative. In speaking about the education of Chernyshevskiy's eldest son, Aleksandr, N. A. Pypin writes: "Sasha's [a nickname for Aleksandr] education already began long before his entrance into the gymnasium: out of devotion to Chernyshevskiy he was taught at home by the best educators of the time (Gerd, Stranolyubskiy and others); great interest was also shown by Chernyshevskiy's and Pypin's friends, I. M. Sechenov and P. I. Bokov."[9]

The generally accepted assumptions concerning the prototypes of the personages in the novel What is to be Done? testify also to the personal contact between Chernyshevskiy and Sechenov. According to well-established opinion, Sechenov represents the prototype of Kirsanov. A number of Sechenov's close friends are also represented in the novel: his future wife, M. A. Bokova, served as the prototype for Vera Pavlovna, while Bokov himself appears in the novel as Lopukhov. If it is taken into account that Chernyshevskiy began his novel in the Petropavlovsk fortress where he was imprisoned in 1862, the assumption that Chernyshevskiy met Sechenov in 1860-1862 appears confirmed.

It is possible that Chernyshevskiy conducted negotiations with Sechenov concerning the latter's participation in the journal The Contemporary which for many years proceeded to intensely propagandize the achievements of the natural sciences. So far, however, positive documentary data concerning this point are not available.

Following Chernyshevskiy's imprisonment in the Petropavlovsk fortress, the editorship of The Contemporary passed to N. A. Nekrasov,

---

[9] N. A. Pypin. Chernyshevskiy's Sons (Reminiscences). Links, pub. Academia, 1932, no. 1, pp. 266-267.

who contacted Sechenov in regard to an article for The Contemporary. In 1940 the author of this volume was able to find and publish an excerpt from Sechenov's letter to M. A. Sechenova-Bokova which offered a key to understanding the history of the relationships between Sechenov and The Contemporary with regard to the monograph Reflexes of the Brain.

In a letter from Paris dated February 11, 1863, Sechenov wrote to Maria Aleksandrovna Sechenova-Bokova:

"Thank you, Maria Aleksandrovna, for your attention, and my thanks to Peter Ivanovich (Bokov) for his efforts on my behalf with Nekrasov. I find the conditions proposed by the latter advantageous, but cannot accept them right now for the following reasons. Experiments have convinced me that I am unable to write in a popular style. At least an article which I intended to be popular did not come out that way. It was as if I had "started with a toast and and ended with a dirge." However, I do not despair of learning this art sometime in the future. We shall then renew our negotiations with Nekrasov. . . ."

In his Autobiographical Notes Sechenov reminisces that while in Paris he was already pondering the basic ideas of the Reflexes of the Brain. Precisely during that period of planning of his remarkable work, Sechenov received the invitation to become a collaborator of The Contemporary. Having completed this work after his return to Russia, Sechenov sent it to The Contemporary. Of course the editors of the journal accepted Sechenov's work and sent it to the printer. Reflexes of the Brain was to appear in The Contemporary under the title "An attempt to introduce physiology as the basis of psychic processes." However, tsarist censorship prohibited the printing of Sechenov's work under this title, and, furthermore, did not permit its publication in the journal The Contemporary, which was under the special surveillance of the censors.

In an article commenting on The Problems of Psychology, a book by Kavelin, Sechenov formulates the original title of his book differently. He writes: "When the article was submitted for censorship its real title was 'An attempt to reduce the mechanism of origin of psychic phenomena to a physiological basis.'" This original title, as we shall see, deeply reveals Sechenov's creative design, since the origin of psychic phenomena was constantly in his field of vision.

The article was supposed to appear in issue No. 10 of The Contemporary in the fall of 1863. But the second half of 1863 was a period of most cruel censorship of the journal. According to Yevgen'yev-Maksimov's count during this time, the journal lost 46 sheets as a consequence of persecution by the censors.* Of eight and three-eighths printed sheets prohibited by the censor in issue No. 10 of The Contemporary of that year, five and three-fourths sheets were expurgated from Sechenov's article "An attempt to introduce physiology as the basis of psychic

---

*Translator's note: A sheet is equivalent to 16 regular pages.

148

processes."[10] In response to the presentation of Sechenov's article for publication in the journal The Contemporary, the Council on Printed Books made the following resolution: ". . .to prohibit the printing of this article in The Contemporary and permit its publication in a medical or other journal with the observance of the following conditions: first, that a change be made in the title of the article, which points much too clearly to the final conclusions which are to be drawn from it. . . ." This resolution clearly illustrates the line of thinking of the chairman of the St. Petersburg Committee on Censorship, Turunov, who declared he would prohibit the publication of articles in The Contemporary which he would approve for some other journal.

After prolonged procrastination, the product of Sechenov's genius was finally published in 1863 in the journal Medical Herald.

We shall refrain here from narrating in detail the tremendous social reverberation which Sechenov's Reflexes of the Brain encountered and the interesting fate that awaited this work when it appeared as a separate book. The reader will find a detailed presentation of these events in our other works.

We shall only note here that an indictment was returned by the courts against Reflexes of the Brain and its author on July 9, 1866, and that during a number of years this physiological discovery was "under court investigation." When Sechenov was asked about the lawyer he intended to engage for his defense in court, according to the statement of the famous columnist, N. F. Annenkov, he replied: "Why should I need a lawyer? I shall take a frog with me to court and perform my experiments in front of the judge; then let the State's attorney refute me."

These events occurred after Karakozov* had fired his shot (April 4, 1866), when the Extraordinary Investigating Commission feverishly searched for breeding grounds from which the idea of killing the Tsar could have been originated. The chairman of this Commission, General Murav'yev, the Hangman,** called the Tsar's attention to the literature of the 1860's and to the editors and collaborators of certain journals which "sharing anti-government ideas have systematically spread during the course of many years all kinds of destructive theories aimed at the overthrow of order and power of the government."

---

[10] V. Ye. Yevgen'yev-Maksimov. The Last Years of The Contemporary, 1863-1866. Goslitizdat, 1939.
*Translator's note: D. V. Karakozov, famous as a revolutionary terrorist but criticized for his individualistic philosophy. For an unsuccessful attempt on the life of the Emperor Alexander II on April 4, 1866, he was executed by public hanging on the third of September of the same year.
**Translator's note: Murav'yev gained the by-name of "Hangman" for his extremely cruel and violent suppression of a Polish revolt against Russian domination.

On May 2, 1866, the Minister of the Interior, Valuyev, directed a special communication to the Chairman of the Extraordinary Investigating Committee in which the following is stated:

"Various information pertinent to the investigations of the Committee under your chairmanship in many respects concerns the tendencies of the organs of the press and the principal directors and collaborators of these organs. It is of utmost importance for me to obtain your opinion concerning the behavior of the press." [12]

At the same time the Minister of the Interior enclosed with his letter a special memorandum concerning the environment where the ideas of killing the Tsar could emerge. The memorandum begins with the following postulate:

"For the purpose of a more successful investigation concerning the personality of the criminal making an attempt on the life of the emperor, it is not without usefulness to investigate the social-literary environment in the midst of which ideas of attempts on the life of the Tsar could grow. From an attentive examination of certain periodical journals as well as from observation of printing plants and bookstores in St. Petersburg, we have discovered. . . ."

Valuyev then proceeds to enumerate the persons and periodicals which are directed "towards dissemination of communistic and materialistic theories." First of all he turns attention towards the militantly progressive journal, The Russian Word [Russkoye Slovo]. Among the staff, Valuyev names the editor, Blagosvetlov, and his collaborators, Pisarev, Shelgunov, Zaytsev and Shchapov, whose articles and reviews contributed in no small way towards publicizing Sechenov's views. In a special paragraph (3) of the memorandum, Valuyev writes:

"Besides, I must call to your attention the following publications: a) the anthology Ray [Luch], published by the collaborators of The Russian Word for free distribution among the subscribers to the journal after it had been stopped; b) the writings of Pisarev (mentioned above) in the printing establishment of Golovachev; c) Reflexes of the Brain by Sechenov (a professor of the Medical-Surgical Academy and the most popular theoretician in nihilistic circles), also at Golovachev's printing establishment; this book propagandizes in a popular form the theories of extreme materialism; d) The Apostates by Sokolov. . .also at Golovachev's. In the latter book the early Christians and the socialists of our times are characterized, while all other people are nothing but pharisees, against whom the renegades advocate the most extreme form of revolutionary tactics."

---

[12] Central Archives of the Revolution. Inventory no. 279. "On the harmful tendencies of certain journals and the people collaborating in them."

[13] In listing the collaborators of the Russian Word, Valuyev adds next to Pisarev's name the remark "up to now imprisoned in the fortress."

The Minister writes further (in item 5):

"Most of these books appeared during the week of April 4. Various Essays, The Apostates and Reflexes of the Brain have been impounded; the other works could not be subjected to such a punishment within the letter of the law."

In conclusion, the Minister of the Interior poses the question to Murav'-yev: "In view of the facts presented the question arises as to whether it would not be useful to turn our attention without delay towards the persons mentioned. . . ." And attention was turned. Already on June 9, 1866, court action was initiated against Sechenov. And later on, up to the last year of his life, the watchful eye of the Tsarist government continued to follow the activities of the great scientist-philosopher incessantly and to hamper his work by all available means.

Before we proceed with an analysis of the basic conclusions of Reflexes of the Brain, as well as the development which these achieved in Sechenov's further investigations, and go on to examine how and with whom the great physiologist struggled for new psycho-physiological concepts, let us turn towards a scrutiny of certain historical events which took place during the thirteen years (1863-1876) following publication of Reflexes of the Brain and which are closely connected with the history of physiology in two most important foci of our science of that period: the faculty of physiology at the Medical-Surgical Academy and that at the Petersburg University.

This wonderful period in Sechenov's life, full of social events, creative achievements, and personal experiences attracted the penetrating attention of I. P. Pavlov.[14] Pavlov incessantly linked the appearance of Reflexes of the Brain, which he considered "a stroke of genius in Sechenov's thought," with a kind of "personal passion." Having first formulated the matter in 1922, Pavlov returned to it repeatedly in subsequent years. In this connection his two letters to a disciple of Sechenov, M. N. Shaternikov, are of special interest; we reproduce them here in full.[15]

In his letter to Shaternikov dated September 23, 1929, Pavlov writes:

"Dear Milhail Nikolayevich! I am turning to you with an important request. For the better understanding of an adequate appraisal of the scientific image of Ivan Mikhaylovich Sechenov, I need some information concerning the events of his private life. Do you have such data available? Do you know when, in what year and under what circumstances the friendship and marriage of Ivan Mikhaylovich and Maria Aleksandrovna occurred? I have heard from somebody that in Chernyshevskiy's novel, What is to be Done?, the love and marriage of Kirsanov and Vera Pavlovna represent the love

---

[14] See the introduction to Twenty Years of Experience of Objective Study of Higher Nervous Activity of Animals.
[15] Published here for the first time from copies at the Moscow division of the Archives of the USSR Academy of Sciences.

151

and marriage of I. M. and M. A. Is this correct? If so, a strong emotional upheaval must have taken place. And it is important for me to know in what year that occurred. I have returned from America[16] in good health and good spirits; all the best, your I. Pavlov."

On Pavlov's birthday, September 27, 1929, M. N. Shaternikov apparently sent him a greeting. In a reply dated October 3, 1929, I. P. Pavlov thanks Shaternikov for his good wishes and again returns to the question bothering him. He writes:

"Dear Mikhail Nikolayevich! Thank you very much for your greetings on the occasion of my 80th birthday. I propose to continue living if fate is merciful. Thank you indeed for the information concerning Ivan Mikhaylovich and Maria Aleksandrovna. I shall make use only of the most general fact that Ivan Mikhaylovich was possessed by the emotions of love during the writing of the Reflexes, without entering into further details. I still do not know when the centennial of the birth of Ivan Mikhaylovich will be celebrated and what program is planned. Of course you will be informed of all this in due time. I am getting ready to work. With best wishes, the sincerely devoted to you, I. Pavlov.
Sincere regards to you from Sof'ya Vasil'yevna with thanks for remembering her."

More than 80 years have passed from the time Sechenov created the immortal pages of the pearl of Russian physiology, Reflexes of the Brain, but the fascination and greatness of this brilliant period in the history of our science still continue strong.

---

[16] This refers to Pavlov's return from Boston where he had attended the XIII International Physiological Congress.

CHAPTER XII

Sechenov's departure from the Medical-Surgical Academy. I. F. Tsion. Sechenov's work in D. I. Mendeleyev's laboratory. Sechenov in Novorossiysk (Odessa) University. Sechenov's return to Petersburg University. The general upswing in physiology in the 1860's-70's.

Sechenov created his militantly materialistic treatise Reflexes of the Brain while serving as professor of the Medical-Surgical Academy. Naturally, his lectern was converted into a platform in the struggle against idealism in science. Not only students of the Medical-Surgical Academy but also numerous progressive young people of the time crowded to hear the lectures of the author of Reflexes of the Brain. It was at that time that Sechenov's lectures were attended by young women disguised in men's clothing who strove towards science, and among them was Sof'ya Kovalevskaya.*

Thanks to Sechenov's endeavors, in the mind of the Russian intelligentsia physiology became the most progressive experimental science, confirming the materialistic ideas which were close to a wide segment of the people. Thus it was not without cause that the faculty chair of physiology played such an outstanding social role in the preparation of Russian intelligentsia wholly dedicated to science and the highest social ideals. This was also the cause of a most suspicious and soon hostile attitude toward Sechenov and his scientific pedagogical activities on the part of the reactionary circles and the tsarist bureaucracy, which finally led to the resignation (in fact, discharge) of Sechenov from the Medical-Surgical Academy in 1871.

In the archives of the Special Division of the Police Department, we read: "From the secret information obtained by the special division of the department of police, it can be seen that in 1872 (obviously a mistake in the record) very many listeners attended the lectures of Sechenov and Botkin whom the Government subsequently deigned to dismiss from the Moscow Academy, because through their lectures they acquired great

---

*Sof'ya Kovalevskaya (1850-1891), considered the first woman professor in the world, corresponding member of the Academy of Sciences, mathematician, and progressive writer on social issues. According to the Great Soviet Encyclopedia, she entered into a fictitious marriage (which later became actual) with the famous paleontologist V. O. Kovalevskiy (1842-1883) in order to be able to devote herself to scientific studies.

153

popularity among the students."[1] On the surface, the cause that compelled Sechenov to leave the Academy was the blackballing of Sechenov's friend I. I. Mechnikov for a professorship at the Medical-Surgical Academy.

Having lost the professorship in physiology at the Medical-Surgical Academy, Sechenov began taking steps towards obtaining a professorship in Novorossiysk University in Odessa, where he expected to be working with I. I. Mechnikov.

But the matter was delayed, and for Sechenov life without a laboratory appeared unthinkable. In this difficult period for Sechenov, he was given a post by the great chemist D. I. Mendeleyev in the latter's laboratory. Mendeleyev offered his friend a corner in the laboratory and even suggested a subject for scientific investigation. According to the theme proposed by Mendeleyev, Sechenov accomplished the synthesis of nitrous-methyl ether and gave a detailed description of its properties. In a letter to Mechnikov dated December 11, 1870, Sechenov dramatically wrote that his medical career might be coming to an end: "It is possible that I shall become a chemist. But of course, this is but a dream."[2]

Much later, in his Autobiographical Notes, Sechenov wrote: "The results of this unpolished work have been described by Dm. Iv.[Mendeleyev] himself. To be a student of such a teacher as Mendeleyev was of course both pleasant and useful, but I had already bitten too deeply into physiology to be unfaithful to it, and I did not become a chemist."[3]

Sechenov took steps to clarify the causes of delay in confirmation of his position as professor of physiology at the University of Odessa. He was given a specious excuse: there were no funds in the budget of the University for the salary of a physiology professor. Sechenov then informed the Rector of the University of his readiness to work on the salary of an extraordinary professor, or even on the salary of a docent, and that he would accept any title just so "there would be no possibility of being disapproved for financial reasons."[4]

However, the cause of the delay in approving Sechenov's appointment was not financial but political in nature. Sechenov himself eloquently commented on this when he had to pay a visit to an important tsarist official in order to express his thanks for assistance rendered to one of

---

[1] Central Archive of the Revolution. Police Department, record no. 1872. "Case of the professor of Moscow University, Ivan Mikhaylovich Sechenov."

[2] Anthology. The Struggle for Science in Tsarist Russia. Sotsekgiz, Moscow-Leningrad, 1931, p. 73.

[3] I. M. Sechenov. Autobiographical Notes. USSR Academy of Sciences, 1945, p. 132.

[4] Anthology. The Struggle for Science in Tsarist Russia. Moscow-Leningrad, Sotsekgiz, 1931, p. 72.

his students (Drozdov).[5] Assuming that Sechenov had come to petition the matter of his own appointment as professor this "high personage" met him with a cynical phrase that he should not have published the Reflexes of the Brain. To that Sechenov replied (the conversation took place in German): "Man muss doch die Courage haben seine Ueberzeugugen auszudrücken" (one must have the courage to express one's convictions).[6]

Worried about his friend, Mechnikov, in one of his letters, advised Sechenov to consult Ye. Pelikan, Sechenov's former opponent at the defense of his dissertation and then an important functionary in the Department of Health. But Sechenov, true to his principles, rejected this approach. "A request to Pelikan is, of course, out of the question for me, and I ask you not to do it either; I would much rather obtain the position in Odessa by fighting for it than through such influence."[7]

The director of the Odessa District of Education at that time, Dr. S. P. Golubtsov, actually panicked at the idea that Sechenov, a man "dangerous and harmful to youth," should teach in a university entrusted to him. And, indeed, Golubtsov's position was a difficult one. He had already received a warning from the Deputy Minister of Education, I. Delyanov, who wrote about Sechenov thus:

"Mr. Sechenov has the reputation of an inveterate materialist who is trying to introduce materialism not only into science but into life itself. Not being a specialist in the field of physiology, I do not dare judge Mr. Sechenov's scientific merits, which I shall not consider here since they have been recognized by scientific institutions. But I consider it my duty to call Your Excellency's attention to Sechenov's reputation and respectfully request that you inform me whether you feel certain that Sechenov's teaching at Novorossiysk University and his close contacts with youth will not have harmful consequences for their moral development and will not have a harmful influence on the peace of the University."[8]

In his Autobiographical Notes Sechenov tells how this question concerning his professorship in Odessa was finally settled. Mr. Pelikan, who acted without Sechenov's request, was still able to reassure the frightened director of the Odessa District, Dr. S. P. Golubtsov. "Knowing

---

[5]V. I. Drozdov graduated from the Medical-Surgical Academy in 1872; he executed his first scientific project in Sechenov's laboratory: "On the effect of curare on the white blood corpuscles" (Medical-Surgical Academy, 1873, 116, vol. VI, pp. 1-12).

[6]I. M. Sechenov. Autobiographical Notes. USSR Academy of Sciences, 1945, p. 133.

[7]Anthology. The Struggle for Science in Tsarist Russia. Moscow-Leningrad, Sotsekgiz, 1931, p. 74.

[8]LOTsIA. Department of Public Instruction record no. 14062, vol. V, folio 65. Quoted from G. A. Knyazev and M. F. Knyazeva. I. M. Sechenov and the Academy of Sciences. Annals Inst. Historical Sciences and Tech., series 1, issue 7, p. 408.

I. P. Pavlov (early 1880's).

from rumors," wrote Sechenov, "that he was personally acquainted with me, Golubtsov was interested to learn whether I actually was such a dangerous and harmful person for youth and added that this circumstance was preventing my appointment at the University. In reply, Pelikan even broke out in laughter and assured Golubtsov of my harmlessness to such an extent that the latter undertook my appointment at his own risk, and I was confirmed. This whole story was told to me by Pelikan himself."[9]

Thus, in 1871 Sechenov moved to Novorossiysk University. Together with him, in the capacity of an assistant, came a student of his from the Medical-Surgical Academy and subsequently a professor, Spiro. By that time Spiro was a fully prepared worker, and in 1870 he published a very interesting investigation concerning the physiology of the spinal cord.[10]

In Odessa, Sechenov spent about six years in the capacity of professor and during this time completed a number of most important works. At that time he devoted special attention to his classical works on the gases of the blood, the results of which he published in the Annals of the Novorossiysk Society of Natural Scientists.[11] In Odessa also Sechenov elaborated on the principles of his Reflexes of the Brain and wrote his famous treatise "Who must investigate the problems of psychology, and how?"[12] Without abandoning the problems of the nature of the inhibitory influence of the vagus on the heart, in that period Sechenov, together with Mechnikov and the student Repyakhov,[13] performed his famous experiments on the effects of the nerves on the heart.

In Sechenov's place, the appointment as professor of physiology at the Medical Academy went to I. F. Tsion. Sechenov's departure and Tsion's appointment were the center of general controversy for a number of years.

What was the cause of this wide interest? First of all, the progressive strata of Russian society deplored the enormous loss for science and the education of revolutionary youth caused by the departure of Sechenov. It was a matter of great political importance that Sechenov's place on the faculty of physiology was filled by Tsion, a man who openly declared his negative

---

[9] I. M. Sechenov. Autobiographical Notes. USSR Academy of Sciences, 1945, p. 120.
[10] Spiro. Physiologisch-topographische Untersuchungen am Rückenmark des Frosches. Mémoires de l'Académie des Sciences de St. Pétersbourg, 1870, VII serie, t. XVI, no. 7.
[11] See notes and records of the Novorossiysk Society of Natural Scientists for 1873.
[12] Herald of Europe [Vestnik Evropy], no. 4, 1873. In the Pushkin house of the USSR Academy of Sciences are deposited a number of I. M. Sechenov's manuscripts and articles published by him in the journal Herald of Europe.
[13] Sechenov and Repyakhov. Duration of reflex excitation from the vagus and sympathetic nerves of the frog (Proc. of Novorossiysk Soc. of Natural Scientists, 1873).

attitude to everything new, a man who was linked to the most reactionary circles. Moreover, the Minister of War appointed Tsion in spite of the fact that the Council of the Academy had not chosen him but another candidate. Analyzing this fact (which at first sight appears insignificant), the revolutionary circles of the 1870's unveiled the political aspect of this event and so attacked the autocratic reign of the Tsar.

The journals of progressive public opinion, i. e. , Notes of the Fatherland and Knowledge [Znaniye], as well as the revolutionary journal Forward [Vpered],[14] published abroad, devoted their pages to discussion of this event.

First of all, these articles were permeated with great love and high respect for Sechenov and were full of regret with regard to his departure from the Medical-Surgical Academy. Thus, in Notes of the Fatherland we read: "It is known that in the winter of 1870 our Medical-Surgical Academy lost one of its best professors, and in addition, a professor in one of the most important subjects: Iv. Mikh. Sechenov resigned and soon afterwards transferred to the University of Novorossiysk. Thus the chair of physiology was vacant, and the council was confronted with the task of finding a successor for this remarkable scientist and widely loved professor."[15] At the same time, a special article in the Notes of the Fatherland presents in detail the circumstances which led to the appointment of Tsion as professor of the Academy against the wishes of the majority of professors and exposes the reactionary background of Tsion's activities. Two candidates were under consideration for the chair left vacant by Sechenov's departure: the Kiev professor Shklyarevskiy and Tsion. As can be seen from the special record of the Council of the Medical-Surgical Academy, a definite part of the Council voiced a negative opinion concerning Tsion's work, and he obtained a minority of votes in the balloting, but, as Tsion himself wrote most cynically: "In spite of the exaggerated respect for the principle of majority rule, the Minister of War confirmed my appointment, administering at the same time a strong reprimand to the Commission for its report, which did not correspond either in form or in context to the dignity of an institution of higher learning."[16]

Expressing its indignation at such a flagrant infringement of the elementary rights of the majority of the Professors' Council and the abortive result of the drawn-out procedure of the election of Sechenov's successor, Notes of the Fatherland wrote:

"One could think that nothing extraordinary had happened; however, a great deal happened. The possessor of the chair suddenly lost it, the one who didn't have it suddenly obtained it, thus demonstrating the truth of the pious saying with regard to the frailty and perishability of everything on earth, and its transitoriness and insecurity; an elected professor was unconfirmed; a blackballed one was appointed; the one thought to be in

[14] See for instance Notes of the Fatherland, no. 5-6, 7-8, 1874; Knowledge, no. 11, 1873.
[15] Notes of the Fatherland, no. 7, 1874, p. 23, ("Contemporary Review").
[16] I. Tsion. Nihilists and Nihilism. Russian Herald, 1886, vol. 183, p. 751.

the right was found guilty; a well presented report brought a reprimand instead of gratitude. And thus Mr. Tsion became a full professor of physiology." [17]

With extraordinary clarity, this event demonstrated the stubborn desire of the ruling circles to isolate the student body from the influences of progressive professors and progressive ideas and to place their upbringing in the hands of reactionaries, of whom Tsion was a true representative. Thus Sechenov's dismissal and Tsion's election in his place was but an expression of a definite policy. It was precisely to this that Notes of the Fatherland was calling the attention of public opinion: "Science and scientific problems apparently play a much greater role in this 'regrettable event' but nevertheless you somehow feel that there is 'something' more, that something is being carefully concealed and is nevertheless cropping up everywhere, something that has nothing to do with science or the interests of the students. This 'something' is a matter of 'politics' and the attitudes which have always played such a prominent role up to now. In local government and in science and in other spheres of our society you can always find this 'something' in every 'well-intended beginning' and in every 'sad finish.' It is for this reason that the facts under discussion do not stand separately from the many other facts which fill our life, and herein lies their lesson; if these events were only 'misunderstandings' or 'exceptions' they would simply arouse our curiosity, and there would be no reason to dwell upon them for any length of time." [18]

Having established himself in the chair of physiology at the Medical-Surgical Academy with the help of the Secretary of War, Tsion proceeded to execute the tasks entrusted to him by the tsarist government. In his first introductory lecture he began to attack the progressive scientific ideas and social ideals which were cultivated in the Medical-Surgical Academy. In his lectures he openly argued against Darwinism and with all his strength attempted to discredit his predecessor, I. M. Sechenov; with pointed expressions, he criticized the books in the natural sciences on which the progressive elements of the 1860's were raised. Tsion took it upon himself to destroy nihilism and undertook to eradicate the materialistic outlook from the minds of youth. Right from the start Tsion's activities encountered a sharp resistance from the revolutionary circles in the Medical-Surgical Academy. The students reacted violently toward the conduct of the reactionary professor, and once when Tsion brought into his lecture a specially-published polemical article directed against his adversaries ("Work and critical articles," 1874) and began to distribute it among the students with appropriate commentaries, "The students broke out in whistles and hissing and proceeded to throw the pamphlets back at the professor." [19]

---

[17] Notes of the Fatherland, no. 7, 1874, p. 39.
[18] Notes of the Fatherland, no. 7, 1874, p. 38.
[19] From a letter of N. N. Strakhov to L. N. Tolstoy. Tolstoy Anthology, 1914, vol. II, p. 54.

The Tsion affair served as the beginning of the so-called student riots. In an article "Nihilists and nihilism," Tsion himself wrote that in 1874 he had requested the head of the Medical-Surgical Academy to station two gendarmes at the doors of his lecture hall "to keep order." The student riots continued, and Tsion was finally compelled to abandon the chair of physiology at the Medical-Surgical Academy. At the same time he also stopped teaching at the Petersburg University, where he had been lecturing on certain fields of physiology and had been working with students since 1868.

Having linked his fate with the most reactionary forces of Russia, Tsion found himself more and more isolated from those workers in Russian physiological science who had the most progressive scientific and social ideals. Tsion's outstanding scientific accomplishments could not shield him from the hostility that his reactionary social views generated. In 1875 he went to France, and thus his scientific activity in Russia came to and end (Tsion's scientific work shall be discussed later on).

In 1875 a young physiologist, I. R. Tarkhanov (Mouravi Tarkhnishvili, 1846-1908), was elected to take Tsion's place at the Medical-Surgical Academy. He had already gained recognition through a series of special investigations in the field of physiology performed in Sechenov's laboratory as well as in the laboratories of the most prominent European physiologists.

I. R. Tarkhanov headed the department of physiology at the Medical-Surgical Academy for almost twenty years. Upon his retirement in the academic year 1894-95, he began lecturing on general physiology in the capacity of privatdocent at the Petersburg University.

His lectures at the University and in the Academy, as well as his numerous popular science lectures, scored a great success. His close friend, the painter I. Ye. Repin, remarked about Tarkhanov as a lecturer in one of his letters: "His lecture in Kuokkala was an unforgettable event; everyone is talking about it and praising it, and those who did not attend it regret having missed it. A marvelous lecturer!!!"[20] A man of broad education, Tarkhanov devoted a great deal of time to allied scientific fields, as well as to art. For a long time he and his wife, the sculptress Ye. P. Tarkhanova-Antokol'skaya,[21] were close friends of the great Russian painter I. Ye. Repin and those outstanding men of arts and letters who frequently gathered at Repin's home. In the State Museum of Literature there is a photograph of a gathering at Repin's estate, "Penates" (Penaty), on May 27, 1905; the people in the picture are: I. Ye. Repin, Leonid Andreyev, A. M. Gorkiy, I. R. Tarkhanov, their wives, and V. V. Stasov.

---

[20] I. Ye. Repin. Letter to Ye. P. Tarkhanova-Antokol'skaya and I. R. Tarkhanov. Moscow Leningrad, Art [Iskusstvo], 1937, p. 31.

[21] Ye. P. Antokol'skaya, the niece of the famous sculptor M. M. Antokol'skiy came to St. Petersburg from Vilna in order to study the natural sciences; for some time she worked with the physiologist N. O. Tsybul'skiy but soon turned to sculpture.

I. R. Tarkhanov (1846-1908)

In reference to one of his meetings with Tarkhanov at Repin's home, A. M. Gorkiy made an interesting notation: while scrutinizing a new portrait of a young man painted by Repin, Tarkanov commented as a physician-physiologist on the mastery with which the artist portrayed the degenerate features of the young man; Tarkhanov did not suspect that the portrait was of Repin's son, Yuriy.[22]

Repin painted three portraits of Tarkhanov (1892, 1895, and 1906). One of these portrays Tarkhanov at the lectern, reading a lecture in the Military Medical (Medical-Surgical) Academy.

After Tsion left there was also a professorial vacancy at the Petersburg University. For this part Professor Ovsyannikov chose Sechenov, who was able to return to Petersburg, but not without great tribulations connected with the police surveillance over him. Upon his return, but now occupying the chair at the University as a supernumerary ordinary professor, in 1876 Sechenov began to give lectures on physiology at the physics-mathematics faculty of the University. In his Autobiographical Notes, Sechenov reminisces: "With regard to my double migration from the Medical-Surgical Academy to Odessa and from Odessa to the Petersburg University, somebody, not without humor, made the remark, 'It took Sechenov five years to get across from the Vyborg side to Vasil'yev Island.'"

Sechenov's work at the Petersburg University over a period of twelve years (1876-1888) laid the basis for the Petersburg physiological school, which advanced it to one of the highest places in world neurophysiology. Suffice it to note that it was precisely at Petersburg University, under Sechenov's guidance, that his most outstanding disciple, N. Ye. Vedenskiy,[23] began his work.

Meanwhile, along with the emergence of a young group of physiologists, the social interest in physiological problems grows steadily. It was in the 1860's and 1870's that translated versions of a number of books on physiology by prominent European scientists began to appear.

M.A. Antonovich spent much of his time translating these books; he was known as a propagandist of the achievements of physiology in the journal The Contemporary. His translation from the English of Foster's

---

[22]Some interesting details of Tarkhanov's biography and especially of his friendship with I. Ye. Repin may be found in the above mentioned letters from Repin to Ye. P. and I. R. Tarkhanov. See also: I. S. Zilberstein. Repin and Gorkiy. Moscow-Leningrad, Art, 1944. This work contains valuable literary references, notes, and illustrations referring to I. R. Tarkhanov in connection with his friendship with Repin.

[23]Interesting data about Sechenov's work in the Petersburg University have been assembled by the academician A. A. Ukhtomskiy in his article "The physiological institute of Leningrad University in connection with its inception." Physiol. Jour., USSR (Fiziologich. Zhurn.), vol. XIX, 1935, p. 307.

Physiology was published in 1875, and his translation of one of the masterpieces by the French physiological genius Claude Bernard, General Physiology, or the Phenomena of Life Common to Animals and Plants, appeared in 1878. Still earlier, in 1862, Agassiz' and Gould's Essays in Comparative Physiology (St. Petersburg) were published in a translation by the author, D. V. Averkiyev. At about the same time Moleschott's Physiological Sketches, Liebig's Letter on Chemistry, and a number of other books on physiology were published.

During this period D. I. Pisarev emerged as an ardent progagandist of physiological problems. His articles, "Moleschott's physiological sketches" (1861): "The process of life" (1861): "Physiological essays" (1862); "Lewes and Huxley," which was written as an introduction to Huxley's book Lessons in Elementary Physiology (1867); revealed with exceptional thoroughness the content and ideological significance of the various problems of physiology. They were a call to youth towards further work in the fascinating realms of this science. I. P. Pavlov invariably emphasized the influence which Pisarev's articles had exercised on him during the years of his preuniversity education, (1864-1870).

Under Sechenov's editorial supervision, the following books were published during the years 1864-1877: the revisions and supplements to the translation of Herman's textbook Basis of Physiology (St. Petersburg, 1864), A Textbook of Physiological Chemistry by Kühne (St. Petersburg, 1866), Textbook of Physiology by Funke (St. Petersburg, 1875). Sechenov's wife, M. A. Sechenova-Bokova, is credited with a substantial part in the translating of these books, and Sechenov's personal friend and an outstanding Russian paleontologist, V. O. Kovalevskiy, collaborated in the editing. Jointly with other outstanding Russian physiologists, Sechenov undertook and completed a translation of Brücke's Textbook of Physiology (St. Petersburg, 1876. In 1866 Sechenov's Physiology of the Nervous System (St. Petersburg) was published; it is a work of astounding clarity of presentation, depth, and novelty of content. During the same period, I. F. Tsion published his Course of Physiology, and two years later a richly illustrated two-volume work by Tsion on methods of physiological experimentation and vivisection was published in Leipzig, in German.[24] This book is the best that was written in the nineteenth century on problems of physiological methods.

A high evaluation of I. Tsion's merit as one of the most outstanding workers in the field of methods in contemporary physiology was given by the authors of a work published in the United States in 1942, A Calendar of Biologists and Physicians.[25] They wrote of Tsion: "He was also one of

---

[24]E. Cyon [I. Tsion.] Methodik der physiologischen Experimente und Vivisectionen. Leipzig, 1876.

[25]P. F. Clark and A. S. Clark. Memorable Days in Medicine. Madison, University of Wisconsin Press, 1942, p. 74. It is interesting that in addition to I. Tsion, this 'calendar' of famous biologists and physicians mentioned only N. I. Pirogov, I. I. Mechnikov and I. P. Pavlov among the Russians.

the most important contributors to the development of modern methods of research in physiology."

We have dwelled here upon one of the most significant periods in the development of science in our country.

In his brief essay on the history of the natural sciences at Russian universities, Sechenov, touching upon the history of physiology and related fields for the period beginning in the early 1830's, wrote: "For the whole preceding thirty year period I am unable to find in the field of microscopic anatomy, physiology and experimental pathology a single specialized work credited to a purely Russian name belonging to a university scientist. However, from 1863 to 1882 inclusive i. e., during a twenty year period, foreign journals in these fields published more than 650 articles by authors with purely Russian names."[26] Thus, due to the self-sacrificing service of a few dedicated and outstanding Russian scientists to science and to the nation, a wave of research work surged up with brilliant results, particularly in the field of physiology.

[26]I. M. Sechenov. A brief essay on the scientific activities of the Russian universities in the field of natural sciences for the last two decades (separate brochure, 1883).

CHAPTER XIII

Reflexes of the Brain as the basis for Sechenov's psycho-physiological views. Subsequent development of these views. Critical rejection of German idealistic philosophy and psychology. Controversy between Sechenov and Kavelin, and the public interest in this controversy. Elements of Thought. Historical significance of Sechenov's psychophysiological works.

Sechenov's experimental investigations on the nature and significance of the phenomenon of inhibition of reflex acts that he had discovered, and his attraction since his student years to the basic problems of psychology, led him to the creation of his immortal work Reflexes of the Brain (1863), in which he was the first in world literature to make a most logical and decisive attempt to introduce a physiological approach in the analysis of complex psychic processes. It was not without reason that the original title of this work read An Attempt to Reduce the Mechanism of Origin of Psychic Phenomena to a Physiological Basis. And even under the pressure of censorship, Sechenov insisted on the title: An Attempt to Introduce Physiology as the Basis of Psychic Processes.

Sechenov advanced an idea that was new for his time: "All acts of conscious and unconscious life are reflexes with regard to their origin;" the whole psychic life with all its motor manifestations is maintained and stimulated by external influences on the sense organs and by stimuli of the sensory nervous system which arise within the organism. In a most original form and with many examples, he proved the formative influence of environmental factors on the nerve processes.

With exceptional conviction, Sechenov developed his proposition that "the primary cause of all human activity is external" and that without external sensory stimulation psychic activity would be impossible.

Sechenov's most important and most promising idea for future science was that not only the beginning and the end of the reflex act could be investigated by physiological methods but that its middle part, which is called the psychic element, could also be investigated by physiological methods. Here is how Sechenov formulated this most important part of his idea.

Sechenov wrote: "All psychic acts which occur in the manner of reflexes must be entirely subject to physiological investigation because

165

their inception, an external sensory stimulus, and their termination, movement, concern this science [i.e., physiology]; the middle, i.e., the psychic element in the narrow sense of the word, must also be subject to physiological investigation, since it too is very often and perhaps always an integral part of a process rather than an independent phenomenon, as was thought before."[1]

Reflexes of the Brain marked a new era in world science. I. P. Pavlov, in evaluating Sechenov's work, wrote "It must be stated as a matter of honor to the Russian intellect that Sechenov was the first to study psychic phenomena."

We cannot elaborate here in detail on the scope of Sechenov's work in this direction, and we direct the reader to the relevant publications of the great physiologist.[2] We shall but point out that in his day these ideas sounded like a new word in world science, and it is regrettable that they remained unknown to foreign scientists.[3] There are some indications that Vladimir Kovalevskiy undertook some steps toward the publication of Reflexes of the Brain in England, but without success.

This particular work of Sechenov, which is of such exceptional significance in the development of the natural sciences in the world and which found its greatest development in the works of Russian physiologists, was formulated in its ideological aspect under the influence of the progressive ideas of Russian philosophers-materialists.

Sechenov's basic ideas concerning the revision of psychology on a strictly materialistic basis and the introduction of objective physiological methods for the study of processes of consciousness, which were conceived during his student years at Moscow University, finally matured during Sechenov's sojourn abroad. Although the physiological laboratories of Western Europe provided a wealth of material for a probe into the mysteries of the physiology, physics, and chemistry of nervous processes, the level of the philosophical formulation of the problems of psychology which concerned him was not high. Moreover, Sechenov had to complete a great deal of work in order to critically overcome the idealistic, metaphysical trends that prevailed at that time, particularly in Germany. This is clearly indicated in the excerpts from I. M. Sechenov's letters from abroad to his wife, which we recently published for the first time.

Thus in a letter from Paris, dated October 29, 1867, Sechenov writes:

By now I am positive that for a man studying psychology it would be futile to scrutinize the German transcendentalists, i.e., Kant, Fichte, Schelling and Hegel, and that the only German

---

[1] I. M. Sechenov. Selected Works. Pub. VIEM, 1935, p. 248.
[2] I. M. Sechenov. Reflexes of the Brain. USSR Academy of Sciences, 1942; The Elements of Thought, collection of articles edited by Professor K. Kh. Kecheyev. USSR Academy of Sciences, 1943.
[3] The French translation appeared much later, in 1884.

psychological school worthy of study is Herbart's school. And at present I am reading his works with great delight because I find very much lucidity and sanity in his theories; yet I cannot help but wonder when, along with the sane aspects, I see his naive conviction that it is possible to create a theory of psychic activity on the basis of metaphysical elaboration of the soul concept, i.e., to attribute an aspect of sufficiency and completeness to the science of psychic life. Just think, this is the concept that constitutes the point of insanity not only of Herbart's entire new school but of all non-naturalist psychologists in general in Germany. When my head tires of Herbart, I turn for diversion to Bain, whose works contain a wealth of good material but also a wealth of trivialities. At any rate, from his works it becomes obvious that in time I shall have to acquaint myself with British psychology.''

One may say without exaggeration that during Sechenov's sojourn in Europe, in 1867–1868, along with his experimental work, he consistently and seriously was occupied with the theoretical exploration of psychological problems. It was precisely at that time that Sechenov was particularly involved in the study of British and primarily German psychologists and came to a most definite evaluation of psychology as a science.

His appraisal of the German psychological school is most interesting. We learn of it from a letter to his wife, dated February 12, 1868. He writes:

"Thus, even in Germany, a country with a prevailing speculative approach, only one school still adheres to the view that metaphysics is necessary solely to build psychological theories, in order to lend to the whole discipline of psychic manifestations the character of unity and completeness. For an individual brought up in the spirit of the natural sciences there is no need for theories from the moment that he deals with things which cannot be explained positively, such as all psychic acts; he merely states in such cases that we do not understand the essence of these phenomena nor can we understand them for the present; consequently metaphysics is useless in psychology.

"I shall not write to you about my general plans because they will be subject to constant change as I read new material and reflect upon it. It is strange indeed how the proverb 'as in the cradle, so to the grave' finds its realization in my case. At one time, precisely during my first trip abroad, I thought my former passion for philosophy was a whim and a hypocritical streak in my life, and now I am concerned about something that seemed most strange to me in my student years, i.e., the absence of psychology in the curriculum of medical schools. Let me tell you in confidence that psychological experiments are already taking shape in my mind. They are still in embryonic form, but I am sure they will develop in time.''

In addition to reading psychological literature, Sechenov also diligently studied philosophical literature, especially that of German authors. But it depressed him exceedingly. We learn of this from a letter to his wife on October 18, 1867. He writes in part:

"Since I ordered the local bookstore to send me all philosophical books, I have recently been receiving such new gibberish that when I attempted to read it, I was positively unable to understand a word. And it seems a vast number of Germans are occupied with it. I frankly confess (as I have recently mentioned to you) I just shall not have the heart to study German metaphysics."

Sechenov's broad experience in physiological experimentation on the central and peripheral nervous system and the vast theoretical studies which he conducted in connection with the formulation of the brilliant postulates in his Reflexes of the Brain permitted him to raise the daring problem of reorganization of one of the most important sciences, i.e., psychology. Gradually Sechenov elaborated a plan of a discussion with the representatives of the official psychological science, the majority of whom took a stand for idealistic philosophy.

Thus in a letter to his wife dated November 4, 1867, he writes:

"With regard to psychology, I have developed the following plan. The principle proponents of the Herbartian school live in Leipzig; I shall have to be there in any case (to keep my appointment with Ludwig). I have therefore conceived the following idea: to address these gentlemen along these lines. . . . You say that you want physiologists to participate in the elaboration of psychological theories; I am a physiologist and I have such intentions; so would you like to arrange some systematic debates on the basic problems of psychology while I am in Leipzig. It would be most beneficial for me if such an idea could materialize."

However, the discussion flared up in Russia, and Sechenov's pretext for it was the philosopher-publicist K. D. Kavelin's book The Problems of Psychology which appeared in 1871, and which, in fact, was directly aimed against the psychological principles expounded in Sechenov's Reflexes of the Brain.

Kavelin's attack on Sechenov's consistently materialistic views was not unexpected, since Kavelin, from the time of Chernyshevskiy's arrest in 1862, repeatedly voiced his opposition to the ideology of revolutionary democracy and set himself up as the defender of the tsaristic government and reactionary ideology.

After reading this book of Kavelin's, Sechenov, with his characteristic directness and abruptness, published a critical article aimed at Kavelin's idealistic views and later released another article which caused a sensation entitled: "Who must investigate the problems of psychology, and how?"

The history and scope of this controversy, which was of great significance in the development of new scientific approaches in the physiology

168

of the nervous system and especially in psychology, as well as in the development of Russian public opinion, is presented in detail in our monograph Sechenov. We shall discuss here only the most important points.

Sechenov's comments on Kavelin's book Problems of Psychology and his second article, "Who must investigate the problems of psychology and how?," were published in the journal Herald of Europe at different times (1872 and 1873). The great interest in the controversy that Sechenov had aroused on the pages of this journal is evident from correspondence between the journal's editor, the famous writer M. Stasyulevich, and K. D. Kavelin. In a letter dated December 24, 1873 (the year of publication of Sechenov's article, "Who must investigate the problems of psychology, and how?"), Stasyulevich wrote to Kavelin:

"Dear Konstantin Dmitriyevich!
Allow me to hear at least a brief summary of your arguments against Sechenov: we expect him for dinner next Wednesday, but if you refuse to dine with us on that day together with him, it will be an admission of your defeat, and we shall be compelled from that time on to think that the soul is nothing more than digestion.
"I shall also consider your refusal to dine with us as a personal defeat since from that moment on there will be nothing left for me to do but to throw myself into the arms of materialism."[4]

However, in spite of this letter, Kavelin declined to meet Sechenov. In a letter of December 25, 1873, in reply to Stasyulevich, Kavelin wrote in part:

Dear Mikhail Matveyevich! No matter how tempting the thought is of spending a few leisurely hours at your home and with you, to my great regret I must decline. Sechenov was scarcely polite or even courteous with me, so that our meeting could hardly be pleasant for anyone. Judging from Sechenov's writing he is ill-mannered, and I am very quick-tempered. These bad traits of ours are so inharmonious with the usual hospitality of the charming hosts and the invariably peaceful mood of their guests that my meeting with Sechenov could unexpectedly leave a black mark on this bright picture. I surely hope that you will not construe my words to be other than my sincere desire to retain the privilege of visiting your home on the old friendly footing without having to remember any past embarrassments."[5]

I. M. Sechenov apparently was in error in his appraisal of K. D. Kavelin when he wrote in his Autobiographical Notes the following words: "I was embarrassed about my "comments" when I met Konstantin Dmitriyevich [Kavelin] personally and felt he had the friendliest feelings towards me from the first meetings."[6]

---

[4] M. M. Stasyulevich and his Contemporaries in their Correspondence. St. Petersburg, 1912, vol. II, p. 123.
[5] Ibid., p. 123.
[6] I. M. Sechenov. Autobiographical Notes, p. 129.

The persuasive voice of Sechenov, the materialist, aroused irritation in the reactionary circles. Reflecting precisely this mood, F. M. Dostoyevskiy, in a letter to A. F. Gerasimova in March, 1877, wrote about Sechenov with regard to his controversy with Kavelin:

"It is not the same in Europe; there you can meet Humboldt and Cl. Bernard and other such people with universal ideas, with tremendous education and knowledge not only in their own speciality. In our country, however, even very gifted people, for instance, Sechenov, are basically ignorant persons and uneducated outside of their own subject. Sechenov knows nothing about his opponents (the philosophers), and thus he does more harm than good with his scientific conclusions. As for the majority of students, male as well as female, they are an ignorant lot. What is the benefit in this for mankind."[7]

And all this was being written at a time when Sechenov enjoyed recognition as a scientist in Europe!

Sechenov's long-standing controversy with Kavelin in defense of a truly scientific-materialistic approach to problems of psychology found a strong response in Russia during the 1870's. In the metaphoric expression of the hero in one of Shchedrin's novels, the voice of Sechenov in this controversy sounded like a basso profundo while the voice of Kavelin was like a tenore di grazia. Its penetration into the literature attests to the broad interest in the Sechenov-Kavelin controversy. We present here a characteristic excerpt from a story published in the Notes of the Fatherland of 1874. "I don't know about you, the reader, but I am a glutton for the fantastic element. By nature I am even somewhat of a mysticist and in the Sechenov-Kavelin controversy am rather inclined to side with the latter. There was a time when this element played a great role in Western literature. Great masters served its cause; it was the foundation on which rested the glory of Hoffmann, whom we, in times gone by, read avidly. We also produced our own Hoffmanns; somewhat weaker than the real one but good enough for the Russian public. These golden days have passed. At present, when the minority representing the ideology of the natural sciences is growing noticeably from day to day and is becoming the majority, realism will supplant the fantastic altogether, and I. S. Turgenev alone has revived it for a moment through his ghosts, telling us of his flight over the earth with a certain enigmatic Ellis. . . . To me this is most distressing."[8]

The idealist, anti-Darwinist N. N. Strakhov was a very active participant in the Sechenov-Kavelin controversy. He was not content with his critical notes against Sechenov's Psychological Studies and wrote a special book in which he expounded his views concerning the matter and

---

[7] Dostoyevskiy's Letters, vol. 3, p. 259.
[8] Notes of the Fatherland, 1874, no. 7, p. 106 ("Contemporary Review").

scope of psychology. This book was published in 1878 under the title On the Basic Concepts of Psychology.[9]

The contents of Strakhov's book were in diametrical opposition to Sechenov's works; indeed it could not have been otherwise, since Strakhov, being an idealist, started from a premise opposite to Sechenov's. For Strakhov, man is the center of the universe; for Sechenov, man is a link in the development of nature; for Strakhov, the soul exists separately from the body, and these two elements live according to different laws; for Sechenov, the integration of "soul" and body is the basic idea, and that which is called psychic activity is one of the manifestations of matter at a definite stage of development of organic nature.

"Psychic phenomena in themselves," wrote Strakhov, "do not and cannot constitute a subject of physiology; they enter into physiology as ready-made concepts of psychology, just like the laws and phenomena of mechanics, physics, chemistry. . . . Usually physiologists invade psychology without scruples as if it were a field still lacking a full-fledged master and a strictly established order, which to some extent is correct but by far not to the extent assumed by many physiologists."[10]

In appraising this book, L. N. Tolstoy wrote to Strakhov in part: "Indeed, you are only establishing the basis for psychology, but you are the first to prove, and without a polemic or a quarrel, the falsity of Kant's and Schopenhauer's idealism and the falsity of materialism. But this is not all; you have proved [the existence of] the soul. . . ."[11]

For the history of the development of the concepts of such an important field as the psychic processes, Kavelin's subsequent position with regard to them is most interesting. In 1878 (four years after the controversy with Sechenov began), Kavelin wrote the following letter to Stasov after receiving and reading Strakhov's book On the Basic Concepts of Psychology:

"I am very grateful to N. N. [Strakhov] for remembering me. There is nothing more one could desire from the standpoint of presentation of his work. As for his point of departure and his conclusions I stand diametrically opposed to him. Strakhov is a dualist. But dualism is completely unthinkable at the present state of knowledge. Hereafter it is possible to work only in the direction followed by physiologists and Sechenov, and it is only necessary to supplement what they may have omitted. In his last articles Sechenov makes some stipulations which make it impossible to disagree with him and which allow the possibility of supplementing his conclusions while recognizing them in full. One feels that the time is not far

---

[9] N. N. Strakhov. On the basic concepts of psychology. Journal of the Ministry of Public Education, 1878.
[10] N. N. Strakhov. On the Basic Concepts of Psychology and Physiology. Separate edition, 1894, pp. 51-52.
[11] L. N. Tolstoy's Correspondence with Strakhov, Tolstoy Museum, vol. II, 1914, p. 175.

away when this supplementation will be done, and all the misunderstandings which appear to justify the efforts of the dualists will sink into oblivion. But in any case it is impossible to attain this coveted goal on the basis of Strakhov's viewpoint and approach."[12]

We learn of this letter from Kavelin to Stasov from a letter from Strakhov to L. N. Tolstoy. The irritated Strakhov adds the following remark to Kavelin's letter: "And that's all. Here is Kavelin in all his glory. He thinks he is discussing my ideas, but actually he does not even wish to think about me."

In his articles which appeared in the reactionary journal The Citizen,[13] N. N. Strakhov criticized not only Sechenov's views but also some of Kavelin's ideas. This "internal quarrel" and the insults that Strakhov and Kavelin threw at each other in connection with Sechenov's Psychological Studies caused a turmoil in the corresponding circles and first of all among the "holy fathers." In the clerical "Black Hundred" journal Conversation at Home, under the by-line of a homespun writer who specialized in the persecution of the natural sciences, an article appeared under the colorful title "He did not acknowledge his own kind." This article was written in connection with Strakhov's article in The Citizen. First of all the journal undertakes to advise Sechenov: ". . . the path of materialism is slippery, and it is in vain that our talented scientist has decided to tread on it. It leads its followers to the most absurd conclusions, obviously contradicting everything that common sense teaches every ordinary mortal."[14]

Deeply hurt by the fact that Strakhov was not able to shatter Sechenov's views completely and that Strakhov's criticism was also directed against Kavelin, the ideological editors of the journal wrote: "This is what always happens with us: while individuals who adhere to materialism staunchly stick together and stand up for one another, our thinkers who do not cater to materialism are disunited and are even ready to trip up those people who follow the same path with them. . . consequently they are under 'confusion within their own ranks.' "[15]

In the period of his labors on the difficult problems of the origin and development of consciousness, Sechenov studied the basic problems advanced by the Darwinian theory. We see him as a participant of a great cultural undertaking in Russia—the translation of Darwin's works into Russian. In 1871, Darwins book Origin of Man and Selection in Relation to Sex was published under Sechenov's editorship (and translated by his wife, M. A. Sechenova). He also made a thorough study of the works of the English philosopher Spencer, who developed the evolutionary theories of Darwin in a series of books. He devoted special attention to Spencer's book The Principles of Psychology. Prompted by the development of her husband's scientific work, M. A. Sechenova, at the end of

---

[12] Ibid., p. 183.
[13] The Citizen, 1873, no. 47, p. 1162.
[14] Conversation at Home, 1874, no. 34, p. 885.
[15] Ibid., p. 884.

1872, wrote to Vladimir Kovalevskiy, who was living abroad at that time, asking him to send this volume to her husband.

Sechenov devoted a great deal of attention to the problems of origin and development of psychic processes in children from their infancy. This is, of course, understandable, since "the mode of origin" of psychic acts was Sechenov's prime concern. In a series of psycho-physiological treatises we see the constant elaboration of this problem.

The analysis of the individual behavioral development in the child permitted Sechenov to present an unusually clear picture of the changes in the nature of motor reactions of the child in the process of develop-ment. At first any stimulation can elicit general muscular activity in the infant; later, the muscle group participating in these reflex acts becomes more restricted, and, finally, it is limited only to the group or muscles which is related to the given reaction of the child. The sight and sound of a bell may elicit the movement of all the muscles of the body in the very young infant; in an older child, when this bell has become a toy, only the muscles of the hand are involved (grasping of the toy); and, finally, when the child learns to speak only the muscles of the larynx are involved and he utters the word—"bell."

During the same period, beginning with the second half of the 70's, these problems of psychological development in the child also drew the attention of Charles Darwin, who was working intensively on his "Expres-sion of feelings in animals and man," which served as the basis for investigations in the field of evolution of the processes of higher nervous activity. In 1881, a translation of Darwin's article appeared in the journal The Word, no. 3, under the title "A biographical sketch of the infant," first published in Great Britain in 1877.[16]

Sechenov deemed it necessary to combine his articles "Who must investigate the problems of psychology, and how?," "Comments on Kavelin's book Problems of Psychology," as well as his treatise Reflexes of the Brain, and to publish them in a separate volume. This book came off the press in 1873[17] under the title Psychological Studies. Its appearance aggravated the climate created by his controversy with Kavelin. Inasmuch as the very title of Sechenov's book (not to mention the contents) invaded the very "sanctum sanctorum" of his adversaries, i.e., psychology, powerful forces emerged to fight against Sechenov. The metaphysician–idealists could not imagine how a scientist-physiologist who acknowledged his ignorance of psychological theories could attempt to refute these theories and to create a new positivistic psychology on the basis of experimental physiological methods. The approach and the

---

[16] Charles Darwin. A biographical sketch of the infant. Mind (a quarterly review of psychology and philosophy), vol. II, 1887, pp. 285-294. Also, Nature (a letter to Talbot).

[17] In 1884 the Psychological Studies were published in Paris in the French language: I. Setchenoff. Etudes Psychologiques, traduites du russe par Victor Derély. Paris.

views of such metaphysician-psychologists were brilliantly presented by V. I. Lenin in his criticism of the metaphysicians in his work Who are 'the friends of the people'? . . . (1894). This book also presents a clear picture of the historical significance of Sechenov's work in the period of the struggle of the Russian revolutionary democracy against its ideological enemies. V. I. Lenin wrote:

"The metaphysician-biologist commented on life and life force. The metaphysician-psychologist discussed the nature of the soul. The very approach was already absurd. One cannot discuss the soul without a specific explanation of psychic processes: here progress must consist precisely in rejecting general theories and philosophies about what the soul is, and placing the study of the facts which characterize the various psychic processes on a scientific basis. Thus, Mikhaylovskiy's accusation is identical to that of the metaphysician-psychologist who, having spent his entire life on 'investigations' of the soul (without knowing the exact explanation of a single, simple psychic phenomenon), would accuse the scientific psychologist of failure to examine all of the known theories about the soul. He, this scientific psychologist, has rejected the philosophical theories on the soul and has undertaken the direct study of the materialistic substratum of psychic phenomena, i.e., the nerve processes, and has presented, let us say, an analysis and an explanation of some psychic processes. And now our metaphysician-psychologist reads this work, comments that the processes are well described and the facts have been investigated, but still he is dissatisfied. 'I beg your pardon,' he argues, overhearing others discuss this scientist's entirely new concept of psychology and his special method in scientific psychology, 'I beg your pardon,' says the philosopher excitedly: 'In what book has this method been presented? This volume offers only pure facts, there is no mention in it of revising all the known philosophical theories about the soul? This is quite an inadequate piece of work!' "[18]

For a full appraisal of Sechenov's psychological views, it is important to stress the difference between them and those of Helmholtz. As it is known, Helmholtz' views became the basis of the so-called "theory of symbols." Hermann Helmholtz, a most outstanding German physicist and physiologist, advanced the following postulate in his book Physiological Optics. ". . . I have designated sensations as symbols of external phenomena and have rejected any analogy between them and the objects that they represent."[19]

Helmholtz analyzed his basic conclusion with particular detail through examples of visual sensations. Engels, in his notes referring to 1881-1882, demonstrated all the inconsistency of Helmholtz' theoretical views. Lenin, rejecting the theory of symbols (and with it Plekhanov's

[18] V. I. Lenin, vol. I, pp. 64–65.
[19] Ibid., vol. XIII, p. 191.

theory of hieroglyphs), formulated the Marxist-Leninist theory of reflection as follows. "Undoubtedly the image can never be entirely compared with its model, but an image is one thing, and a symbol, a conditioned sign, is another thing. An image necessarily and inevitably presupposes the objective reality of what it "reflects." "The conditioned sign" the symbol, the hieroglyph, are concepts which introduce an entirely unnecessary element of agnosticism."[20]

"The viewpoint of life, the practical viewpoint, must be the first and basic one in a theory of cognition. And this leads inevitably towards materialism, rejecting right from the start the endless inventions of professorial scholasticism," Lenin points out in his work Materialism and Critical Empiricism.[21]

The very fact that man in his everyday activities, particularly in a period of development of precise sciences and technology, subordinates the varied world of matter and energy in the surrounding nature to his will, his purposes, and his needs proves that the reflection of phenomena of nature in the consciousness of man corresponds to that which really exists in nature. And this cognition of nature is all the nearer to the objective truth as man's scope of influencing nature becomes broader and deeper and as the artificial tools created by man to analyze the phenomena of the external world become better and more varied and enrich and broaden the scope of man's innate sensory organs. Man has created an enormous arsenal of the most diverse measuring instruments, of optical systems, chemical reagents, the most complex machinery and technological procedures through which he is able to demonstrate in practice the reality of that which is reflected in his consciousness. These complex problems that are completely alien to idealistic psychology confronted Sechenov, the great reformer of psychology, who put it on a materialistic foundation.

Having established at the beginning of his article "Impressions and reality" that there are opinions to the effect that "we receive only a kind of conditioned signs from objects of the external world through our sense organs," Sechenov posed the question: "How is it then possible to reconcile the fact of such apparently conditioned cognition of the external world with the enormous achievements of the natural sciences, through which man subdues more and more the forces of nature? It would then appear that this science bases its work on the conditional sensory signs from inaccessible reality, and as a result a more and more harmonious system of knowledge, of real knowledge is obtained since it is incessantly confirmed by brilliant practical applications, i.e., by the achievements of technology."[22]

Insofar as the investigator was confronted with this problem, it was bound to lead him to the formulation of postulates entirely opposed

[20] Ibid., vol. XIII, p. 193.
[21] Ibid., p. 116.
[22] I. M. Sechenov. Selected Works, p. 292.

to the Helmholtz-Plekhanov theory of symbols. Indeed, when Sechenov analysed the scope of visual sensations, he arrived at conclusions which give us reason to believe that, on the one hand, Sechenov adhered to Helmholtz' theory of symbols, and, on the other, that Plekhanov made one-sided use of Sechenov's views for the construction of his own erroneous "theory of hieroglyphs."

Here are these conclusions:

". . . the seen image, i.e., the sensory sign of the external object as well as the last causative visual component, becomes observable to the same extent as any other material object; and this immediately obviates this incommensurability of the impression (as a sensory act) with the external source (as the material object) which made their comparison impossible in principle for many thinkers."[23]

We present here Sechenov's concrete conclusions concerning each of the elements of the complex visual perception of objects:

a) ". . . that which is called perspective in the visual picture has its basis in reality."[24]

b) ". . . in addition to the linear contour, the eye transmits with approximate accuracy, i.e., in accordance with reality, the relative placement of objects on limited portions of the earth's surface."[25]

c) ". . . Beside the shape and placement of objects, the eye (and the touch of the blind) also provides true indications of the size of objects."[26]

d) ". . . with regard to movements which the eye is capable of following, the perceived and the real concur."[27]

Sechenov substantiated all these conclusions with a most important philosophical conclusion that he had already formulated in his doctoral dissertation and had subsequently elaborated in his Reflexes of the Brain: "It goes without saying that my arguments are based on the inherently absolute conviction of every man as to the reality of the external world."

These Sechenov postulates do not leave any doubt that the great Russian physiologist traveled a long way from Helmholtz' original views, and, through his exceptionally deep approach to the problem of the relationship between the subjective and the objective, he arrived at a consistently materialistic point of view.

It therefore appears all the more surprising that many authors constantly comment that both Sechenov and Helmholtz adhered to the

---

[23]Ibid., pp. 293-294.
[24]Ibid., p. 297.
[25]Ibid., p. 298.
[26]Ibid., p. 299.
[27]Ibid., p. 300.

theory of symbols or conditioned signs. One should remember that, in the corresponding chapter of Lenin's Materialism and Empirical Criticism devoted to the criticism of the theory of hieroglyphs, Lenin has Helmholtz in mind and does not mention Sechenov at all, although Lenin followed Sechenov's work closely.

In 1903 Lenin wrote from Geneva to M. A. Ul'yanova: "Mother dear! . . . I request. . . that you buy some books for me. I have already written to you about a Russian-French dictionary. I am now adding Sechenov's Elements of Thought (a book just recently published)."[28]

Sechenov's work Elements of Thought is of paramount significance, since it formulated, for the first time, on a strictly scientific basis, the problem of formation of ideas, and it revealed the physiological basis of the so-called abstract thinking in the process of development of man and his active encounter with objects of the external world.

Sechenov devoted more than 40 years of his scientific career to the penetrating study of psychic phenomena. K. A. Timiryazev, in evaluating the most outstanding achievements in the natural sciences of the world during the 19th century, emphasizes Sechenov's tremendous role and considers him "in all probability the most penetrating investigator in the field of scientific psychology," who never faltered before the most complex problems and undertook to solve them "with. . . the caution of a scientist and the discernment of a thinker."[29]

Sechenov's work was the starting point for the creation of the theory of conditioned reflexes, which is the most outstanding achievement of contemporary science in the field of physiology of the nervous system. I. P. Pavlov especially emphasized the enormous significance of Sechenov's work, particularly of his book Reflexes of the Brain, in developing the theories of conditioned reflexes.

"The beginning of our investigations dates back to the end of 1863 when Sechenov's famous essays Reflexes of the Brain were published," stated Pavlov in one of his first public speeches on conditioned reflexes (1906).[30]

[28]V. I. Lenin, Letters to Relatives, Partizdat, 1934, p. 292.
[29]K. A. Timiryazev. Collected Works, vol. VIII, p. 100.
[30]Proceedings of the St. Petersburg Society of Russian Physicians, 1906, March–May, vol. 73, p. 416.

CHAPTER XIV

Historico-logical connection between Sechenov's and Pavlov's work in the field of physiology of the higher nervous system. Sources, methods of formation, and achievement of the theory of conditioned reflexes.

The basic similarity and historico-logical relationship between Sechenov's and Pavlov's investigations lie in the fact that for both of them the leading role in the formation of the most complex processes of psychic activity belongs to the environment of the organisms. Pavlov's theory of conditioned reflexes has shown that all the varied manifestations of higher nervous activity are the result of constant interrelationships between the organism and the environment, and that they arise in conjunction with specific conditions under which the organisms exist. Sechenov's basic theory, that an organism cannot exist without the external environment that sustains it, was experimentally confirmed and, so to speak, made complete in the Pavlovian doctrine of conditioned reflexes.

An objective physiological approach to the study of complex psychic phenomena is characteristic of both Sechenov and Pavlov. Up to their times, none of the prominent investigators of nature investigated so-called psychic activity because they could not find the means for an objective study; therefore, they remained confined by philosophical dualism. Sechenov and Pavlov were the first to escape this confinement and to present most convincing proof of the unity and interdependence of psychic and physical phenomena. It was precisely this fact that justified Pavlov's proud and bold statement in a letter to the Leningrad Physiological Society which bears Sechenov's name. "Yes, I am glad that together with Ivan Mikhaylovich and a host of my dear collaborators we have gained for mighty physiological investigation not just a fragment, but the whole integrated animal organism. And this is entirely our own incontestable Russian contribution to world science, to general human thought."[1]

Were we to proceed only from a chronological sequence, the history of the theory of conditioned reflexes would have to be presented much later, since Pavlov's first publication in this field was in 1903. However, from a historical-logical aspect the development of the theory of conditioned reflexes must directly follow the history of the development

---

[1] I.P. Pavlov. Complete Works, v. I, USSR, 1941, p. 27.

of Sechenov's views, first presented in his book Reflexes of the Brain, since this is a single chain in the great progress of Russian theoretical thought. It is precisely in the theory of conditioned reflexes that we have the end of a long trial of quests followed by both the philosophers and the natural scientists of our country in their persistent attempt to overcome the constant contraposition of spiritual processes against the organic ones.

V.I. Lenin indicated with exceptional clarity that the philosophical works of Belinskiy, Gertsen, and Chernyshevskiy were the forerunners of the enormous ideological conquests that were made by the Russian revolutionary democracy and that led to the formulation of Russian Marxist thought. As a result of their gigantic creative labor, the Russian philosophers and natural scientists produced a theory of unity of the psychic and the organic, and through the work of such Russian physiologists as Sechenov and Pavlov this theory of unity of soul and body achieved its indisputable proof. This completes, as it were, a particular stage of extensive scientific explorations that passed through the philosophical concepts of Radishchev, Belinskiy, Gertsen, and Chernyshevskiy and arrived at the ideas of the Russian physiologist-materialists of the 19th-20th centuries.[2]

The intense and creative struggle of generations of Russian thinkers for experience, observation, and an experimental method as the only means of gaining knowledge about nature, including the phenomena of consciousness, the struggle to overcome the dualistic conceptions of organic nature, to prove the unity of the spiritual and the physical — all this attained brilliant fulfillment in the works of Sechenov and Pavlov.

The historico-logical connection between Sechenov's and Pavlov's work is linked to one significant date. In 1903, a memorable year for Russian physiology, Sechenov, just one year before his death, published the revised edition of his famous work Elements of Thought; this was the great reformer's last message on the theory of the nature of consciousness. That same year, 1903, Pavlov read his first paper on the conditioned reflexes before the assembly of the International Congress in Madrid.

In the light of the general problems in the history of Russian science, one fact is of utmost importance. Pavlov never was a student of Sechenov's in the usual, scholastic sense of the word. Pavlov's student years in Petersburg, at the Medical-Surgical Academy, and at the University (1870-1875) coincide with the years of Sechenov's absence from Petersburg. I.P. Pavlov entered Petersburg University in 1870, so that he began to attend lectures in physiology in the year that Sechenov left Petersburg. Sechenov returned to Petersburg in the capacity of professor at Petersburg University in 1876, while Pavlov completed his studies at the

---

[2] About 20 years ago in my article "The biological views of La Mettrie," I was too one-sided in my statement concerning only the one ideological trend that could be traced from La Mettrie through Du-Bois Reymond to Sechenov.

university and at the Medical-Surgical Academy in 1875. Pavlov's teachers at these institutions were I.F. Tsion and F.V. Ovsyannikov.

It must be stated that, subsequently, during the period of over 10 years that Sechenov remained in Petersburg (1876-1888), Pavlov, who was already doing independent work in the field of physiology, was primarily concerned with the physiology of digestion, as well as the cardiovascular system and pharmacology; in other words, the scope of his interests was almost entirely outside Sechenov's field.[3] While Sechenov, along with experimental investigations in the field of physiology of the nerve conductor, nerve centers, and physio-chemical explorations concerning the gas content in the blood, was also doing intensive research on psychophysiological problems, Pavlov's interests were directed towards the exploration of the functional mechanism of the digestive glands and the nervous regulation of circulation of the blood. At the beginning of the 1890's, at the height of Pavlov's work on the physiology of digestion and at the start of his tormenting search for the nature of a "psychic secretion," Sechenov left Petersburg and moved to Moscow. After Sechenov moved to Moscow there was apparently no opportunity for these two great physiologists to meet.

To date there are no indications that there was any correspondence between Sechenov and Pavlov. At my request, Serafima Vasil'yevna Pavlova made a special search of Pavlov's archives and was unable to find any letters from Sechenov. Nor have any letters from Pavlov been found in Sechenov's archives. At the same time, it is difficult to conceive that in the period of Pavlov's activities as a mature scientist he was not constantly under Sechenov's ideological influence, when Sechenov had been recognized as the teacher of all Russian physiologists, and, according to Pavlov himself Sechenov had exercised a tremendous influence on him even in his youth, before he enrolled at the University.

Pavlov himself indicates that the enormous impression made by I.M. Sechenov's Reflexes of the Brain in his youth (during his last years at the Ryazan Theological Seminary) gave impetus to his work on the important problems of physiology of higher nervous activity which developed into the theory of the conditioned reflexes. This is extremely interesting in the complex problems of the history of science, the history of the inception of various important theoretical generalizations in the field of a science, and their connection with the generalizations of scientists of previous periods. It is for this reason that we consider it most appropriate to quote here in full a remarkable excerpt from Pavlov's writings which characterizes with greater clarity than any other document the influence that a genuine teacher exerts upon his disciple. Ideas early implanted in the soul, perplexing phenomena of nature, personal examples from the life of a scientist and thinker, an independently developed daring

---

[3] We say "almost" because in a little-known Sechenov article "On tryptic digestion," published during the Petersburg period (1888), important problems on the difference between the effect of trypsine and pepsin on albumin were advanced for the first time.

idea concerning the ways of learning and explaining the most complex phenomena of nature, and much more that is linked with the youth of the scientist persistently clings and stir his thoughts, sometimes until he is very old. The excerpt from Pavlov's observations that we are quoting also speaks of the great power of his scientific message, of his book.

"When Tolochinov and I began our investigations, I only knew that with the extension of physiological investigations (in the form of comparative physiology) over the whole animal kingdom, beyond the favorite laboratory specimens of that period (dogs, cats, rabbits and frogs), there was no choice but to discard the subjective viewpoint and attempt to introduce objective investigative procedures and terminology (J. Loeb's theory of trophism in the animal kingdom and a proposed objective terminology by Baer, Bethe and von Uexküll). Indeed, it would have been difficult and unnatural to think and speak about the thoughts and desires of some amoeba or infusoria. But I think that in our case my decision to work with the dog, man's closest and most loyal companion since prehistoric times, was prompted long ago, in my youth although I did not realize it then, by the impression made by the fascinating brochure by Ivan Mikhaylovich Sechenov, the father of Russian physiology, Reflexes of the Brain, 1863. Such an influence is powerful through its novelty and adherence to reality of thought, especially when it is exerted in one's youth; it is a deep, persistent and, one must add, often a subconscious influence. In this brochure an attempt was made, both brilliant in form and extraordinary for those times (of course, theoretically, in the form of a physiological scheme), to represent our subjective world in purely physiological terms.

At that time Ivan Mikhaylovich made a most important physiological discovery (concerning central inhibition), which made a strong impression on European physiologists and it was the first Russian contribution to an important branch of the natural sciences which had just previously made such strides through the achievements of German and French scientists. The tension and joy of discovery and possibly the impact of some personal emotion account for this brilliant stroke of the Sechenov genius."[4]

In summarizing the results of the gigantic amount of scientific work he and his disciples accomplished, Pavlov in 1935 presented a general historical analysis of the development of physiology of the higher levels of the central nervous system at the end of the 19th century and defined the place and significance of his theory thus.

"Many years have passed (more than one millennium) since psychic activity became the subject of a special science, psychology. Whereas physiology only in remarkably recent times, beginning with the 1870's, was able to discover, by the standard method of artificial stimulation, the first precise facts concerning certain (namely, motor) physiological functions of the cerebral hemispheres; using another standard method, that of partial destruction, additional data were obtained with regard to the

---

[4] I.P. Pavlov. Twenty Years of Experience of Objective Study of Higher Nervous Activity (Behavior) of Animals, 1932, p. 12-13.

connections of different parts of the hemispheres with the principle receptors of the organism: eyes, ears and others. This seemed to arouse the hopes of both the physiologists and the psychologists of a close connection between physiology and psychology. On the one hand, it became customary for psychologists to begin their textbooks in psychology with a preliminary presentation of facts concerning the central nervous system and especially the cerebral hemispheres (sense organs). On the other hand, the physiologists, when performing experiments with extirpation of various portions of the hemispheres, began to discuss their results on animals psychologically, by analogy with what would have occurred in our own experience (for instance Munk's concept "sees" but does not "understand"). But soon disappointment took hold of both camps. The physiology of the hemispheres came to a noticeable standstill after these first experiments and did not make any appreciable further progress. Yet, there appeared again a considerable number of resolute individuals among the psychologists who, again, insisted on the complete independence of psychological investigation from the physiological. There were also attempts to link the victorious natural sciences with psychology through a statistical treatment of psychological phenomena. At one time it was even considered to establish in physiology a special branch of psychophysics, owing to the fortunate discovery by Weber and Fechner of the law of a definite numerical relationship between the external stimulus and the intensity of the sensation. But this new branch did not progress beyond the single law. More successful was the attempt of Wundt, a former physiologist who subsequently became a psychologist and philosopher, to apply experimentation with numerical measurements to psychic phenomena in the form of so-called experimental psychology; thus a significant amount of data was assembled and is still being assembled. Some apply the term psychophysics to mathematical treatment of numerical data in experimental psychology. But nowadays it is not rare to encounter many psychologists and especially psychiatrists who are very disappointed in the active contributions of experimental psychology. Thus what was to be done? However, yet another path towards the solution of this fundamental problem was sensed, imagined and outlined. Would it not be possible to find an elementary psychic phenomenon that could also be justifiably considered a pure physiological phenomenon? And by studying the conditions of its origin with strict objectivity (as everything has to be done in physiology) could we obtain an objective physiological picture of the whole higher activity of animals, i.e., the normal function of the higher region of the brain instead of the various earlier experimental procedures of artificial stimulation and destruction of brain tissue? Fortunately, such a phenomenon had been right under the eyes of many, for a long time; many had dwelled on it, and a few even began to study it (Thorndike should receive special mention), but for some reason stopped right at the beginning, and did not elaborate the study into a basic method of systematic physiological exploration of higher activity of the animal organism. This phenomenon was precisely that which is now designated as "conditioned reflex" and the intensive study of which had completely justified the expressed expectation."[5]

---

[5] Physiological Journal, USSR, v. XIX, no. 1, 1935, pp. 261-262.

A comprehensive exploration of the history of development of the theory of conditioned reflexes deserves an entirely independent study and presentation, and future investigations are bound to demonstrate the whole unusually complex and interesting path followed by Pavlov and his coworkers during the process of formation of this most outstanding achievement in the natural sciences in the 20th century. In our Essays we are able to present but a broad outline of the development in this important area.

Our task, as well as that of future investigator of the history of physiology, is greatly facilitated by the fact that Pavlov himself left a remarkable history of his theory: Twenty Years of Experience in the Objective Study of Higher Nervous Activity (Behavior) of Animals, completed in 1922.

In the preface to the 5th edition (1932) of this remarkable book, Pavlov himself wrote: "The present book is a vivid history of this enormous field of human knowledge in, we dare say, one of the active points of its development. As in any history, there were and still are numerous mistakes, observations lacking in precision, faulty set-up of experiments, insufficiently founded conclusions; but in return there were also many instructive instances showing how much of this was avoided and rectified, and on the whole a constant accumulation of scientific truths was achieved."

And indeed, reading Twenty Years of Experience... article by article, report by report, one clearly pictures the conditions of work, the enthusiasm and devotion of Pavlov's students to their labors; one sees clearly the bright manifestations of Pavlovian thought, his tedious pondering over contradictions that emerged in the process of exploring this complex problem, and the errors and doubts that arose in the course of this work.

The beginning of this great scientific achievement dates back to a report Pavlov presented at one of the general meetings of the International Medical Congress in Madrid in 1903. Pavlov's paper bore the title "Experimental Psychology and Psychopathology in Animals." Pavlov's introductory words to this report before the Congress are particularly characteristic. He began with a simple and clear statement. "Considering the language of facts as the most eloquent one, I am taking the liberty of referring directly to the experimental material that gave me the right to speak on the subject of my paper." It is possible that Pavlov's listeners, the participants of the International Medical Congress, from the title of the paper expected it to be a flow of logical constructions and casuistic descriptions of the manifestations of the pathological activity of the nervous system in animals under experimental conditions. However, Pavlov's paper dealt with something entirely different. It dealt with the results of observations of the function of the salivary glands under various physiological experimental conditions. It goes without saying that his communication, both in the formulation of the problem and in its factual material, presented as a basis for the most complex psychological problems, reverberated at the Congress as something entirely new, and we may say without exaggeration that Pavlov's report created the impression of an exploded bombshell.

In this connection let us consider the generally known fact that Pavlov's work in the field of physiology of higher nervous activity was closely

183

connected with his brilliant cycle of investigations which brought him the Nobel Prize; this work dealt with his classical investigations in the field of physiology of the digestive glands. The outstanding characteristic of Pavlov's work, as well as that of his disciples in the field of physiology of digestion, is that they succeeded in analyzing with exceptional detail the most complex problems of neural regulation of the digestive glands. One may say that the problems of reflex regulation of the glands of the digestive tract have obtained the most vivid and comprehensive elucidation in Pavlov's investigations. But in the course of this important experimental work, Pavlov and his disciples stumbled onto the fact that the forms of neural regulation of the secretion of the digestive glands are frequently governed not only by physiological factors but also by psychological ones. Pavlov and his disciples were absorbed by the fact that a reflex influence on the salivary glands was elicited not only through direct contact of food stimuli with the body of the animal (with the various sensory zones of the digestive tract), but also in cases when the food stimuli were far from the animal. Let us recall a forgotten detail, that originally Pavlov often used to add after the words "conditioned reflexes" the words "remote reflexes," parenthetically.

The historico-logical connection between Pavlov's works in the field of physiology of digestion and the conditioned reflexes spreads over a vast territory; these two physiological fields covered by the work of Pavlov's genius are connected not only by the kinship of ideas but also by the kinship of methodological approaches. The technique Pavlov perfected for the preparation of animals for physiological experiments after successful surgical procedures, in order to preserve the neural connections intact in animal played an outstanding role in the discovery of the real relationship of digestive processes and made it possible to use a new approach to the study of relationships in the organism. It goes without saying that as long as the function of the various glands in the digestive tract, including the salivary and gastric glands, was studied in ignorance of this basic fact (these glands were studied either in an isolated state or in the intact animal, but their central nervous connections were frequently impaired), it was difficult to see and, what is most important, to analyze this special form of reflexes - i.e., the reflexes at distance which emerged only under definite conditions.

I.P. Pavlov approached this problem after a thorough study of the special forms of secretory activity of the digestive glands which he himself called "psychic secretion." Pavlov uses this term in his Lectures on the Function of the Main Digestive Glands, which appeared in 1897. In this book, Pavlov presents in detail the most varied instances of psychic secretion but does not mention at all that this form of secretion can also be analyzed by experimental physiology. Academician L. A. Orbeli, who attended Pavlov's lectures at the Military Medical Academy in 1909, recalls that Pavlov, speaking of psychic secretion, had pointed out that "the function of a gland may be governed by purely physiological as well as by psychic factors."[6]

---

[6] L.A. Orbeli. Lectures on the problems of higher nervous activity. AS USSR, 1945, p. 8.

During the second half of the 1890's, I.P. Pavlov began in earnest to make an experimental analysis of the essence of "psychic secretion." Although his observations were indicative of this kind of secretion in both the gastric and the salivary glands, his attention was concentrated on the latter. By that time his closest coworker, D.L. Glinskiy,[7] had developed an excellent technique for making a permanent fistula of the salivary gland which made it possible to perform experiments on the salivary glands of the dog repeatedly for months and years.

Pavlov assigned Dr. S.G. Vul'fson for a special exploration of the problem of "psychic secretion" of the salivary gland. He found that just showing the food to the animal was enough to cause salivation from the sublingual as well as the parotid glands. A most amazing fact in Vul'fson's experiments was that the saliva differed qualitatively and quantitatively, depending on whether the animal was presented with a nutritive or distasteful substance. In other words, salivation that occurred upon being shown a substance seemed to be a copy of the salivation that occurred upon direct stimulation of the buccal cavity with the same substances - true, to a somewhat lesser degree. Similar results were obtained also upon stimulation with usual food substances (meat, milk, rusks, meat powder), by introducing them into the mouth and by showing them.

Concurrently with Vul'fson, similar experiments were performed by Dr. A.B. Snarskiy, who obtained very interesting data. Thus, for instance, Snarskiy introduced an acid that had been dyed black into the mouth of a dog, several times; this would cause profuse salivation. After that Snarskiy would pour plain water, also dyed black, into the dog's mouth, and this water also caused increased salivation. The conclusion appeared most unexpected for those times; "black" water would stimulate the glands at a distance only when the dog had been previously given black colored acid.

Another of Snarskiy's experiments consisted in the following. He established that various odorous substances, anise oil for instance, have no effect on salivation. If a dog with permanent fistulae of the salivary glands smells anise oil for the first time, no salivation occurs. If, however, simultaneously with the effect of the odor, the buccal cavity is in contact with the same oil, which causes a strong local irritation, then, subsequently, the odor alone will start the flow of saliva.

These results led Snarskiy to an even deeper exploration of the problem Pavlov had presented concerning psychic secretions. He, as Pavlov before him but in a more definite and sharper form, raised the question of the thoughts, desires, and sensations of experimental animals. Snarskiy, in discussing with Pavlov the results of his experiments, stressed the enormous significance of the inner world of the dog, and indicated that the whole behavior of the animal he had observed was its psychic reaction, and that the salivary glands but reflect some inner state of the animal which would be difficult to submit to physiological investigation.

_____

[7] D.L. Glinskiy. An Experiment on the Function of the Salivary Glands. Works of the Society of Russian Doctors, SPb, 1895.

These events took place at the very beginning of the 20th century, since Snarskiy's dissertation was published in 1901. By this time, Pavlov was firmly convinced that it was necessary to replace the concept of psychic secretion with a very definitely physiological concept. This is why his controversies with Snarskiy became very acute, and this is why in this period certain events occurred in Pavlov's laboratory which were extremely significant in the history of the theory of conditioned reflexes. Pavlov himself speaks very clearly of these events, and he began his paper in 1906 with a description of this very episode.[8]

"Permit me to begin with an incident that occurred in my laboratory a few years ago. Among my collaborators a young doctor stood out. He displayed a quick mind susceptible to the joys and triumphs of an investigative thought. How great then was my astonishment when this loyal laboratory friend became truly and deeply indignant when he first heard of our plans to investigate the psychic activities of the dog in this same laboratory and with the same means that we had been using for the solution of various physiological problems. No amount of persuasion could affect him; he predicted and wished us all kinds of failures. And all that, as we could understand him, because in his eyes the sublime and unique phenomena which he assumed to lie in the spiritual realm of man and higher animals could not be investigated successfully and, furthermore, the crudeness of procedures in physiological laboratories was almost insulting. Admitting that this particular presentation contains an element of exaggeration, it appears to me however not devoid of the characteristics of certain typical attitudes. We cannot close our eyes on the fact that a genuine and consistent scientific approach towards the last boundary of life will not occur without considerable misunderstandings and resistance on the part of those who since time immemorial have had a different approach to this field of natural phenomena and have considered their viewpoint the only acceptable and legitimate one in this particular case."

Pavlov returned to this problem again in 1922, beginning the introduction to his Twenty Years of Experience. . . with a description of this crucial period in the development of the theory of conditioned reflexes.[9]

"I began to elaborate on the problem of this stimulation of the salivary glands with my coworkers, Drs. S.G. Vul'fson and A.T. Snarskiy. At that time Vul'fson had collected new data concerning the details of psychic excitation of the salivary glands that attributed great importance to the subject. Snarskiy undertook the analysis of the inner mechanism of such excitation from the subjective viewpoint, i.e., considering the inner world of the dogs (our experiments were done on them), which he imagined by analogy with humans, i.e., their ideas, sensations and desires. This led to an unprecedented incident in the laboratory. We thoroughly disagreed with one another in the interpretation of this inner world of the dog,

---

[8] Lecture "On the New Advances in Medicine and Surgery" delivered in honor of T. Huxley on Oct. 1, 1906 in London. Publ. in Twenty Years of Experience... , 1932, pp. 56-57.
[9] See Introduction, Twenty Years of Experience...

186

and in spite of all further attempts we could not agree on any general conclusion, notwithstanding the usual laboratory practice whereby experiments undertaken by mutual agreement usually solved all controversies and arguments.

Dr. Snarskiy persisted in his subjective interpretation of these phenomena while I, astonished by the fantastic nature and scientific sterility of such an approach to the problem at hand, sought another solution to this most difficult situation. After persistent deliberation and a most difficult mental struggle I finally decided to remain in the role of a pure experimenter with regard to this so-called psychic excitation and to deal exclusively with external manifestations and relationships. To carry out this decision I took on a new collaborator, Dr. I.F. Tolochinov, and our work went on for 20 years with the participation of many of my dear collaborators.''

Pavlov's early lectures and papers on the conditioned reflexes, including his famous Madrid speech in 1903 and the article "On the Psychic Secretion of the Salivary Glands," published in 1904 in French in the International Archive of Physiology, were devoted to the Vul'fson, Snarskiy, and Tolochinov experiments.

During the early 1900's, the most talented students of the Military-Medical Academy as well as of Petersburg University were attracted by Pavlov to experimental work in the field of conditioned reflexes. During the period of 1906-1910, Pavlov's laboratory published a series of dissertations and other publications by his students, who subsequently became outstanding Russian physiologists. Suffice it to mention that the following articles and dissertations appeared during this period: L.A. Orbeli - "Concerning the Localization of Conditioned Reflexes in the Central Nervous System;"[10] G.V. Fol'bort - "Data Concerning the Physiology of the Conditioned Reflexes;" A.V. Palladin - "The Formation of Artificial Conditioned Reflexes by an Aggregate of Stimuli;" V.N. Boldyrev - "The Formation of Artificial Conditioned (Psychic) Reflexes and Their Properties;" B.P. Babkin - "Data on the Physiology of the Frontal Lobes of the Cerebral Hemisphers in Dogs; I.V. Zavadskiy - "Experience in Applying the Conditioned Reflex Method of Pharmacology;" G. P. Zelenyy - "Orientation of the Dog in the Area of Sounds;" V.A. Demidov - "Conditioned (salivary) Reflexes in a Dog Devoid of Anterior Halves of the Cerebral Hemispheres." During this same period one of Pavlov's closest collaborators, N.I. Krasnogorskiy, began his valuable studies on the development of conditioned reflexes in the ontogenesis of children.

In the works of these intimate coworkers of Pavlov, basic facts were compiled which permitted Pavlov to describe the patterns that characterize the new type of reflex associations that he had discovered, and that he termed "conditioned reflex associations." These collaborators are the ones who revealed the full scope of conditions for the formation, development, and extinction of conditioned reflex reactions from the sense organs,

---

[10] L.A. Orbeli, Dissertation "Conditioned reflexes from the dog's eye," 1908.

and by various combinations of indifferent stimuli with unconditioned stimuli, primarily with food stimuli.

Pavlov became more and more convinced of the correctness of his chosen path, and this brought up the problem of creating special laboratory conditions that would enable him to make a precise study of the conditions under which conditioned reflexes are elicited.

First of all, Pavlov was faced with the problem of the financial requirements for building a laboratory of a new type, where the necessary conditions could be provided for close observation of the formation of reflex relationships of the animal with the environment under given conditions, without interference by superfluous environmental conditions. This presented not only a methodological and administrative problem but also a question of principle. This is why Pavlov delivered his remarkable address in 1910 at the meeting of the Society for the Promotion of Experimental Sciences and Their Practical Applications (a society founded in Moscow in honor of Kh. S. Ledentsov), calling the attention of the Russian scientific community to the problems that arise before the further development of the theory of conditioned reflexes, and to the urgent need for the organization of a new type of laboratory, necessary for the solution of emerging problems on a proper methodical level.

The Ledentsov Society responded to Pavlov's appeal, since this Nobel Prize Laureate was held in very high esteem. Pavlov called upon one of his closest assistants, Ye. A. Ganike, to design this new laboratory, and from that time on Ganike was engaged for many years in equipping Pavlov's laboratories with special apparatus for the study of conditioned reflexes. His efforts were very significant in the development of this theory.[11] Pavlov's idea of erecting special buildings for the study of conditioned reflexes, born in 1910, found its realization only in Soviet times, when the famous "Tower of Silence" was completed; in it Pavlov and his students, completely isolated from any external interference, were able to explore occurrence and development of the conditioned reflexes under strictly isolated conditions of the effect of specific external stimuli.

The period from 1910 to 1914 was particularly fruitful. During these years a number of extremely valuable works in the field of conditioned reflexes authored by Pavlov's new collaborators were published, among them: M. K. Petrova - "On the Theory of Irradiation of Excitation and Inhibitory Processes;" N.A. Rozhanskiy - "Data on the Physiology of Sleep;" I.S. Tsitovich - "The Origin and Formation of Conditioned Reflexes;" M.N. Yerofeyeva - "Electrical Stimulation of the Dog's Skin as a Conditioned Stimulus for the Activity of the Salivary Glands;" N.I. Krasnogorskiy - "On the Process of Delaying and Localization of the Skin and Motor Analyzer in the Cerebral Cortex;" N.M. Saturnov - "Further Investigation on the Conditioned Salivary Reflexes in a Dog Deprived of the Anterior Halves of the Cerebral Hemispheres;" S.P.

---

[11] Ye. A. Ganike. Concerning the Construction of Soundproof Chambers. Reports from the Lesgaft Scientific Institute, vol. V, 1922.

Kurayev - "Investigations on Dogs with Damaged Frontal Lobes of the Hemispheres in the Late Post-operative Period;" N.I. Leporskiy - "Data on the Physiology of the Conditioned Inhibition."

The specific characteristic of the research done in this period is the pioneer work in investigating the significance of the cerebral cortex in the development of conditioned reflexes. In the remarkable communications of G.P. Zelenyy under the title "A Dog Without Cerebral Hemispheres," it was demonstrated that in animals who have recovered completely after bilateral removal of the cerebral cortex it becomes impossible to develop reflexes to sight, smell, and sounds linked with various kinds of food stimuli. This was the first proof of the significance of the cortex as a completely indispensable organ for the formation of conditioned reflexes in the dog.

During this same period, thanks to Tsitovich's excellent work at the Women's Medical Institute in Professor Vartanov's laboratory, published in his dissertation under the title "Origin and Formation of Natural Conditioned Reflexes," for the first time there was a most precise experimental confirmation of Pavlov's views with regard to the existence of two types of reflexes: - inborn or unconditioned, and individually acquired or conditioned. Tsitovich demonstrated that puppies with permanent fistulae of the salivary glands reared for a long period on milk alone had complex forms of conditioned reflex associations with everything that was related to the milk. But the sight, the odor, and the sounds linked with other foods and conditions of feeding, such strong food stimuli as meat or bread, did not cause conditioned salivation in these puppies until they were only once given an admixture of meat or bread in their ration. A single administration of these foods was the condition after which the smell of meat or bread already caused profuse conditioned salivation.

This was also the time when Pavlov's extremely important doubts arose concerning the method of both total and partial cortical extirpation, employed by his students (Demidov, Saturnov, Kurayev) to study conditioned reflexes. In 1912, in Pavlov's report to the Society of Russian Physicians, presenting a summary of results of experimental extirpation of various regions of the cerebral hemispheres by the method of conditioned reflexes, he concluded his communication with the following statement.

"Is it really possible to be satisfied with the results obtained? Of course, the answer is yes, and primarily because they have paved some good ways for the further productive study of the subject. Yet it is clear the work has only just begun and the most complex and important aspects are ahead. And now if we are to imagine the further course of investigations, our attention is first riveted to our present methods of dissection of the apparatus under study. These methods are frightful. The more one extirpates from the cerebral hemispheres, the more one is astonished that so much was obtained by earlier investigations. With extirpation we almost never obtain a constant condition, but always a fluid and changing one. You have touched the brain with your hands, your clumsy hands, you have injured the brain by removing certain parts. This injury stimulates the brain, the effect of such stimulation lasts for an undetermined time,

189

and you are in ignorance as to its scope. You cannot predict when it will terminate. That such stimulation exists is confirmed by many generally known experiments of which I shall not speak now. Finally, the desired moment comes: the stimulation of the injury has passed and the wound has healed. But then a new stimulus emerges: the scar. And possibly you have only a few days during which you may work with some assurance that all of the observed changes depend, for the time being, only on the absence of the removed parts of the cerebral hemispheres. And here is what happens next: first there appear phenomena of depression. And you guess correctly that the scar has become active. Such a state lasts for several days, then follows an onset of convulsions. After the convulsions, after the excitation, there is either a new period of depression or an entirely new particular state of the animal. Before the convulsions the animal had one mode of behavior. Then came the convulsions and you are unable to recognize the animal, it now appears much more damaged than it was immediately after surgery. Obviously the scar not only stimulated, but also compressed, stretched, tore, in other words, again caused destruction.

"Under such abhorrent conditions would you expect to analyze successfully a function so complex as the function of the cerebral hemispheres?"

And thus Pavlov the natural scientist, with all his experimental skill and energy in the achievement of his aims, the man who endeavored to study various phenomena on the complete animal, was again confronted with the problem of finding a method of exclusion of specific cortical regions that would not be accompanied by the gross effects described above. He assigned the development of such new methods, and in particular a method of local cooling of the brain, to his closest disciple, L.A. Orbeli.

These new attempts of the Pavlovian school, in 1912, obtained further broad development through the investigations of other Pavlovian disciples, especially through the work of A.D. Speranskiy.

In a comparatively short period of time (the decade from 1903-1914) for the development of a new major trend, the Pavlovian laboratories accumulated a vast store of factual data that have become the basis of the Pavlovian theory of conditioned reflexes, with all the ensuing new and unexpected conclusions bearing both on physiology and on psychology.

In 1914 Pavlov accepted an invitation to participate in the International Congress of Psychiatry, Neurology and Psychology which was to be held in Switzerland, and he prepared a paper. However, this congress was postponed due to the beginning of the First World War, and Pavlov's report, " 'The real physiology' of the brain," was published in the journal, Nature (1917).

This article (report) summarized the actual achievements of Pavlov and his disciples in the field of exploration of the physiology of the higher areas of the central nervous system and the complete description of the

190

patterns of formation and of the significance of the new type of reflexes, the conditioned reflexes; it also marked a new milestone in the progress of the basic materialistic tradition of Russian science. As a genuine follower of Sechenov, Pavlov concluded his paper with the following postulates.

"One may rest assured that on the road which the strict physiology of the brain of animals has chosen, it will attain similarly the astounding discoveries and with them just as great a mastery over the higher nervous system that in no way will yield in significance to other achievements of the natural sciences. I understand and respect the mental efforts in the work of the old and the newest psychologists, but at the same time it appears to me, and this can hardly be disputed, that this work is being performed in a highly inefficient manner, and I am deeply convinced that the pure physiology of the animal brain will greatly facilitate and will crown with success the gigantic efforts of those who have dedicated themselves and continue to dedicate themselves to the science of the subjective states of man."[12]

During the years of the first World War, the experimental work in the Pavlovian laboratories was greatly curtailed as a consequence of the departure for active military service of a significant number of his closest coworkers, physicians, alumni of the Military Medical Academy.

However, Pavlov himself during this period published a series of remarkable lectures and reports, among which the papers that he read before the Philosophical Society of Petrograd, at the Third Congress of Experimental Education in Petrograd on Jan. 2, 1916, and an article written in collaboration with M.K. Petrova and published in an anthology dedicated to K.A. Timiryazev (1916) are most noteworthy.

During these same years, Pavlov published his well-known articles "Reflexes of purpose" and "Reflexes of freedom."

As Academician Orbeli has pointed out, it was in these years of reduced experimental laboratory work that Pavlov began to visit the psychiatric hospitals and in particular the hospital in Udel'nyy where his closest friend and coworker, A.V. Timofeyev, together with V.P. Golovina, acquainted him with abundant psychiatric material, which prompted Pavlov to consider the feasibility of applying his theory of conditioned reflexes to the conditions of pathological disturbances of the nervous system.

Of this important turn in his work, Pavlov wrote in 1919: "During the summer of 1918 I had the opportunity to realize my long-standing intention of getting better acquainted with the field of mental illnesses. Thanks to the kind permission of the director of the Home for the Care of the Mentally Ill at Udel'nyy, Dr. M.K. Voskresenskiy, and the kind cooperation of V.P. Golovina, who gave me much of her time, I was able to observe a considerable number of mentally ill patients. I express my sincerest gratitude to both of these colleagues. My plan was to find data

---

[12] I.P. Pavlov. Twenty Years of Experience... , 252-253.

191

in the disturbances of higher brain activity for the analysis of this activity. With this in mind, I endeavored to stand on a purely physiological viewpoint as I did in the laboratory study of the physiology of the cerebral hemispheres, constantly translating psychic phenomena into physiological concepts."[13]

Subsequently, especially in Soviet times, Pavlov made an extensive exploration of mental diseases in relation to data of the physiology of the brain. In this endeavor he found a number of close collaborators and assistants, primarily among the specialists in psychiatry and neurology (Professor P.A. Ostankov and Dr. I.O. Narbutovich), and, subsequently, a number of his close collaborators, primarily M.K. Petrova, A.G. Ivanov-Smolenskiy, and others, turned to this work.

In 1930, on the basis of these observations and investigations, Pavlov appeared for the first time in the international press in the Jubilee Volume in honor of Gley and Heymans, with an article under the title "A Physiologist's Excursion into the Field of Psychiatry."

This most valuable trend in Pavlov's theory attained its highest development during the last years of his life, due to his collaboration with the experienced clinician and neuropathologist, S.N. Davidenkov.

The problems of the relationship between normal physiology and pathology of the higher nervous activity were studied in Pavlov's laboratory during the most difficult years in Leningrad, 1918 and 1919, when, according to Pavlov, "one had to work with emaciated, and starved animals." Under these conditions "even the slightly preserved reflexes disappeared rapidly, evoked sleep, so that further work became impossible."

In these difficult times Pavlov's closest collaborators were his students and assistants, N. A. Podkopayev, I. S. Rosenthal, and Yu. P. Frolov.

The great flood of 1924 in Leningrad also served as a direct impetus toward the exploration of these problems of pathology of higher nervous activity; the old physiological laboratory at the Academy was also affected. In a report which Pavlov delivered in French to the Paris Psychological Society, in December of 1925, under the title "Inhibitory Types of the Nervous Systems of Dogs," Pavlov describes in detail observations on the behavior of dogs with various types of nervous systems under the flood conditions. Most interesting are the facts dealing with the experimental confirmation of certain suspected causes of disturbance of nervous activity in dogs under such conditions, which were obtained by Pavlov, together with his student A.D. Speranskiy. The interesting conditions of these experiments and other circumstances belonging to this remarkable period of Pavlov's laboratory were beautifully described by Pavlov himself. He wrote:

---

[13] I.P. Pavlov. The Auxiliary Role of Psychiatry in the Physiology of the Cerebral Hemispheres. Russian Physiological Journal, v. II, no. 4-5, 1919, p. 257.

"The extraordinary catastrophe, namely the great flood that occurred in Leningrad on September 23, 1924, presented us with the opportunity to observe and study the chronic pathological state of the nervous system of our dogs, brought about under the influence of this event that served as an extremely strong external stimulus. The animals' accommodations, which stood at ground level and were located a quarter of a kilometer away from the laboratory building, began to be flooded. In a frightful storm, with large waves of oncoming water beating against the walls of the building, under the crackle and noise of breaking and falling trees, it became necessary for swimming rescue parties to transfer our animals quickly to the second floor of the laboratory in a strange environment. All this apparently acutely inhibited every animal without exception, so that during that time none of the customary fights occurred. As the flood passed and the dogs were returned to their own kennels, some of them reverted to their previous patterns of behavior; others, precisely the ones of the inhibitory type, were found to be neurotic, this condition lasting for a long time, as was substantiated by experiments on their conditioned reflexes."[14]

During this period (1923-1925), problems connected with the phenomena of inhibition in the animal's brain were studied with particular intensity in Pavlov's laboratory. Valuable work on this subject was continued by M.K. Petrova as well as by I.P. Razenkov, who at that time had just begun working in Pavlov's laboratory and was to become a famous Soviet physiologist.

The work of these two Pavlovian students, as well as that of others, led to the synthesis of the theories of the conditioned reflexes with the views on the relationships between excitation and inhibition formulated by N. Ye. Vedenskiy, and this is very important in the history of physiological thought in our country. We have already dwelled on this in connection with the discussion concerning the development of the theory of inhibition in our country.

In 1925 a remarkable piece of work by Pavlov's disciple V.A. Krylov was published under the title On the Feasibility of Creating a Conditioned Reflex by Stimulation through Blood (an Automatic Stimulus). As the title itself indicates, Krylov discovered a new form of conditions under which conditioned reflexes appeared. Thus it was found that after repeated injections of morphine, which made the dog vomit, injection of water would also cause vomiting, due to repetition of the procedure of hypodermic injection.[15]

During the same period, in 1923, Pavlov brought up the question of the necessity of setting up research of higher nervous activity at a comparative physiological level. As Professor Ye. M. Kreps has recently pointed

---

[14] I.P. Pavlov. Lectures on the Function of the Cerebral Hemispheres. GIZ, Moscow-Leningrad, 1927, p. 272-273.
[15] In a verbal communication N.A. Podkopayev indicated that he observed this important phenomenon in Pavlov's laboratory in 1914, but the war prevented completion of the experiment and publication of its results.

ПОСТАНОВЛЕНИЕ

СОВЕТА НАРОДНЫХ КОМИССАРОВ

Принимая во внимание совершенно исключительные научные заслуги академика И.П ПАВЛОВА, имеющие огромное значение для трудящихся всего мира, СОВЕТ НАРОДНЫХ КОМИССАРОВ П О С Т А Н О В И Л

I. Образовать на основании представления Петросовета специаль ную Комиссию с широкими полномочиями в следующем составе тов. М Горького, Заведывающего Высшими учебными Заведениями Петрограда Кри. сти и члена Коллегии Отдела Управления Петросовета тов. Каплуна,которой поручить в кратчайший срок создать наиболее благоприятные условия для обеспечения научной работы академика Павлова и его сот рудников.

2.- Поручить Государственному издательству в лучшей типографии Республики отпечатать роскошным изданием заготовленный академиком Павловым научный труд, сводящий результаты его научных работ за последние 20 лет, причем оставить за академиком И.П.Павловым право собственности на это сочинение как в России, так и за-границей

3.-Поручить Комиссии по Рабочему снабжению предоставить академику Павлову и его жене специальный паек, равный по каллорийности двум академическим пайкам

4 Поручить Петросовету обеспечить профессора Павлова и его жену пожизненным пользованием занимаемой ими квартирой и обставить ее и лабораторию академика Павлова максимальными удобствами

Председатель Совета
Народных Комиссаров.

Москва.Кремль
-24-го Января 1921 года

Постановление Совета Народных Комиссаров от 24 января 1921 г.
(Фотокопия)

Resolution of Soviet of People's Commisars, January 24, 1921.
(Photostat)

RESOLUTION

OF THE SOVIET OF PEOPLE'S COMMISSARS

In consideration of the entirely exceptional scientific services of Academician I.P. PAVLOV, which are of utmost significance for the working people of the whole world, THE SOVIET OF PEOPLE'S COMMISSARS HAS RESOLVED

1. To form a Special Commission, as proposed by the Petrosoviet, with broad powers, and consisting of the following: comrade M. Gorkiy, comrade Kristi, director of institutions of higher learning of Petrograd and comrade Kaplun, member of the college of the department of government of the Petrosoviet. This Commission will provide at the earliest possible date the most favorable conditions for the scientific work of Academician Pavlov and his collaborators.

2. - To instruct the Government publishing house to have the best printing establishment of the Republic print a magnificent edition of Academician Pavlov's scientific work summarizing the results of his scientific research for the last 20 years, Academician Pavlov retaining the property rights on this work in Russia as well as abroad.

3. - To instruct the Commission of Workers Supply to give Academician Pavlov and his wife a special ration equal in its caloric value to two academic rations.

4. - To instruct the Petrosoviet to grant Professor Pavlov and his wife the lifelong occupancy of the apartment that they now occupy and to furnish it and the laboratory of the Academician Pavlov with maximal conveniences.

The Chairman of the Soviet of

People's Commisars. /signed/

V. Ul'yanov I. Lenin

Moscow, Kremlin

24 January 1921

out, in 1923 Pavlov addressed the scientific council of the Murmansk Biological Station and "suggested that a laboratory be created at the Murmansk Station for the study of higher nervous activity in lower animals for the purpose of following through the evolution of higher nervous activity from its earliest stages. The scientific council of the station responded with the great eagerness to this undertaking and in the summer of 1923 a laboratory began to function." [16]

Pavlov assigned Kreps to organize and direct these investigations, and the latter subsequently performed the physiological investigation dedicated to the study of the conditioned reflexes of ascidia. In the same year, 1923, Frolov made a report at the 50th Petrograd Physiological Debate on the subject "Conditioned Motor Reflexes in Fresh Water Fish." These two papers served as the beginning of a comprehensive series of comparative physiological investigations for the study of conditioned reflexes, which subsequently achieved a broad development.

From the early 1920's, the last 15 years of Pavlov's life were a period of maximal development of the Pavlovian school. By that time the number of his disciples had greatly increased; they were able to establish independent laboratories; substantial funds were allocated to the existing Pavlovian laboratories for expansion and equipment; and in addition, the famous Koltushi biological station was built especially for Pavlov's work.

The turning point in this direction is marked by the famous decree justifiably called the Pavlov decree. This decree was signed by V.I. Lenin in 1921 and ordered provision of all necessary conditions for Pavlov's scientific work. Lenin appointed A. M. Gor'kiy as chairman of the commission for the execution of all necessary measures for the assurance of normal working and living conditions for Pavlov during the difficult times of the early 1920's. This decree began with a statement of the enormous historical significance of Pavlov's works for the laboring people of the whole world.

Pavlov's own assessment of this period is extremely interesting. In November 1922 Pavlov wrote:

"Our research has continued without interruption and is still going on. It did slow down and weaken in 1919 and 1920, years of extremely difficult working conditions in the laboratories (cold, darkness, starvation of experimental animals, etc.). From 1921 on the situation improved and now gradually conditions are almost back to normal, except for the shortage of instruments and literature. Our factual data is accumulating satisfactorily. The scope of our research is gradually widening and little by little we are beginning to visualize a general system of phenomena in the field of physiology of the cerebral hemispheres as an organ of higher nervous activity." [17]

---

[16] Ye. M. Kreps. Comparative physiology. See The Progress of Biological Sciences in USSR in 25 years. Publ. Academy of Sciences, USSR, Moscow-Leningrad, 1945, p. 69.
[17] I.P. Pavlov. Twenty Years of Experience... , p. 15

In 1922 the State Publishing House released Pavlov's immortal book Twenty Years of Experience in the Objective Study of Higher Nervous Activity (Behavior) of Animals, which is an anthology of articles, reports, lectures, and speeches dealing with this important branch of the natural sciences which Pavlov and his numerous disciples developed. Soon this volume was translated into a number of foreign languages.

In the spring of 1924, Pavlov delivered a series of lectures for a vast audience of physicians and natural scientists at the Military-Medical Academy. These lectures summed up Pavlov's work, as well as that of his disciples, on the physiology of the cerebral hemispheres, over a period of almost 25 years. After having spent more than a year and a half editing the stenographic account of these lectures, Pavlov decided to publish them. Pavlov's comprehensive book Lectures on the Function of the Cerebral Hemispheres was published in Leningrad in 1927; it and Twenty Years of Experience. . . may be considered major contributions to the development of physiology in the 20th century.

The theory of conditioned reflexes was soon reflected in the allied field of pharmacology. I.V. Zavadskiy's dissertation on "Experience in Applying the Conditioned Reflex Method to Pharmacology" was published in 1908; and the dissertation of P.M. Nikiforovskiy, "Pharmacology of Conditioned Reflexes as a Method of Studying Them," came out in 1910. These early works, done in Pavlov's laboratory, opened up new horizons for physiology as well as pharmacology. I.S. Tsitovich and his disciples, Soviet physiologists and pharmacologists (A.I. Smirnov, N.A. Popov, A.M. Chernikov and others), particularly developed this work.[18]

M.K. Petrova's brilliant experiments, begun during Pavlov's lifetime, on the effect of various doses of bromates on the higher nervous activity, are closely related with this group of investigations. In P. Nikiforovskiy's work it was already demonstrated that there is a predominance of inhibitory processes under the influence of sodium bromide.

The work of Pavlov and his disciples clearly demonstrated that, in addition to the inborn reflexes that are based on the anatomical connection of the central nervous system and its conductors to the peripheral organs (muscles, glands), there are additional reflexes that may arise in a particular animal's life as a result of coincidence of functions of various, up to a given moment, indifferent, environmental stimuli with stimuli that act as unconditioned stimuli of a reaction (secretory, motor and other). Herein lies the basic theoretical premise in the development of methodological approaches lying at the basis of the Pavlovian theory of conditioned reflexes, according to which such indifferent stimuli for the alimentary food reaction as light, sound, pin-pricks, etc., become conditioned stimuli for the digestive glands, if they coincide with the effect of the unconditioned alimentary stimulus of the food itself. From a general

---

[18] I.S. Tsitovich and A.I. Smirnov. See Archives of Biological Sciences, vol. XX, no. 1, 1917. Also N.A. Popov and A.M. Chernikov. Archives of Theoretical and Practical Medicine. Baku, vol. I, issue 1-2, 1923; A.M. Chernikov, ibid., vol. I, no. 3-4, 1923.

biological standpoint, the above experiments with newborn animals (Tsitovich's experiments) are of particular value.

Pavlov arrived at a completely new conclusion that the animal organism has two kinds of reflexes: constant or inborn, and temporary or acquired. "They represent an organ of the animal organism which is specialized in constantly achieving a more and more perfect adjustment of the organism with the environment, an organ for proper and direct reactions to the most varied combinations and fluctuations of phenomena of the external world, an organ that is intended, to a certain degree, for the uninterrupted further development of the animal organism."[19] And elsewhere: "The basic function of the higher level of the central nervous system is to close the circuit of the new and temporary associations between the external phenomena and the function of the various organs and breaking down the complex elements of the external into individual ones; in short, into the activity of the closing and analyzing apparatus. These activities establish more exact and more refined relationships of the animal organism with the environment, in other words, a more perfect balance between the system of matter and forces that comprise the animal organism and the matter and forces of the surrounding environment."[20]

Pavlov as a natural scientist attributed a much greater significance to the conditioned reflexes than to the usual physiological method. He constantly returned to the important problems of general biology. Thus, in classifying the reflexes, he spoke of the inborn reflexes as reflexes of the species and of the acquired reflexes as individual reflexes. He stated further: "We gave the name of unconditioned reflex to the former, and conditioned reflex to the latter, so to speak, for purely practical reasons. In all probability (and there are already some isolated factual indications), new reflexes that arise under unchanged living conditions for a number of successive generations are continually transformed into permanent reflexes. This would then appear as one of the permanently active mechanisms in the development of the animal kingdom."[21]

In his last summarizing article written for the Great Medical Encyclopedia in 1935, Pavlov again returned to the general biological significance of conditioned reflexes; in it, he indicates that the conditioned reflexes assure all that is necessary for the well-being of the individual organism, as well as for the species.

In a speech delivered at the International Congress of Physiologists in 1913, Pavlov emphatically declared: "It may be assumed that some of the conditioned, newly formed reflexes become converted to unconditioned ones later on, through heredity."[22]

---

[19] I.P. Pavlov. Twenty Years of Experience... , pp. 238-239.
[20] Ibid., p. 244.
[21] I.P. Pavlov. Twenty Years of Experience... , 1932, p. 245.
[22] Ibid., p. 239.

In the early 1920's, N.P. Studentsov[23] began special investigations to confirm this idea in Pavlov's laboratory; and, naturally, Pavlov's speech concerning these experiments was received with tremendous interest by biologists, since it dealt with the important problem of the heredity of acquired characteristics. The outstanding American geneticist T.G. Morgan (1924)[24] took a stand against these experiments and their interpretation, and Pavlov had to agree with the basic arguments of the geneticists.

It must be stated that Pavlov not only did not abandon the exploration of this problem precisely in this biological direction but rather developed it further.

This is when a new segment in Pavlov's activities begins, concerning the exploration of the genetics of higher nervous activity. This new field of investigation, which was put at the basis of the investigations at the new biological station in Koltushi, was to complete Pavlov's complex ideas on the biological significance of conditioned reflexes.

Pavlov and his students explored with great detail the typology of behavior of various dogs, making this the biological basis for the techniques of experiments on various animals and for the possible conclusions in each individual case. In the above-mentioned summary article on conditioned reflexes written in 1935, Pavlov indicates that "the study of conditioned reflexes in numerous dogs gradually brought forward the problem of different nervous systems in individual animals, and eventually modalities were found for the systematization of nervous systems according to certain basic features."

As to types of nervous systems, Pavlov presented a comprehensive description that is in full agreement with contemporary general biological concepts.

Pavlov writes: "Thus a type is an inborn constitutional form of an animal's nervous activity, a genotype. But since an animal, from the day it is born, is subjected to the most varied environmental influences to which it must inevitably respond with certain activities that often become permanent eventually, the ultimate nervous activity of the animal is a fusion of type characteristics and changes governed by the external environment, i.e., the phenotype or character."

These Pavlovian ideas were a grandiose plan for new investigations of higher nervous activity of animals by methods of genetics and physiology which open entirely new approaches to this problem. Pavlov's death prevented his carrying this undertaking to the same degree of completion as

---

[23] N.P. Studentsov. Inherited tameness in white mice. Report to the 48th Petrograd Physiological Discussion. 1923.
[24] Yale Review, July, 1924. See also in Russian: T.G. Morgan and Yu. A. Filipchenko. Are acquired characteristics inherited? Leningrad, 1925, pp. 8-10.

in the creation of the three branches of physiology: digestion, conditioned reflexes, and the trophic role of the nervous system.

In the last period of his scientific endeavors Pavlov exclusively and consistently stressed that physiologists must study genetics and the application of genetics to the analysis of types of function of the nervous system of animals. This attitude was symbolized by the artistic design of the Koltushi Biological Station at Pavlov's suggestion. As is known, in front of Pavlov's laboratory in Koltushi three sculptures were erected: one represents the originator of the concept of the reflex, Rene Descartes; the second, the founder of the strictly scientific physiology of the nervous system, Ivan Mikhaylovich Sechenov; and the third, the founder of contemporary genetics, Gregor Mendel.

The Soviet government gave its special attention to the construction of the Biological Station in Koltushi. The large amount of funds allocated for its construction made it possible to create one of the best biological institutes in the world, and in it Pavlov's work, as well as that of his students, gained the broadest scope. Special attention was devoted to the problems of the development of higher nervous activity. Here, during the course of a decade, Pavlov and his disciples made the widely known observation on the higher nervous activity of primates (Rosa and Rafael).[25]

Shortly before his death, Pavlov formulated his theory on the second signal system, which outlined the fruitful path of exploration with regard to the formation of conditioned reflexes in man as distinct from animals.

"In the evolution of the animal kingdom to the level of man," wrote Pavlov, "something unusual was added to the mechanisms of the nervous system. For the animal, reality is signalled almost exclusively by stimulation and its effects on the cerebral hemispheres, directly reaching special cells of the visual, auditory and other receptors of the organism. We have this too in the form of impressions, sensations and images of the surrounding external environment, natural as well as social, except for the heard or seen word. This is the first signal system of reality which we have in common with the animals. But the word has formed our special second signal system of reality, as a signal of the first signals. A multitude of word stimuli has on the one hand removed us from reality, and we must constantly keep this in mind in order not to distort our relationships with reality. On the other hand, it is precisely the word that made us human, on which of course, we need not dwell here. However, there is no doubt that the basic laws established for the first signal system must also govern the second, because the latter too is a function of the same nervous tissue."[26]

Pavlov first expressed these extremely important ideas in such a vivid form in the article "Conditioned Reflex," which he wrote upon special

---

[25] Prior to these investigations and concurrently with them, the conditioned reflex activity of apes was studied in detail at the subtropical branch of VIEM in Sukhumi.

[26] Physiological Journal of the USSR, vol. XIX, issue 1, 1935. p. 270.

request for the Great Medical Encyclopedia. This was the last summary Pavlov wrote of the achievements attained by the Pavlovian school and of his views on the nature of higher nervous activity and the role of conditioned reflexes. Pavlov wrote this article somewhat more than a year before his death. Before sending the article to the editors of the encyclopedia, he read it at one of his usual "Wednesday" meetings. As one of Pavlov's closest collaborators reminisced, all present at this "Wednesday" were astounded by the depth and newness of Pavlov's formulation of the problem. And, of course, the concept of a second signalling system was the more striking because it showed his disciples a new approach in the field of physiology of higher nervous activity, an approach pointed out for future generations of physiologists by their great teacher. Pavlov's ideas concerning the second signal system also echo the remarkable psycho-physiological views of I.M. Sechenov, who, in his times, posed the profound question of concrete and abstract thinking. Sechenov, too, had emphasized that abstract thinking is generated by man's interrelationships with the surrounding objects, and, although their verbal expression is at times very remote from the original concrete reality, the expression with all its roots is related to reality.

Great strides have been made in the theory of conditioned reflexes during the last 25 years, thanks to the efforts of Soviet physiologists, mostly disciples of Pavlov. A concise but comprehensive evaluation of these achievements was recently presented by Academician L.A. Orbeli in his paper at the Jubilee session of the USSR Academy of Sciences. He stated:

"Frolov (Moscow) and Tsitovich (Rostov on the Don) have applied the method of conditioned reflexes for the evaluation of the effect of noxious substances of industrial and military significance.

Research in the direction of comparative physiology of conditioned reflexes was developed by Frolov (fish), N.A. Popov and Bayandurov (birds), Kreps (ascidia), Asratyan (turtles), Nikiforovskiy (amphibians).

Popov and Bayandurov broadened the investigations of conditioned reflexes by including a new stimulation of a receptor that had not been used by Pavlov—the vestibular apparatus as a conditioned stimulus of food reflexes.

Anokhin (Moscow) developed a method for the study of higher nervous activity under conditions of free movement with bilateral application of stimuli and with possibility of choice of response reaction, and he has used this method extensively.

Bykov (Leningrad), with a large contingent of collaborators, extensively developed the theory of interoceptors and proprioceptors, having found adequate procedures of stimulation for each of the internal organs and organs and applying the method of conditioned reflexes for the objective discovery of the effects. Kupalov, who was in charge of the physiological division of the Institute of Experimental Medicine in Leningrad, a division where the theory of conditioned reflexes originated and was developed for

33 years, with his collaborators, continued to broaden and develop this theory in the direction of meticulous analysis of the dynamics of cortical processes and clarification of the mechanism of origin of "functional structures."

Fol'bort and his collaborators (Khar'kov) developed Pavlov's theories of depletion and restoration of the salivary gland at work and at rest, transferred the conclusions from this theory to the central nervous system and thus linked two lines of Pavlov's investigations into a unified concept with regard to the role of depletion and restoration in the function of the nerve centers."

Exploration of higher nervous activity on Pavlovian principles reached its maximal scope at the Pavlov Physiological Institute of the Academy of Sciences, USSR, and at the Pavlov Institute of Evolutional Physiology and Pathology of higher nervous activity, of the Academy of Medical Sciences, under the direction of Orbeli.

The staff of the Pavlov Physiological Institute chose as its primary task the parallel investigation of higher nervous activity with the conditioned reflex method, with the physiology of sense organs and with objective electrophysiological registration of cortical activity, for the purpose of obtaining an accurate conception of the functions of the brain (Gershuni, Strogonov, Tonkikh, Fedorov and others).

Concurrently, the work continues on the study of the "second signal system" initiated by Pavlov, which is a most important super-structure specifically characteristic of the higher nervous activity of man (Strogonov, Sosuntsova, B.V. Pavlov).

One of Pavlov's closest collaborators, Petrova, who, while Pavlov was still living had assembled the greatest collection of data with regard to the origin of neurotic states in dogs under the influence of functional overstrain of the cortical processes, has continued her work in this direction untiringly and has perfected the theory of experimental neurosis.

At the Institute of Evolutional Physiology and Pathology of Higher Nervous Activity (Koltushi), the work already initiated in Pavlov's time concerning the genetic study of higher nervous activity continues, and it is directed toward clarification of the role of the heredity factor in the development of the nervous type of animals. Work is also being done with systematic application of the principle of evolution to the study of higher nervous activity. On the basis of the concept that the process of formation of conditioned reflexes and establishment of their interaction with previously existing reflexes (inborn and acquired) is the key to the functional evolution of the nervous system, Orbeli and his collaborators studied the formation of inborn reflex activity in the embryonic and early postnatal period. The investigations of Volokhov, Stokalich, Obraztsova, and Tsobkallo have demonstrated the correctness of this idea and made it possible to establish a number of analogies between the two types of processes.

Vasil'yev and, subsequently, Promptov turned towards exploration of the interaction between inborn and acquired reflexes in young birds and made an important contribution to our conceptions concerning the so-called instinctive forms of behavior in birds.

Ye. A. Ganike's investigations deserved special mention; he established an unsurpassed brilliant method for the study of conditioned reflexes in mice, a method that assures absolute perfection of the experiment due to the automatization of all of the steps such as plotting (or charting), graduation, and scheduling the stimuli, as well as recording the animals' reaction under conditions of a group experiment.

The analysis of higher nervous activity of primates—in the chimpanzee—allowed Vatsuro to clarify, from the standpoint of Pavlovian teachings, all of the futility of the psychological enthusiasm of certain authors.

All the accumumated data on animals has formed the basic foundation for the objective study of higher nervous activity in man. The brilliant work of Krasnogorskiy and Ivanov-Smolenskiy has demonstrated the complete applicability of the Pavlovian method (with corresponding methodological adjustments) to the exploration of higher nervous activity of the child. Ivanov-Smolenskiy also succeeded in demonstrating the applicability of this method to the study of the disintegrated nervous system in patients with certain forms of mental illness. In the field of psychiatry, however, introduction of physiological principles encounters much greater resistance than in the field of neurology, where the Pavlovian theories find an enthusiastic reception as well as a practical application in the understanding and treatment of sequelae of traumatic and concussion[or shell-shock] injuries to the central nervous system, as well as of purely functional neuroses.

Pavlov's views on the protective role of inhibition and on sleep as a pervading form of internal inhibition were to acquire a great significance in practical medicine. These views are confirmed by the success of sleep therapy in schizophrenia (Ivanov-Smolenskiy), in traumatic shock (Asratyan), in the treatment of trophic afflictions of the skin (Petrova), and in the treatment of burns and wounds (Polyakov). Asratyan's developments of the theory of "plasticity of the nervous system," indicating the vast organizing role of the cerebral hemispheres in compensatory phenomena in the central nervous system, is also very promising. There is no doubt that this theory will play a significant role in the developing new motor acts in injured soldiers."[27]

The theory of conditioned reflexes has been widely disseminated; the conditioned reflex as a form of the organism's reaction, based on temporary connections, is spreading to the broader field of biological processes. Attempts are being made to extend these concepts to the

---

[27] L.A. Orbeli. Academician Ivan Petrovich Pavlov and the Russian physiological school. An address at the Jubilee meeting of the Academy of Sciences, USSR. Moscow-Leningrad, 1945. Publ. AS USSR, p. 12-13.

phenomena of immunity (Metal'nikov and others); it is possible that conditioned associations play a distinctive role in the development of ontogenic characteristics in animals, and, finally, extensive data have been obtained recently indicating that development of conditioned reflexes is at the basis of a number of complex biological laws of animal behavior. A most interesting attempt was made in this direction by the zoologist A.A. Mashkovtsev (1939), in his investigations of the patterns of breeding among various vertebrates.

The work of Pavlov and his collaborators for over 30 years in the field of physiology of higher nervous activity revealed numerous deep secrets to science of the function of the brain of higher animals and man. They have established experimentally the existence of a particular, heretofore unknown, type of reflexes that arise only under specific conditions and that become extinguished when these conditions are eliminated. The theory of conditioned reflexes has been associated, and is still associated, by everyone with the name of the genius who created this theory - I.P. Pavlov.

All the more strange then is the attempt of the important American physiologist Fulton to make it appear that before Pavlov the English physiologist Sherrington discovered a special form of reflex that was named the conditioned reflex.[28] Furthermore, Fulton disregards dates and actual facts. Sherrington's work, to which Fulton refers, appeared in 1900;[29] it contains a descripton of experiments on the cardiovascular system that have only a remote resemblance to the conditions of formation and stabilization of a conditioned reflex as described by Pavlov and his students. Pavlov himself, in making a historical review of the development of the theory of conditioned reflexes, referred to the American investigator Thorndike, whose work appeared in 1898 and who had formulated the question of comprehensive exploration of animal behavior under various conditions imposed by the experimenter. Indications of the existence of a special form of reflex activity of the digestive glands, depending on environmental conditions, or the so-called psychic reflexes, can be found in Pavlov's "Lectures on the Function of the Main Digestive Glands," published in 1897.

In April of 1903, at the general session of the International Medical Congress in Madrid, Pavlov presented a report under the title "Experimental Psychology and Psychopathology on Animals," which opened a new era in the field of physiology of higher nervous activity and psychology. In this report, Pavlov showed the historico-logical connection between his new investigations in the physiology of higher nervous activity and the series of his previous investigations in the field of physiology of digestion. Pavlov uses his disciples' findings as the basis for his experimental data: Vulf'son, whose dissertation was published in 1898,[30] Snarskiy (dissertation published in 1901);[31] and Tolochinov, whose special article on the

---

[28] J.F. Fulton. Physiology of the Nervous System, 1938, p. 134.
[29] C. S. Sherrington. Experiments on the Value of Vascular and Visceral Factors for the Genesis of Emotions. Proc. Roy. Soc., 1900, v. 66, p. 394.
[30] S.G. Vulf'son. The Functions of the Salivary Glands, SPb., 1898.
[31] A.T. Snarskiy. Analysis of the Normal Conditions of Function of the Salivary Glands in the Dog. SPb., 1901.

physiology and pathology of the salivary glands was published in Helsingfors in 1902.[32] In this last article, the term "conditioned reflex" appears
in print for the first time.

The experimental investigations, especially in the field of neuropsychic
regulation of the function of the salivary glands (so-called psychic salivation), referrable to the late 1890's, led Pavlov to a most important and
entirely new conclusion as to the existence of two types of reflexes, conditioned and unconditioned. As may be seen from Pavlov's Madrid address
of 1903, he had presented a system of new and unexpected views rather
than isolated experimental facts. These views pointed towards new paths
for the understanding of the genuinely physiological basis of activity of the
higher levels of the central nervous system, in relation to both simple and
complex acts of adaptation in the various forms of animal behavior.
Sechenov's ingenious idea concerning the reflex basis of the most complex
manifestations of nervous activity received further development in
Pavlov's theory of conditioned reflexes. Herein lies the essential difference between Pavlov's investigations and those of other scientists,
among them such authorities as Sherrington.

In a historical review (first lecture) in his classical work Lectures on
the Function of the Cerebral Hemisphere (1927), Pavlov evaluates Sherrington's works highly and speaks of his research on the reflex nature of
locomotor activity. He compares his own research on the physiology of
the brain with Sherrington's studies of the physiology of the spinal cord.

Thus there remains no doubt that Fulton's attempt to attribute the
priority in the discovery of the conditioned reflexes to Sherrington is entirely unfounded. This is attested first of all by Sherrington's own attitude toward the theory of conditioned reflexes as a special trend in
physiology. Thus in a lecture he delivered in May of 1934, under the title
"Experimental Pathology of the Higher Nervous Activity," Pavlov incidentally reports: ". . . I was in London on the occasion of the Jubilee of
the London Royal Society, and had the opportunity to meet the greatest
English physiologist-neurologist, C.S. Sherrington. He told me: 'Do you
know that your conditioned reflexes will hardly enjoy any success in
England because they smack of materialism.' "[33]

In the same lecture, Pavlov dwelled on the manner in which his theory
of conditioned reflexes had spread and how it had influenced scientific and
cultural developments in other countries. He remarked: "Indeed, it is

---

[32] I. Ph. Tolotschinoff [I.F. Tolochinov]. Contribution a l'etude de la
physiologie et de la pathologie des glandes salivaires. Forhåndl. vid.
Nordiska Naturforskare och Läkaremötet. Helsingfors, 1902, p. 42.

[33] It is interesting to note that during Sherrington's visit to Pavlov's
laboratory when an experiment was demonstrated for him, one that had
been described by Yerofeyeva on conditioned salivation from a pain
stimulus, he exclaimed: "Now I understand the Christian martyrs."
Such was the first association of the physiologist, Sherrington, at the
sight of his experiment.

precisely in the country about which Sherrington had warned me that matters took a different turn; at present the theory of conditioned reflexes is being taught in all the schools in England. It also has found a broad recognition in the United States of America. But such is not the case everywhere. In Germany, for example, this theory is not as popular."

Many editions of Pavlov's Lectures, and of his famous book Twenty Years of Experience of Objective Study of Higher Nervous Activity (Behavior) of Animals have been published in almost all of the European and American countries. A book by Pavlov's student Professor N.A. Podkopayev, which presents the entire methological aspect of research in the field of conditioned reflexes, was also published abroad. (Methods for the Study of Conditioned Reflexes, 1926; second edition, 1935; this book contains a most valuable bibliography on the conditioned reflexes.)

Foreign scientists visited Pavlov in order to familiarize themselves with the method of conditioned reflexes. Within a relatively short time, research in the field of conditioned reflexes was instituted on a broad scale in England and in the U.S.A. This can be seen, for instance, from the vast bibliography of works on conditioned reflexes that was given in a special summary published in the U.S.A. in 1940.

During the course of almost 35 years, in addition to accumulating the most valuable physiological data that shed a new light on the "real physiology" of the brain, Pavlov was constantly and intensely concerned with the problem of the nature of consciousness and urged that this problem be analyzed on a strictly objective physiological basis. He conducted this work through a constant critical analysis of those tendencies in foreign physiology and psychology that stood on the old idealistic and subjectivistic positions. Therefore, Pavlov's authority spreads far beyond the physiology of the brain; in world culture his name has become a symbol of the materialistic, strictly scientific approach to the most difficult problem of the natural sciences - the problem of consciousness.

At the XIVth International Physiological Congress in 1932, Pavlov stated in his paper: "I am convinced that we are approaching an important milestone in human thought, when the physiological and psychological, the objective and subjective will genuinely fuse, when the disturbing contradiction or opposition of my consciousness and my body will be factually solved or eliminated in a natural way."

Pavlov's deep influence in forming an ideology was felt in all of the physiology of the 20th century. Thus, the dean of French physiologists, the Sorbonne professor Louis Lapicque, concluded his address to the XVth International Physiological Congress in 1935 with the following words. "We are entirely justified in our hopes that the influence of higher nervous activity on the motor organs—an unsolvable problem if it were treated by the formulation of the philosophers, as a relationship between the spirit and the body—will be revealed in a new light now that we are able to combine chronaxymetrics with the method created by the genius of Ivan Petrovich Pavlov."

The extensive investigations of Pavlov and his numerous disciples in the field of physiology of the cerebral hemispheres by means of the method of conditioned reflexes revealed many aspects of the function of this organ. The analysis and synthesis of perceived sensations, the dynamics of the processes of excitation and inhibition in the cerebral cortex, the various forms of this inhibition (external and internal), the mobility or lability of the functional properties of the cortical nerve cells, the role of the cortex in adaptive processes of organisms, and, finally, a detailed exploration of the ways and means of formation, stabilization, and extinction of conditioned reflexes - all this has been a major contribution to the development of neurophysiology and has given impetus to investigations in many laboratories all over the world. Pavlov developed his theory of individual types of higher nervous activity on the basis of numerous experiments and observations.

Most valuable data which has made a significant contribution to the understanding of the pathogenesis and therapy of disturbances of higher nervous activity, were also obtained at his institute (the Institute of Physiology and Pathology of Higher Nervous Activity, Academy of Sciences, USSR).

The work of Pavlov and of his collaborators, in the laboratory as well as clinics, has exerted a great influence on world neurophysiology and neuropathology, and, at present, the scientists of the USA are attributing a particular importance to these achievements of the Pavlovian school.

As Pavlov wrote: "For physiology, the conditioned reflex has become the central phenomenon and its use has greatly facilitated a comprehensive and precise exploration of the normal as well as pathological activities of the cerebral hemispheres."

The conditioned reflex theory was, so to speak, the culmination of a prolonged and intensive search by Russian physiologists and thinkers, who had persistently sought for the pattern of function of the nervous system in its relationships with the external world. The conditioned reflex theory was a major milestone in the elaboration of problems of the relationship between the psychic and the physical. At the start of this chapter we showed the historico-logical connection between Pavlov's theory of conditioned reflexes and the basic postulates developed by Sechenov in his immortal treatise, Reflexes of the Brain. And the development of Russian physiology has followed a vast historical path towards this achievement. It began in 1863, the year of the publication of Reflexes of the Brain.

Having completed our examination of this basic trend in the development of Russian physiology, we now pass on to the further aspects of Sechenov's and Pavlov's activity, as well as that of their coworkers, and to the development of those remote physiological fields that have been cultivated predominantly in the physiological laboratories of our country.

CHAPTER XV

The discoveries and general conclusions of Sechenov and his coworkers, and their significance in the development of contemporary concepts on the functions of the nervous system. Sechenov's investigations on the blood gases; their theoretical significance and application. Sechenov's transfer from Petersburg to Moscow University; his last investigations. M. N. Shaternikov.

Sechenov's discovery of central inhibition appeared as one of the most important gains of contemporary physiology. We have mentioned that an analysis of this remarkable phenomenon by Sechenov and his disciples indicated the necessity for detailed exploration of the paths along which the cerebro-spinal reflexes are accomplished, their reflex regulation, and the significance of the various sections of the central nervous system in this regulation.

In the first half of the 1860's, in a relatively short time Sechenov and his coworkers had obtained such a wealth of new data and had delved so deeply into the nature of coordinated reflex acts that it became difficult for them to adhere to the theoretical views that prevailed in all the existing textbooks and summaries.

During the summer of 1864, while living at a country home on the shores of the Neva, Sechenov began to write his Physiology of the Nervous System, which was to become both a summary of the new facts obtained by him and his disciples and a new theoretical formulation of the focal problems of the physiology of the nervous system. This remarkable book by Sechenov was published in Petersburg in 1866.

Physiology of the Nervous System demonstrates that Sechenov was well informed on all contemporary data and conclusions on the physiology of the nervous system, and that he also reformulated a series of important problems in this physiological field; what is also important, he had an entirely new approach in the presentation of the voluminous material on the physiology of the nervous system.

In the introduction to his Physiology of the Nervous System, Sechenov himself comments on the newness of his work. "I was prompted to write a physiology of the nervous system mainly by the fact that in all, even the best, textbooks of physiology, the description of nervous phenomena is based on purely anatomical elements, i.e., first of all the functions of the nerve stems are described, the spinal cord, the medulla oblongata, the cerebellum and the other parts of the brain are mentioned, and in the form of an appendix the function of the sympathetic nerve. The major defects of this method of description of neural phenomena are such that from my very first year of teaching physiology I followed a different plan, namely, in my lectures I described nervous acts as they occur in reality."

One can only regret that this remarkable work was not available to foreign physiologists, as also was the case in its time with Reflexes of the Brain.

One is especially struck by the attempt, entirely new for that time, to represent reflex acts as integrated processes and to present the purposefulness of separate reflex acts as a consequence of anatomical-physiological peculiarities of relationships between the peripheral and central nervous apparatus that have developed in the process of growth.

There is much originality in Sechenov's ideas concerning the systemic nature of the peripheral sensory elements, as a consequence of which stimulation of a particular system of receptors elicits reflex acts of a systemic nature rather than isolated (having no significance) or chaotic ones.

We know how very significant the phenomena of summation of stimuli are in the origination of processes of excitation in the peripheral as well as in the central nervous system. We have on hand all the facts to substantiate that this basic process in the nervous system was discovered by Sechenov, and only later did many foreign scientists become interested in it. This is best documented by an excerpt from a Sechenov letter to M. A. Sechenova-Bokova, of February 4, 1868. In this letter we read:

"I yesterday wrote to you that the effects of successively switching on and off a direct current applied to a sensory nerve are cumulative. Today I arranged the experiment thus: a direct current A is switched on and off any number of times per minute by means of a metronome; this makes it easy to count the number of times the current has been switched on and off. As a result I found that for a given strength of current the frequency of clicks necessary to elicit movement remains approximately constant. Consequently by this method perhaps it will be possible to measure a property of the nerve centers that has not been understood thus far, to add up individual excitatory shocks. This opens up a broad field of investigation: the study of the variations in this property under the most varied conditions. I am simply getting dizzy from the vast accumulation of facts requiring explanation."[1]

In spite of the fact that Sechenov shed light on this problem, even Soviet authors do not always associate the discovery of summation phenomena with Sechenov's name.

---

[1] First published in my monograph "Sechenov." 1945, pp. 116-117.

One of Sechenov's students, I. R. Tarkhanov, was one of the first to submit the phenomena of summation, in particular of the sensory nerves, to experimental analysis. His article on the subject was published in 1872 in the Proceedings of the Petersburg Academy of Sciences.[2] In 1879 V. Danilevskiy described the phenomenon of summation in the vagus nerve.[3]

Sechenov's views on the role of the muscular system as a sense organ have attained an important meaning in our days. The theory of so-called proprioception, by which we understand the sensations which arise in the organism under the influence of stimulation of the sensory nerve endings of the various internal organs, including the muscles, is an integral component of contemporary neurophysiology.

In contemporary physiology this most important field is linked most frequently with the name of the English physiologist Sherrington and his disciples. However, Sechenov presented the general concept of the role of muscular proprioception and its physiological significance much earlier than Sherrington. In 1866, in his lectures on the physiology of the nervous system, i.e., 25 years before the publication of Sherrington's investigations, Sechenov described the physiological significance of the so-called "obscure muscle sense," which, in his opinion, "together with the cutaneous and visual sensations serves so to speak as the most important guide of consciousness in the matter of motor coordination." "Sensations from the skin and muscles," wrote Sechenov, "accompanying the beginning, the end and all the phases of every muscular contraction, determine the duration of each of them individually and the sequence in which one muscle contracts after another . . . thus as long as there is a muscular contraction in the body there is uninterrupted sensory excitation from the skin and muscles of the part in motion to the nerve centers, an excitation that becomes altered as the nature of the movement changes and thus determines the further direction of motor acts."

Sechenov drew these conclusions on the basis of strictly scientific clinical observations on ataxic patients, in whom the exclusion of the sensory elements from the muscles causes disturbance of the normal coordinating movements, due to an impaired awareness of these movements. The role of muscular sensitivity was known from the experiments of Claude Bernard before Sechenov made these statements; Bernard's experiments demonstrated that removal of the skin from the extremities of the frog does cause the same disturbances of reflex movements as those obtained after transection of the sensory nerve. Consequently, this is not a matter of cutaneous sensitivity. Sechenov was

---

[2] Ueber die Summierungserscheinungen bei Reizungen sensibler Nerven d. Frosches, (Summation Phenomena upon Stimulation of The Sensory Nerves of the Frog). Bull. de l'Acad. de Sc. de St.-Pet., v. XVI, p. 75, 1872.

[3] V. Ya. Danilevskiy. On the summation of electrical stimulation of the vagus. Memoirs Acad. Sc., 1879, v. XXXV, pt. 2, pp. 69-77.

greatly assisted in the analysis of this problem and the formulation of his views by his friendship with the clinician S. P. Botkin, who was the one who made the observations on ataxic patients deprived of the ability to regulate both the strength and direction of movements of their extremities, due to degeneration of the posterior roots of the spinal cord.

Sechenov raised the same problems in his articles on physiology and psychology dealing with questions of the individual development of the act of walking in man. Assuming the existence of a special signal system of the sensory nerves within the muscles of the child's legs, Sechenov attempted to reconstruct the process of development of walking in man from the interrelationships between these sensory nerve elements and the external environment.

A. F. Samoylov, one of the most authoritative physiologists of recent times, was the first to give Sechenov credit for his achievements in this most important problem of contemporary physiology. He did so in his address at the session of the Russian Physiological Society in Leningrad dedicated to the centennial of Sechenov's birth. His report, "I. M. Sechenov and His Ideas on the Role of the Muscle in our Knowledge of Nature,"[4] greatly impressed those present, among them I. P. Pavlov.[5] In his speech A. F. Samoylov not only proved Sechenov's precedence in this important subject but also emphasized the far-reaching philosophical conclusions that Sechenov made from his views on the role of the muscle as a sense organ.

Indeed, in his monograph Elements of Thought,[6] Sechenov tried a new approach to the most difficult problems of time and space, based on the concept of the muscles as sense organs that transmit to us the basic signals of position in space and timing. In this connection, there is a very interesting letter from Sechenov to Mechnikov, dated the 27th of February 1878.

"The writing of Elements of Thought has finally been completed. It has dragged on so long and has cost me such indescribable efforts that it is unlikely that I shall ever undertake a similar task again; at least may God grant this effort to be of some use. To me it appears that the article should significantly facilitate the study of logic; I should consider it a great practical achievement. Moreover, it contains several points that are close to my heart (for instance, the idea concerning the role of the muscle sense in the analysis and measurement of space and time). But people are often poor judges of their own deeds."[7]

[4] Published in the journal The Scientific Word, no. 5, 1929, p. 44.
[5] See A. F. Samoylov's biography compiled by A. A. Samoylova.
[6] I. M. Sechenov. Elements of Thought. Selected articles. Prof. K. Kekcheyev, editor. Published Academy of Sciences, USSR, Moscow-Leningrad, 1943.
[7] Collection of articles The Struggle for Science in Tsarist Russia. Sotsekgiz, Moscow-Leningrad, 1931, p. 96.

In present times, due to the broad use of the string galvanometer and oscillographs of various types in physiological investigations, it has become possible to record with exceptional precision the bioelectrical phenomena in the central nervous system. Electroencephalography has developed into an independent chapter of contemporary neurophysiology of great importance from a scientific and practical standpoint. The basis for this new trend in physiology was laid by the concurrently published investigations of V. Ya. Danilevskiy[8] and the English scientist Richard Caton. Danilevskiy's and Caton's investigations dealt with the cerebral cortex. Soon Sechenov's classical investigation of galvanic phenomena in the spinal cord and in the medulla oblongata was published (1881),[9] where it was demonstrated that, with the help of the galvanometer, it is possible to detect the presence of periodic rhythmic electrical phenomena in an isolated medulla oblongata and spinal cord. Sechenov was the first to establish this most important fact in the field of neurophysiology, which was subsequently confirmed by the investigations of many foreign scientists and, particularly, by the Cambridge physiologist Adrian.

One must especially note that Sechenov not only discovered the actual presence of rhythmic electrical phenomena, but he also clarified the origin, significance, and functional relationships of the electrical phenomena in the medulla oblongata and spinal cord, and, what is particularly important, he was the first to prove experimentally that their character could change under the influence of centripetal impulses originating in the corresponding nerve trunks.

Sechenov completed this work, important in the history of physiology, at Petersburg University. During the period of his research in this direction, he attracted the attention of the subsequently famous physiologist N. Ye. Vedenskiy, who was then only at the start of his scientific career and had completed an interesting investigation on the periodicity of respiratory movements in the frog in connection with its motor activity, a piece of work that Sechenov submitted at a competition for an award.

The investigations of B. F. Verigo, a student of Sechenov, published in 1889, are of great significance in the development of the theory of bioelectrical phenomena in the central nervous system.

The use of chemical agents as stimuli of the central nervous system in the close investigation of central inhibition led Sechenov to extremely important conclusions with regard to the mechanisms of

---

[8] Danilewsky [Danilevskiy]. Experimentalle Beiträge zur Physiologie des Gehirns. Pflüg. Arch. 1875, II, p. 128-138.
[9] Galvanische Erscheinungen an dem verlängerten Marke des Frosches. Pflüg. Arch., 1881, B. 27; the same in the Russian language: Medic, no. 45, 1882.

the function of the nervous system. He describes this very vividly in a letter to Sechenova-Bokova dated Nov. 14, 1867. He writes:[10]

While I was working on the chemical stimulation of the brain, having selected for this purpose alkaline salts and alkaline earth, the following thought occurred to me: what if I should introduce large quantities of these substances under the skin? One would expect that upon entering the blood they affect the brain in the same manner as they do upon direct contact. I take some table salt and stuff it under the frog's skin...After 3-4 minutes the legs are insensitive when I cut off the fingers with sharp pincers, etc. I dissolve the salt and inject the solution into the stomach— after 3-4 minutes the results are the same. If I now cut off either frog's head, the leg reflexes reappear from a light pinch with the fingers.

Having obtained such results I further conceived the following idea: since table salt introduced into the body depresses the reflexes, one would expect that it could counteract any reflex convulsions, strychnine poisoning, etc. So I take two frogs of equal size, and give both of them equal doses of strychnine, but in addition I stuff some salt under the skin of the abdomen of one of the frogs. The first frog has violent convulsions and becomes exhausted. The second shows only minor convulsive tremors (i.e., absence of tetanus seizures), but following them it exhibits the same exhaustion as the first frog. I have kept these frogs now for more than 24 hours and they are still lying as if dead, insensitive to skin stimulation but this afternoon a heart beat was still present.

Soon (tomorrow, if I get a dog) I shall perform an experiment with strychnine on a dog, i.e., I shall see whether I succeed in stopping or at least in appreciably reducing the convulsions. If so, it should be possible after a few more experiments to pass this experiment on to practicing physicians for the treatment of reflex convulsions, for instance in traumatic tetanus, etc."

We see thus that the broad plan of investigation of chemical stimulation of the various parts of the nervous system led Sechenov not only to conclusions that were extremely important for the understanding of the mechanisms of complex processes that occur in the peripheral and central regions of the nervous system but also to conclusions of great practical significance.

Sechenov did carry out his intended experiment with the dog, and in this regard there is a letter dated November 28, 1867, to Sechenova-Bokova. In this letter he writes:

"My work is progressing further and further. True, I did not succeed in saving the dog from strychnine, but I was able

---

[10]This as well as the next two excerpts from Sechenov's letters to M. A. Sechenova-Bokova were published by me for the first time in the monograph "Sechenov" (1945).

to delay the onset of the convulsions. On frogs our experiment of suppressing strychnine convulsions by introducing salts into the body now proceeds with astounding clearness; but the strychnine dosage must be weak enough to avoid the appearance of tetanus, producing only separate convulsions. Consequently the fact is true and should be adaptable for the good of mankind." [Italics Koshtoyants'].

Further on in the same letter, he asks his correspondent: "Now do you feel. . . how much beauty and practical importance is concealed in the chemical stimulation of nerve centers!?"

The further developments in physiology, pathology, and therapy of the nervous system confirmed Sechenov's expectations in the use of chemical stimuli of the nervous system, both for the clarification of the laws of function of this system and for therapy when these functions are disturbed.

It would not be an exaggeration to assert that Sechenov as a physiologist-experimenter devoted himself most of all to problems linked from a theoretical and methodological aspect most closely with chemistry and physical chemistry. Suffice it to point out in this connection the list of his works compiled by M. N. Shaternikov. Out of 106 publications, 46 titles refer to investigations and articles of a physico-chemical nature.[11]

In his doctoral dissertation (1860), young Sechenov advanced the following postulates. "1. A physiologist is a physical chemist dealing with the phenomena in animal organisms," and "8. In the present state of the natural sciences the only possible principle in pathology is the molecular principle."[12]

The last postulate is a reverberation of the scientific controversy which arose between Sechenov and his friend Botkin during the period when both worked in Ludwig's laboratory in Vienna. Botkin was an ardent admirer of R. Virchow and, on the basis of the principle of cellular pathology, considered all processes in the normal as well as in the morbid state to take place in the cells. Sechenov, on the other hand, "having imbibed the teaching of the dyed-in-the-wool biologists-physicists. . . considered the molecule as the beginning of all beginnings."[13] He attempted to prove that in the life processes of the cells of the organism the important role belongs to the environment surrounding the cell, its molecular composition. The seventh postulate of Sechenov's doctoral dissertation reads: "On this basis cellular pathology which has as its foundation the physiological independence of the cell or at least its hegemony over the immediate environment is incorrect as a principle. This theory is nothing but an extreme degree of development of the

[11] I. M. Sechenov. Autobiographical Notes. Moscow, 1907.
[12] I. M. Sechenov. Data for a Future Physiology of Alcohol Intoxication. Dissertation, SPb., 1860.
[13] I. M. Sechenov. Autobiographical Notes. 1945, p. 93.

anatomical trend in physiology." This was followed by the above quoted eighth postulate, according to which "the only possible principle in pathology is the molecular principle."

Apparently, the quarrel between Sechenov and Botkin was very acute. Once friends, they literally quarreled and parted. "Under other circumstances this controversy could have had a beneficial effect, by way of corrections and concessions by both parties, but in this case it did not happen, and it terminated on Botkin's part with a proverb, true at that time: 'he who mixes the end with the beginning has but rubbish in his head' which offended me to such an extent that we did not see each other any more in Vienna and I departed for Heidelberg."[14] Then Carl Ludwig, the teacher of both of them, entered the controversy. In a letter to Sechenov in Heidelberg dated May 4, 1859, Ludwig wrote, in part:

"Dear Sechenov, Apparently Botkin is married and is presently travelling; I wish him a pleasant time. . . Just as you complained of Botkin's touchiness, he complained of yours. Forgive me for mentioning it to you, but I greatly desire to achieve peace and agreement between two people who, each in his own way, can accomplish so much good. You know my opinion in this matter. Each of you considers himself offended; this is a good sign and a means for speedy forgiveness. . . Give my best regards to Bunsen and to Helmholtz and don't forget your devoted K. Ludwig."[15]

Sechenov writes about the end of this quarrel in his Autobiographic Notes: ". . . a few days after receiving Ludwig's letter I met the happy and kind Botkin and his beautiful wife in Heidelberg. It must have been on some holiday because they and Junge (who was with me in Heidelberg), knowing where I had gone, found me in the park near the castle. Since that time we have never quarreled, neither about cells nor molecules."[16]

All his life, Sechenov developed the view that the physiological processes were basically chemical and physico-chemical.

Here we must elaborate somewhat on Sechenov's concept with regard to the processes occurring in a neuro-muscular system at rest or in action. Twenty-five years after his controversy with Botkin, Sechenov again developed his chemical, molecular views concerning the complex physiological processes. There is a particularly graphic presentation of this concept in his "Physiological Essays" (1884). Sechenov wrote:

"The core of the working processes in the body lies in the chemical instability of the protoplasm; all motor and sensory acts are directly linked with this variability.

---

[14]Ibid., p. 93.
[15]I. M. Sechenov. Selected Works. p. XII, 1935.
[16]I. M. Sechenov. Autobiographical Notes. 1945, p. 93.

"Indeed, these processes have such an appearance as if the muscles and neural masses were composed of explosive substances. Just as the latter represent unstable reserves of energy that is released under the influence of mild shocks, so the neuromuscular functional charges — at times very intense — are generated from impulses that are generally infinitesimal in a mechanical sense. Just as an explosion basically represents a chemical cataclysm of the state of a complex body, so here too the traces of chemical changes are always present. To be sure, these traces frequently are barely noticeable; but this is because in living excitable tissues the results of explosions are immediately compensated in part by elimination of the products of decomposition, in part by restoration of the decomposed substances. And we could not do without restoring processes since the muscles, for instance, would be apt to function only up to the amount of depletion of their explosive reserve, while in actuality the muscle (of course, with a certain amount of rest) continues to function for dozens of years without change in its weight or strength. It is for this reason that the active protoplasm constantly requires an uninterrupted blood supply or, which is the same, a supply of external substances; and the more active it is, the richer this supply must be.

"And thus to the most pronounced characteristics of animals we must add their ability to transform, by means of the organization of their tissues, inert substances of food into unstable chemical combinations which serve as reserves of energy." [17]

Two phases are characteristic for this chemical conception of the processes occurring in the nervous and muscular systems. On the one hand, Sechenov considered that in the tissues of the animal organism there occurs a synthesis of special substances ("unstable chemical combinations"), the presence of which is absolutely indispensable both for muscular contraction and for the conduction of nervous excitation; on the other hand, he advanced the theory that the course of these processes in the nervous and muscular tissues depends on a constant influx of nutritive substances and oxygen. This chemical conception of I. M. Sechenov is confirmed by the contemporary chemical theories of nervous excitation.

Recently, the British physiologist, Dale, an outstanding representative of the contemporary chemical theory of transmission of nervous excitation, expressed in a brief note the belief that the ideas upon which the chemical theory of the nerve process are based had already been stated in the middle of the 19th century by the founder of contemporary electrophysiology, Du-Bois Reymond. According to the modern chemical theory of transmission of nervous excitation, this transmission is effected through synthesis and excretion in the endplates of the nervous system of special chemical associations that have been named chemical transmitters of nervous excitation. Dale quotes from Du-Bois Reymond's articles, from which it can be seen that the famous electrophysiologist, in his search of the causes of muscular contraction upon indirect

---

[17] I. M. Sechenov. "Physiological Essays." SPb., 1884, p. 15-16.

excitation (stimulation of the nerve), had come to the conviction that a "secretion" of stimulating substances occurs at the borders of the contracting elements ("contractile substance").[18]

For the contemporary chemical theory of the nerve process, it is not only the final act of "secretion" of stimulating substances that is very significant; so are the chemical processes of synthesis of these substances and the close link between this synthesis and the general processes of metabolism of the various elements of the nervous system.

In the light of these most recent problems in physiology and physiological chemistry, we may give recognition to Sechenov as one of the pioneers of this new trend. From the above quoted excerpt from the "Physiological Essays," it is apparent that Sechenov attributed a very great significance to the synthesis of unstable chemical associations for effecting complex processes of nervous excitation and muscular contraction. In formulating the most important question concerning the nature of electrical phenomena observed in the nerve at rest as well as upon stimulation, Sechenov provided the following reply.

"How then, after making the above statements, are we to conceive the ability of the nerve to generate currents? It would be most natural to think that they appear as a result of chemical processes in the tissue of the nerve fiber which occur in a manner characteristic of a living organ. Indeed, if the influx of blood to the nervous mass is suspended so that the metabolism in the tissue of these organs is rendered impossible, then both the excitability of the nerve and the electrodynamic phenomena in its tissue disappear."[19]

Not satisfied with a purely physical explanation of the processes occurring in the nerves — namely, with the concept of molecular structure and its modifications, a concept enjoying broad popularity, Sechenov embarked on a road of independent investigations. Quite specifically, he posed the problem concerning those chemical changes that occur in a nerve when it is stimulated, but, being limited by the insufficiency of factual data in physiology at the beginning of the 1860's, he was unable to arrive at the proper conclusions.

"Of course it is impossible to draw any extremely important conclusions from such a meager store of data. But the change in nerve reaction in the transition from rest to activity may serve as a clue that the latter state is related to chemical upheavals within the nerve. New facts will be revealed in the future to confirm that the character of these processes is bound to consist in oxidation."[20]

Together with his collaborators, Sechenov was the first to present convincing proof that a change in the normal process of metabolism in

[18] [in English] H. Dale. Du-Bois Reymond and Chemical Transmission. Journ. of Physiol., v. 91, 1938, no. 2, p. 4.
[19] I. M. Sechenov. Physiology of the Nervous System. 1866, p. 36.
[20] Ibid, p. 21.

the nerve first of all results in disturbance in the excitability of the nerve and a disturbance in the corresponding physiological indices of this excitability. From this standpoint, numerous experiments were performed with an impaired blood supply.

"If the blood supply [to the nerve] is stopped," said Sechenov, "for a short time, 5-10 minutes, resumption of blood supply causes the nerves to regain their excitability; otherwise the excitability disappears and the nerve dies. This fact clearly indicates the close link between chemical acts in the nervous tissue and the physiological property under study" (excitability —Kh. K.).[21]

Similar disturbances in the excitability of the nerve were found upon severance of the nerves from the nerve centers.

With these facts as a point of departure, Sechenov came to the fruitful idea that the ganglia represent "a kind of nutritive centers, i.e., mechanisms whose activity maintains the anatomical, chemical and physiological integrity[22] of the nerve fiber (Sechenov means the sensory fiber).

From all these facts, Sechenov draws the basic conclusion that "activity of the nerve as of any other organ in the body is unthinkable without the consumption of matter."[23]

This idea concerning a specific physiological phenomenon seems to reflect Sechenov's general views on the nature of psychic phenomena.

The great significance, newness, and fundamental acuity of the problems formulated by Sechenov may be understood only if we consider the general level of science in the 1860's — 1870's. In this light, we regard Sechenov as an innovator in world neurophysiology, as a materialistic thinker with a broad view of the entire scope of small and great scientific problems.

These essentially new views developed by Sechenov gave a strong impetus to the development of Russian neurophysiology in a strictly definite direction. In the laboratory of his immediate disciples, Tarkhanov, Vedenskiy, Samoylov, and their followers, the persistent search for metabolic and chemical relationships in the origin and spread of the nerve process continued. The fact that physico-chemical and chemical concepts concerning the nature of the nerve process have obtained special development in the investigations of Russian and Soviet physiologists is unquestionably linked with Sechenov's strong ideological influence.

Sechenov's concern with chemical and physico-chemical problems can also be attested by the circumstances under which he was appointed professor of physiology at Petersburg University in 1876.

---

[21] Ibid, p. 73.
[22] Ibid, p. 77.
[23] Ibid, p. 75.

Professor F. V. Ovsyannikov, in his zeal to attract Sechenov to the physiological laboratory of Petersburg University, submitted a petition on September 27, 1876, to the council of the University concerning the organization of a chemical department in this laboratory. "The laboratory," he writes, "is in great need of chemical equipment since it lacks the necessary glassware, reagents and the most commonly used working tools and measuring tools. Their acquisition is an undelayable necessity."[24]

Indeed, Sechenov, having begun his work at Petersburg University, developed an extensive series of physico-chemical investigations.

Sechenov's interest in physico-chemical problems becomes quite evident when we look into his investigations in the field of the physico-chemical principles of the distribution of gases in blood and in salt solutions. During his whole scientific career, Sechenov was concerned with the exploration of the principles of solution, combination, and movement of carbon dioxide and oxygen in the blood. This interest dates back to the first years of his scientific career. In his second paper, published in 1859, the problems of investigation of blood gases were presented, and new research methods were described. These are the so-called absorptiometric investigations, dictated by the persistent desire of a scientist to discover the secret of one of the basic physiological processes, i.e., absorption by the blood from the tissues and elimination by the lungs of carbon dioxide. These investigations demonstrate with particular forcefulness Sechenov's efforts to understand the very core of the problem, "the molecular" physico-chemical essence of physiological phenomena.

These investigations led Sechenov to significant discoveries in the field of the theory of solutions which in themselves alone could have firmly established Sechenov's name in the history of the natural sciences. He began with the investigation of the state of CO_2 in the blood and gradually shifted from the blood, an unusually complex solution, to artificial salt solutions and made an exceptionally comprehensive study of the principles of absorption of CO_2 by various salt solutions, depending on the solvent as well as on the concentration of the solutions. As a result of these investigations, Sechenov formulated an equation which represents the general Sechenov law for the absorption of gases by solutions of substances indifferent to them.

Sechenov conducted this series of investigations at the Universities of Odessa and Petersburg (1875-1888). "The work with salts and CO_2," reminisced Sechenov, "lasted for about 10 years in Petersburg, with two long interruptions, and it brought me many happy minutes as well as numerous moments of grief. Some biologists accused me of being a physiologist who spent too much time on the solution of non-physiological

[24]Quoted from A. A. Ukhtomskiy "The Physiological Institute at Leningrad University and the History of its Organization" — see Physiolog. Journ., USSR, v. XIX, issue 1, 1935, pp. 310-311.

problems, and I of course recognized the justice of these reproaches, but I was unable to tear myself away from the gradually emerging possibilities of finding the key to a wide range of phenomena not yet touched by anyone. Twice I interrupted my experiments with CO_2 to work on other problems, but both times I again returned to them. Because of this some circles even coined a saying: 'All that I. M. Sechenov is doing is pumping CO_2.'"[25]

Using Bodlender's numerical data on the solubility of salt systems in water, published in 1891, Sechenov demonstrated the application of the law he discovered to phenomena of solubility of salt mixtures in water.

In 1896, when Sechenov's investigations in this field were fully concluded, an article by the chemist A. A. Yakovkin was published under the title "The distribution of substances between two solvents as applied to the study of phenomena of chemical static,"[26] in which Sechenov's law was confirmed as having general significance on an extensive range of phenomena of solutions, with a demonstration of the particular application of this law to the distribution of substances between aqueous phases. In the article mentioned, Yakovkin, basing his analysis on numerous experimental cases, comes to the following conclusion: "Thus Sechenov's law (similarly to Boyle's law for instance) represents the first approximation to the genuine dependence between the extent of absorption and concentration of salts."

The publication of Yakovkin's work was a great event in Sechenov's life. For more than 30 years, Sechenov had persistently endured various difficulties, greatly suffering from each failure in the work, in his search for this secret of nature. And he succeeded. In connection with the publication of Yakovkin's work Sechenov joyfully wrote: "Thus I did find the universal key to a broad range of phenomena."[27] The significance of Sechenov's investigations in the physico-chemistry of solutions has yet to be explored and evaluated. Sechenov proceeded with his work concurrently with the classical investigations of the nature of solutions by Bethelot, Mendeleyev, van't Hoff, Konovalov and others, at a period of greatest controversy with regard to the chemical and physico-chemical theory of solutions. Sechenov's work attracted the attention of the most authoritative physico-chemist, Ostwald, and subsequently the "Sechenov law" gained general recognition.[28] In the history of physiology,

---

[25] I. M. Sechenov. Autobiographical Notes. 1945, p. 159.
[26] A. A. Yakovkin. Scientific reports, Moscow University, Department of Natural Sciences, issue 12, 1896.
[27] I. M. Sechenov. Autobiographical Notes, 1945, p. 167.
[28] Among the latest works see: A. F. Kapustinskiy and B. I. Anvayer "The Sechenov law and the solubility of hydrogen sulfide in hydrochloric acid solutions" DAN, v. XXX, 1941, no. 7; in a review in Chemical Review [in English] (v. XXVIII, p. 519, 1941), the American scientists Markham and Kobe recognize "the Sechenov law" as a basic law of solution of gases in salt solutions, as confirmed by numerous experiments.

Sechenov's work represents an unsurpassed example of consistent analysis of a complex physiological phenomenon with the precise methods of physics and chemistry.

This group of investigations revealed the principle of association and elimination of blood gases in animals under normal as well as pathological conditions. As Sechenov himself remarked concerning these investigations: "the theory concerning the gases of the blood was established on a firm track." The absorptiometer proposed by Sechenov for the investigation of blood gases made it possible to analyze with great precision the absorption of gases of whole blood and blood plasma. Sechenov discovered the role of hemoglobin in the binding and transportation of carbon dioxide in the organism. However, this discovery was definitely recognized only after the investigations of the Belgian scientist O. M. Henriques in 1928. The absorptiometer first introduced in physiology by Sechenov formed the basis for numerous subsequent designs of this instrument. The manometric instruments extensively used at present in the laboratories of the whole world are perfected versions of Sechenov's original instrument.

Having obtained a precise picture of distribution of the gases of the blood capable of a quantitative expression, Sechenov tackled a problem of physiology proper: the exchange of gases between the blood and the tissues and between the organism and the external environment. In doing so, Sechenov laid the scientific foundation for the study of gas metabolism in animals and especially in man. These investigations on gas metabolism were particularly elaborated after Sechenov's transfer to Moscow.

During the period of intensified work on the problem of blood gases, Sechenov made an attempt of utmost significance, namely, to apply the physiological data to analysis of causes of death as a consequence of disturbance of normal breathing conditions. This was undertaken in connection with the tragic end which befell three French balloonists at a height of 28,000 feet in the balloon "Zenith" (1875). Upon the influence of a sharp drop in atmospheric pressure two of the participants in this high altitude flight, Sivel and Croce-Spinelli died, while the third, Tissandier, who kept an unusually valuable diary on the conditions of the balloonists during flight, was found unconscious in the cabin of the airship. In his Autobiographical Notes Sechenov writes: "In 1879. . . I began to wonder why the Zenith airmen suffocated at a height of a 1/3 of an atmosphere, i.e., I began to calculate to what extent was the supply of O_2 insufficient for breathing during each breathing cycle, on the basis of available physiological data."[29]

On December 21, 1879, at the Sixth Congress of Natural Scientists and Physicians in Petersburg, Sechenov read a remarkable paper on the subject "Data related to the solution of the problem of CO_2 and O_2 entering into the blood under normal breathing conditions and under

---

[29] I. M. Sechenov. Autobiographical Notes. 1945, p. 160.

I. M. Sechenov (late 1890's).

downward oscillations of air pressure." This paper, in a somewhat modified form, was published in the journal Medic under the title "On the Problem of Breathing in Rarefied Air."[30] Basically, Sechenov's paper was devoted to a thorough scientific analysis of the causes of death of the two French balloonists.

His conclusions presented with exceptional clarity the need of creating conditions to maintain a constant atmospheric pressure in high flying airships, since the drop in pressure suspends the function of physiological mechanisms of lung ventilation, although the blood itself is capable of oxygen saturation even under conditions of lesser pressures.

Sechenov's report aroused tremendous interest among the delegates at the Sixth Convention of Naturalists and Physicians. In a special review of the proceedings of this convention, the editors of the journal Medic wrote with regard to Sechenov's report: "Needless to add, the members of the section hastened to greet the author with thunderous applause, as an expression of the respect that he had instilled long ago in Russian physicians both as a scientist and as a public figure whose words never diverge from his deeds."[31]

Sechenov's investigation was one of the very first physiological works which posed the problem of the special nature of the physiological processes in the human organism under conditions of low atmospheric pressure at definite altitudes. Just as his close friend Mendeleyev analyzed the causes of the death of the airmen of the airship "Zenith" in his report to the Russian Physico-Chemical Society in October of 1875 and first formulated the idea of a sealed gondola[32] for such airships, so Sechenov, using his prolonged investigations of gas metabolism in organisms for the analysis of the same event, founded a new physiological field — aviation physiology, which has been particularly developed in our times.

It is customary to consider Sechenov's contemporary, the famous French physiologist Paul Bert,[33] as the father of modern aviation medicine. Bert performed his investigations on this subject in connection with an analysis of the causes of death of the balloonists of the airship "Zenith," as well as data on an earlier flight, in 1862, of two balloonists, Glaisher and Coxwell. Bert's classical work presenting the results of his investigations on the influence of reduced barometric pressure appeared in 1878,[34] i.e., during the period when Sechenov had arrived, quite independently, at the basis of his nearly 20-year-long investigations on blood gases and general problems of respiration — the important conclusions that laid the foundation for aviation medicine.

---

[30] Medic no. 21 and 22, 1880; see also: Pflüg. Arch., B. 22, 1880.
[31] Ibid., no. 3, 1880, p. 54.
[32] B. P. Vorob'yev. D. N. Medeleyev and Aeronautics. Sov. Science, no. 8, 1939.
[33] See chapter on aviation medicine in the book: H. Armstrong [in English] Principles and Practice of Aviation Medicine. London, 1943.
[34] B. Bert. La Pression barometrique. Paris, 1878.

In 1887-1888, a number of events occurred that led Sechenov to the decision to leave Petersburg University. The reasons are rather complex: on the one hand, on the surface they appeared connected with the black-balling of Sechenov as an active member of the Academy of Sciences and the government's refusal to confirm him in the title of Honored Professor and, on the other hand, reasons connected with his scientific endeavors. The pertinent facts about the elections at the Academy and his confirmation as Honored Professor are discussed in detail in my monograph "Sechenov."[35]

During Sechenov's last years at Petersburg University, he devoted a great deal of attention (as we have indicated above) to problems of physico-chemical nature connected with the solubility of gases, in particular CO_2 in salt solutions. And it was precisely in this area that he failed to find due response. Speaking of this crucial moment of his life, Sechenov wrote: "Thus life in the laboratory at Petersburg University brought me many happy moments and no little grief. There was some consolation in the fact that I already knew my research had given me a certain standing in the West, but could all this remove the vexation of being told: 'all that you have done is very good, but it represents only a specific instance; prove that your law holds for other gases,' after I had worked for almost a decade with CO_2.

Due to the absolute impossibility of finding such proof, my stay at the Petersburg laboratory seemed to me aimless, even unpleasant, and I decided to exchange my professorship for a more modest status of Privatdozent in Moscow."[36]

Having made this decision, Sechenov turned to some close acquaintances and friends in Moscow with the request to explore to what extent his move to Moscow and the work at the university would find sympathy among the University staff and administration. In this connection we quote here a typical letter from Sechenov of March 18, 1888, to an authoritative professor at the University, the zoologist A. P. Bogdanov.[37]

"Dear Anatoliy Petrovich! My persistent refusal to participate in your beautiful and useful publication (and I express to you my most sincere thanks for having sent it to me) is simply explained by the fact that I considered it intended exclusively for zoologists.[38]

---

[35] See also A. A. Ukhtomskiy. "The Physiological Institute of Leningrad University in the History of its Development" — see Physiolog. Journ., USSR, v. XIX, issue I, 1935, pp. 316-317.

[36] I. M. Sechenov. Autobiographical Notes. 1945, p. 164.

[37] This letter is published here for the first time. The original is preserved in the Moscow Division of the Archives of the Academy of Sciences, USSR, fund 446, list 2, no. 591.

[38] Sechenov is referring to the publication of the biographical dictionary of Russian zoologists undertaken by A. P. Bogdanov: Data for the History of Scientific and Practical Activities in Russia in the Field of Zoology, of which the first volume was published in 1888.

However, when a copy of it came into my hands, and this occurred but about two weeks ago, and I saw that the publication deals also with workers in fields related to zoology, there was no reason for me to refuse, and it is a pleasure to send you the requested data, i.e., my biography and list of publications, except for the picture, which is still not ready. At the same time, I take this opportunity to direct a few questions of personal nature to you and I know in advance I shall receive a very sincere answer, even if it is in the negative.

In September of this year I will have completed 25 years of service, and I feel that I am still capable of being useful; I should like to work at Moscow University in the capacity of a Privatdozent, since I have never ceased to love our mutual alma mater.

In view of all this it would be important for me to know: how would the majority in the natural science and medical departments react to my transfer; would they give me at least a little space for my work and the right to make use of their scientific apparatus during lectures and, finally, can this matter find a favorable response on the part of your administration?

I should like to obtain your personal opinion concerning these questions, i.e., I should not like my request to become the subject of debate in various circles since my transfer is not an irrevocably definite matter yet.

Forgive me if my questions put you in a difficult situation, but I should not think they could, since I shall be entirely satisfied with the sincerity of your answer whatever it may be.

Respectfully yours, I. Sechenov.

Sechenov himself points out another letter. In his Autobiographical Notes he wrote:

"I was corresponding with my old friend Nadezhda Fedorovna Shneyder. She (then a widow) had been married to the professor of histology, Bredikhin (a brother of the famous astronomer) and had connections at the university and could supply reliable information as to whether my intention to act as a Privatdozent at the university could displease some of the professors. I received an answer that there was indeed lack of sympathy for my transfer. In reply I requested that she assure them that I would not inconvenience anyone and would not be a hindrance to anyone. Then I received a satisfactory answer and in the early spring I went to Moscow to submit an application for a privatdozentship."[39]

In the fall of 1889 began the last, the Moscow period of Sechenov's activities; thus he returned to Moscow University 33 years after graduating from it.

Towards the end of Sechenov's activities in Petersburg University, his portrait was painted twice by the great Russian artist I. Ye. Repin. The first portrait was painted in 1884, and at present (since 1939) it

---

[39] I. M. Sechenov. Autobiographical Notes. 1945, p. 164.

decorates the office of the president of the Academy of Sciences, USSR, while the second portrait, dated 1889, is in the Tretyakov Gallery. [40] The latter portrait was considered especially successful by Sechenov's contemporaries, among them I. P. Pavlov and A. F. Samoylov, Sechenov's former assistant at the Moscow University.

In this connection there is a most interesting letter from I. P. Pavlov to Professor M. N. Shaternikov, dated November 28, 1916, presented here in its entirety. Pavlov wrote:

"Dear Mikhail Nikolayevich! My great thanks to Marya Alexandrovna and to you for your readiness to accede to the request of the physico-mathematical Department of the Academy and our own. Of course, I refer to the available portraits and photographs. I had especially in mind a copy of the Repin portrait in the Tretyakov Gallery because I liked it very much and have admired a copy of it many times in Timiryazev's article on "Russian Scientific Workers" that the author had sent to me; I do not know where it was published, I think it was in the Herald of Europe. It is the acme of characteristics and resemblance and of course it is desirable to have larger photographic reproductions, one half or one quarter of the original size. As to the organization of societies and journals in Ivan Mikhaylovich's name, we have decided to convoke the first congress especially for the organization of these matters, not excluding scientific reports, if such are available. The proposed dates are January 5-7, 1917. With all the best. Yours, Pavlov." [41]

The above letter is also of interest because the question of placing I. M. Sechenov's portrait in the Academy of Sciences was obviously raised upon Pavlov's initiative at the end of 1916. At the same time, as is seen from the letter, the idea emerged of creating a journal and a convention of physiologists in I. M. Sechenov's name.

Samoylov has given an exceptionally brilliant description of the appearance of the great physiologist. He wrote:

"His appearance, manners, his behavior, a sort of meaningfulness in his conversation corresponded to the image that I had associated with Sechenov's fascinating name. If I were to say that I saw an old man, of medium height, strong build, lean, a face with large features and faint pock marks, that the face was of a peculiar color: a pale, somewhat

---

[40] I. Ye. Repin painted this portrait over a long period of time with frequent interruptions. In a letter to his wife in 1889, Sechenov, who by that time had returned from the country to Petersburg, informed her that he had met N. V. Stasova, who "urgently pleaded in her own and Repin's name that I grant him about two hours to complete the portrait." Unpublished letters in the possession of Professor O. P. Molchanova.

[41] Published for the first time from a copy in the Moscow division of the Archives of the Academy of Sciences, USSR.

greenish tinge — obviously such a description would offer little. One had to see Sechenov! His eyes and their sharp expression are beyond description. His face was mobile and very expressive of his mood, and his mood was very changeable. He had a fine face when he was kind, or more correctly, when he was in a kind mood. He liked to be kind. He greatly appreciated kindness in others and by nature he was a kind man, but his excitability, temper, anxiety and even some distrust at times prevented him from behaving consistently with his innate kindness. He could be very strict at times and he was in a way enchanting in moments of strictness, severity, in moments of anger and rage that erupted particularly when he saw injustices perpetrated by the authorities. His eyes in such cases were indeed sparking.

"Soon I began to attend his lectures for students, and as his assistant I had to prepare the experiments. There was no limit to my astonishment and delight. Even now, after many years I must say that never in my life either before or after him, have I ever encountered such a gifted lecturer.

"He possessed a rare and fortunate combination of gifts that make a talented lecturer. And with all that he was only a lecturer, not an orator, he was not a tribune, he never raised his voice in order to arouse by intonation or emphasis the attention of his listeners, to appeal to their feelings. He was exclusively a lecturer who presented his book. He lectured quietly and evenly. His speech was an orderly stream of short, concise and strong sentences. His diction was remarkably clear. He pronounced his words with astounding sharpness and clarity without conscious deliberate intent. Apparently, his vocal apparatus with all its resonant parts and appendages for delivering consonant sounds was most fortunately constructed. His voice was remarkable: ringing, slightly harsh, a high pitched baritone quality. Sechenov never strained his voice when lecturing, he spoke as calmly as in ordinary conversation and nevertheless his voice carried and filled the large auditorium.

"The beauty of his diction was well combined with the peculiarities of his language. In general he was a master of speech. He was in perfect command of three foreign languages. He spoke German and French with faultless pronunciation. As to his Russian, it must be said that many excerpts from his popular articles and speeches deserve to be included into readers together with excerpts from our best writers and novelists. He produced examples of exceptional elegance of the Russian scientific language. Sechenov's style distinguishes itself by the picturesque character of expression and by some special keenness, one wants to say of wholesomeness, as if one could feel in it the strength of the country, its fields and its forests. Some rather antiquated expressions lend a certain special flavor to his masterful Russian language.

"But his talent as a lecturer was of course not limited to his diction or the elegance of his style, it also included the strength and special persuasiveness of Sechenovian logic. His logic overwhelmed the listener. From the very first words a reign of silence would spread over the auditorium. This beautiful distinct language flows calmly and one idea is strung with the next with implacable, overpowering logic. More than once the students told me what a pity it was that it was impossible to take notes. And it was true: it was a pity to be distracted by hurried note taking and to lose the unity of impression and enchantment that these lectures imparted. Sechenov spoke with unusual conviction; all his conclusions from demonstrated and described experiments appeared self-understood. At times during the lecture he would step forward from behind the desk, stop before a listener in the first row and would seem to converse with him, endeavoring by words and gestures to convince him of something. He gesticulated somewhat during his lectures and his gestures were both unique and expressive; even at rest his hands were full of expression as was so well depicted by Repin in his magnificent portrait of Sechenov now in the Tretyakov Galleries." [42]

After leaving Petersburg University in 1888, Sechenov found himself without a laboratory of his own. For almost three years he remained in a deeply depressed mood. He spent a whole year in the country (1888-1889). He wrote: "I have retired, and first of all decided to take a rest for a whole year in the country with my wife." The indefinite situation with regard to Moscow University dragged on for over a year; there, the great physiologist, in the capacity of Privatdozent, did not have a room to work in nor any instruments, "with the exception of the absorptiometer, a knife and induction equipment." [43]

Indeed, Sechenov was not very readily accepted in the professorial circle of Moscow University! He found friendly acceptance only by M. A. Menzbir, who put a small room at his disposal for his work. But Sechenov needed a proper laboratory and this he did not have. Just how acute the problem became can be seen from Sechenov's thought, during his first months in Moscow, of equipping his own laboratory in the country, in his wife's home in Klepino. "Perhaps I should install a laboratory in Klepino? I think it could be done," he wrote to his wife on October 5, 1889. He returned to the same question again in a letter to his wife of October 12, 1889: "After all, once the first major investment is made, it would be less expensive to work in the country than in the city since there are no living expenses in the country. However, this possibility lies in the future. . ." [44]

Sechenov began to work at Moscow University as an Privatdozent in the department of physiology on the medical faculty in 1889. Professor F. B. Sheremet'yevskiy (1840-1891) was the chairman of the department. Upon his return from a scientific fellowship abroad, in 1868, Sheremet'yevskiy was first elected dozent (lecturer) and later, in 1870, professor of physiology at the University and took over from Babukhin the

---

[42] A. F. Samoylov. Sechenov and his Ideas Concerning the Role of the Muscles in our Perception of Nature. Speech read to the Russian Society of Physiologists on December 26, 1929 on the occasion of the 100th anniversary of Sechenov's birth.

[43] I. M. Sechenov. Autobiographical Notes. 1945, p. 165.

[44] Excerpts from the unpublished letters of Sechenov to M. A. Sechenova-Bokova. Professor O. P. Molchanova has the originals.

chairmanship in the department of physiology. At the time of Sechenov's arrival in Moscow, Sheremet'yevskiy's closest assistant was L. Z. Morokhovets, and the two together reorganized the pedagogical as well as the scientific research work in the department.

After joining the department, Sechenov displayed a maximum of the tactfulness that characterized all of his activities. Here is what he wrote to his wife in one of his first letters from Moscow in the fall of 1889:

"The most ticklish point with regard to the physiological laboratory resolved itself satisfactorily. The chief and his assistant are finally convinced that I have no designs whatsoever against them and treat me so unpretentiously that I feel quite free to come to the laboratory, to make various trivial inquiries and even to accept small favors. For the sake of peace, I even had a little misunderstanding with the professors of the natural sciences, but it was not my fault. I had requested from the start that no thought be given to an appointment for me as a professor in the department of natural sciences; but apparently they did not believe I was sincere and yesterday I received an official invitation to this effect from the faculty. Of course, I shall refuse and they will be displeased; but I had warned them not to pursue this matter in the department. Consequently I am in the right. Apparently the audience is very satisfied with my lectures because so far there are more comers than there are seats available." [45]

This excerpt reflects all the circumstances that attended the beginning of Sechenov's work at Moscow University. It reflects the attitude of the "bosses" of the department of physiology and the difficulties of obtaining equipment for scientific work, as well as the great desire of a group of professors of the faculty of natural sciences to create an independent course in physiology for Sechenov. The prominent members of the department of natural sciences — Menzbir, Timiryazev, Bogdanov, Markovnikov — persistently approached Sechenov with this proposition. But Sechenov refused: he did not wish to create friction with the physiologists at the medical faculty, and, on the other hand, he doubted that the ministry [of education] would allocate funds for the creation of such an independent department.

Meanwhile, time passed and the working conditions remained very unsatisfactory. Furthermore, in the very year of Sechenov's arrival in Moscow the physiological laboratory in the old anatomical building was torn down, and up to 1893 the laboratory was housed in the crowded and unequipped former apartment of the president of Moscow University. It was proposed to build a special physiological institute at Moscow University, and in 1888 L. Z. Morokhovets was commissioned abroad for a firsthand look at the best physiological laboratories of Europe.

---

[45] A letter of October 5, 1889. Published for the first time. Professor O. P. Molchanova has the original.

Being temporarily located in Menzbir's laboratory of comparative anatomy and without any laboratory facilities of his own, and without hope of help from the University, Sechenov began to read paid lectures to finance his scientific work. He thus earned enought to go abroad for the purchase of needed equipment.

His friends at once sensed Sechenov's great worries, the grief of a man who was actually deprived of an opportunity to fulfill his great scientific plans. I. I. Mechnikov, whom Sechenov saw in Paris, wrote in his memoirs of this period: "We spent much more time together in 1891, when Sechenov came to Paris. He was only 62 years old then and in spite of his preserved vitality age was taking its toll. . . He remained as ever a devoted friend, at times a cheerful conversationalist. But at times his sadness crept through and without any apparent reason he would become apprehensive. "I don't want to bother you," "maybe I am boring you," etc., would he strangely interject in his conversation. . . as before we are in complete agreement in our outlook. He remarked that he does not advise me to return to Russia, where life is especially difficult." [46]

The same moods must have also revealed themselves in Sechenov's conversations with his great teacher K. Ludwig in Leipzig. More than 30 years had passed since the first meeting of teacher and student, but the relationship between them remained the same. Deeply moving is the entry in the Autobiographical Notes:

"On my return to Russia," writes Sechenov, "I paid a visit to my dear teacher Ludwig in Leipzig. In view of the uncertainty of my situation at that time, and without any prompting on my part, he told me that I should have in mind that as long as he lives there will always be a room for me in his laboratory. Upon my return to Russia I learned to my great disappointment that the premises promised me were not available and I almost decided in my mind to work at Ludwig's abroad and only to lecture in Moscow." [47]

But he did not carry out this decision, since he was offered a position in the department of physiology of Moscow University after the sudden death of the professor of physiology, F. N. Sheremet'yevskiy.

Sechenov wrote of this difficult period in his life to his friend Mechnikov on September 29, 1891.

". . . On my return to Russia I learned that the space at the University promised me a year ago does not exist and that I shall again have to live on the street for a whole year since I had planned on staying in Moscow for a whole year at least in order to repay my debts for the instruments by lecturing. Having

---

[46] Quoted from The Struggle for Science in Tsarist Russia. Annotations by S. Shtraykh, pp. 110-111.
[47] I. M. Sechenov. Autobiographical Notes. 1945, p. 182.

received invitations from Ludwig and Ostwald to work in their laboratories, I had already decided to go to Leipzig after payment of my debts when Sheremet'yevskiy (the local professor of physiology) suddenly died and I received an invitation from the faculty and the trustees to take his place. To accept meant having a place to work without living the year around apart from my wife; for this reason I hesitated only for a day and then sold my freedom in exchange for these two advantages." [48]

Ludwig was always concerned about the fate of his pupil. In a letter of November 6, 1891, soon after Sechenov's appointment as professor at Moscow University was confirmed Ludwig cheerfully wrote:

"Dear Sechenov! Having read a month ago in the Viennese press the notice of Sheremet'yevskiy's death, I was extremely worried about your future. I was afraid that they would appoint someone else above you, someone less acceptable. Your letter has freed me from this worry. . .

There is no need for me to tell you that I am glad that you are again on a road worthy of your abilities, and words cannot express the extent of my joy. It suffices that you are again where we all wish to see you.

Living and teaching in Moscow amidst the people you so love, and having wonderful colleagues, you are entering a new era, richer and happier than all that has preceded it. . .

Your new discovery will be of help to me in many ways, when I receive a paper on it; up to now we have known very little about the nature of solutions. I saw our mutual friend Ostwald yesterday and spoke to him of your successes, outward as well as inner. He sends you his regards and congratulations; my wife sends you the same; for years she has been devoted to you. Remember, in Vienna you had such good times with our children; at that time there were only two of them. As ever, devotedly,

Your K. Ludwig" [49]

The beginning of Sechenov's professorial career in Moscow coincides with the deep moral satisfaction at the general recognition of his work on the theory of solutions.

While working at Moscow University, Sechenov continued to keep in touch with I. I. Mechnikov and established new connections among the Moscow scientists.

In addition to a close relationship with Menzbir, Sechenov established a close ideological and personal friendship with the great scientist

---

[48] The Struggle for Science in Tsarist Russia, Letter no. 38, p. 112. Sotsekgiz, Moscow-Leningrad, 1931.
[49] M. N. Shaternikov. Biographical essay — see the volume I. M. Sechenov, Selected Works, p. XXIX-XXX. Pub. VIEM, 1935.

K. A. Timiryazev. Among the professors with whom Sechenov maintained friendly relations, we see the most progressive representatives of the professorial community of that time: the historian Klyuchevskiy, the physicists Stoletov and Umov, and the professor of general literature Storozhenko.

In 1894 in Moscow, there was a congress of natural scientists and physicians. All of thinking Russia listened with great interest to Sechenov's and Timiryazev's addresses delivered at that convention; they received a broad response in the land and in the press. In a caricature published in the journal Budil'nik [The Alarm Clock] for 1894 are pictured the two professorial camps: one headed by Timiryazev and Sechenov fighting against ignorance with the flame of their scientific reports and speeches, the other camp portraying professors "warming" their hands at this flame.

I. M. Sechenov, who according to professor M. N. Shaternikov's very accurate description dedicated his whole life to service to science and his country and sought nothing for himself personally but the opportunity to work, was unable to find a common language with the mass of professors of the medical faculty around him who lived with other interests. "It is impossible to associate with the medics if for no other reason than that they are wealthy, reside in palaces, and live accordingly," wrote Sechenov to Mechnikov in a letter of the 21st of April, 1891. In criticizing his colleagues, the professors of the medical faculty, Sechenov was preoccupied about the fate of science and the future of the young people. In describing the slow pace of work in the physiological laboratory of the university, Sechenov in a letter to Mechnikov of December 23, 1892 writes in part:

". . . among the local youth there is no taste for physiological investigations that are not lucrative, — they are full of ambitions instilled in them by the leaders of the medical faculty who managed to acquire palaces." [50]

Soon, however, Sechenov set going the scientific work of the department at the university. In 1896 A. F. Samoylov arrived in Moscow from Petersburg (he had already worked with Pavlov) and became Sechenov's assistant. In the same year, 1896, Shaternikov (1870-1939) graduated from the department of medicine and was to become one of Sechenov's most favored disciples, and later on a professor at Moscow University. M. N. Shaternikov began his scientific work under Sechenov's guidance while still a student. "Up to now I always worked alone," wrote Sechenov in his Autobiographical Notes; "but as soon as I saw that the student Shaternikov was a potential co-worker with a fine character, a good head and skillful hands, I began to work with him. Our first task was the construction of an accessory to the manometer of my absorptiometer for rapid and accurate repeated analysis of the atmospheric air." [51] After

---

[50] The Struggle for Science in Tsarist Russia, letter no. 41, p. 116, Sotsekgiz, Moscow-Leningrad, 1931.
[51] I. M. Sechenov. Autobiographical Notes. 1945, p. 165.

defending his dissertation on the subject "A new method of determining in the human the amount of exhaled air and its CO_2 content" (1899), Shaternikov was sent abroad, where he studied modern methods of gas metabolism in a number of laboratories, and especially in Voit's laboratory. Later on he designed a special respirator which found a general recognition under the name of Shaternikov's respiratory apparatus. [52]

The joint research of Sechenov and Shaternikov in the field of gas metabolism in the human under various conditions was a brilliant completion of Sechenov's works in the study of blood gases.

In general, Sechenov felt that his seemingly theoretical research on the blood gases should culminate in the investigation of the respiratory metabolism of man during various movements, and in particular while walking and at work. Such investigations were made possible by the design of a portable apparatus for the investigation of man's breathing under various conditions, and this was accomplished jointly by Sechenov and Shaternikov. Much later Sechenov wrote in this connection in his Autobiographical Notes: "I frankly admit that the construction of a portable apparatus was a great joy to me since the investigation of breathing during walking was always a dream of mine yet it had seemed impossible." Sechenov and Shaternikov jointly published a detailed article about this portable apparatus for the investigation of breathing in 1900 in the journal Le Physiologiste Russe. This work was destined to play a very important role in the further development in our country of research of practical value in the physiology of metabolism in the human under various working conditions. Shaternikov's great accomplishment and merit consist in that he elaborated this aspect of Sechenov's heritage in great detail and created an excellent school of physiologists in Moscow specializing in the field of gas metabolism in man and animals under various conditions (B. A. Lavrov, O. P. Molchanova). This aspect of physiology has attained exceptional development in recent times and has made a valuable contribution to public health as well as to the important problems of physiology of farm animals.

M. N. Shaternikov was a loyal friend of his teacher and enjoyed his love and interest. Shaternikov's name is closely linked to the last steps in Sechenov's teaching activities at the Prechistensk courses for workers, where he assisted Sechenov in his lectures on physiology for the workers. There are letters from Sechenov to Shaternikov indicative of the teacher's concern for his disciple. One of these letters clearly depicts the state of physiology in the departments of a number of universities, and it is quoted here in full. The letter dates back to 1903, when both Samoylov and Shaternikov, already well prepared for independent scientific work, were unable to make full use of their abilities under the conditions prevailing in the department of physiology at Moscow University. On July 28, 1903 Sechenov wrote to Shaternikov from his country home on the river Oka: [53]

---

[52] M. N. Schaternikoff [Shaternikov]. Pflüg. Arch, v. 201, 1923, p. 56.
[53] The letter is published here for the first time. Professor O. P. Molchanova has the original.

"In replying to your letter my deal Mikhail Nikolayevich, I am speaking as your friend who discusses together with you the reasons pro and con with regard to the problem without however touching upon your family affairs that are also involved in the matter.

Acceptance of the appointment as prosector in Odessa will give you a definite and secure position, instead of indefinite expectations. What could you expect in Moscow? - A starvation position as Privatdozent if Samoylov remains at his post.[54] If he should leave, your chances are still questionable (because the vacancy may be filled by Yudin[55] or even Statkevich).[56] Besides, you should keep in mind that in case of a competition for the Kazan' vacancy you can enter it (other conditions being equal) with greater expectations for success in the capacity of a prosector in the department of physiology than in the capacity of Privatdozent. The position in Odessa also has the advantage of separating us: as long as we are working in two adjoining rooms, those who are hostile will always ascribe a large measure of your independent achievements to my influence. As prosector you will also have the opportunity to act as an Privatdozent; consequently you will have the opportunity to be active both in practice and in lecturing publicly. There is another significant circumstance: in Odessa there are two excellent workers in

---

[54]After Sechenov's retirement (1901), A. F. Samoylov and L. Z. Morokhovets divided the lecture course in basic physiology between them. But in 1903, Samoylov left Moscow for a professorship in Kazan'.

[55]A. A. Yudin, the assistant in the department, was one of the first to apply in Moscow the Einthoven string galvanometer for investigation of the action currents of nerves. His dissertation "Action Currents of Nerves" was published in Moscow in 1907. Yudin invested much effort into installing the string galvanometer. In his dissertation he writes: "After many disappointments I was finally able to complete this project and at the present time I have an instrument that has brought me much enjoyment in my work." However, his experimental investigations contained basic defects that aroused criticism, particularly by Vedenskiy (see N. Ye. Vedenskiy. The refractory phase and the exhaltation phase. With added remarks concerning Dr. Yudin's dissertation. Publications of the Physiological Laboratory of the St. Petersburg University, v. III, 1908, pp. 133-142).

It is interesting to note that Yudin, in his dissertation, criticized Vedenskiy's telephonic method; working with a string galvanometer, an apparatus that provides an objective record of the electrical changes occuring in the nerves, Yudin was not able to appraise the telephonic method and considered it a method of subjective evaluation. But as we shall soon see, Yudin was mistaken. History has proved the great significance of the results of Vedenskiy's telephonic observations and the telephonic method itself.

[56]P. G. Statkevich — a student and assistant of L. Z. Morokhovets at the Petrov Agricultural Academy; a protege of Kasso, he held the Professorship in 1912 and was fired after the February revolution.

fields closely related to yours, the physiologist Verigo and the hygienist Khlopin. In Russian Universities this is very rare.

Such in my opinion are the arguments in favor of the Odessa position.

In my opinion the following considerations speak against it: 1) A subordinate position under a man who received his appointment undeservedly, due to the influences of a group; [57]

2) A physiological laboratory for the joint use of the departments of medicine and of the natural science, there being hostility between these two, since Verigo openly opposed Zav'yalov's candidacy.

Thus you would find yourself between two fires.

But I might be in error concerning the first of these points since I do not know Zav'yalov's qualities as a person. As to the second point, perhaps I could help you by influencing Verigo favorably (by writing to him about you).

Of all the Russian cities Odessa in my opinion is the best, but I think it is more expensive than Moscow.

Thus my dear Mikhail Nikolayevich, you have my sincere opinion concerning the proposed question, without taking into consideration the family matters.''

During the last years of his life Sechenov's basic scientific interests and research were dedicated entirely to the application of physiological achievements to a deeper understanding of the physiological laws governing the work activities of man and to the search for a physiological basis for a better regimen of his work and rest. He directed his scientific research toward this problem, wrote about it a book and popular articles.

In 1900, in the journal The People's Welfare, an article by Sechenov, "The Participation of the Nervous System in Work Movements of Man," was published; in 1901 in a special anthology, he published a popular article "The Participation of the Sense Organs in the Work of the Hands in Sighted and Blind People; [58] in the same year his book An Essay on the Work Movements of Man appeared. Sechenov's last laboratory investigation on the indefatigability of the hand during proper periodical work appeared in print in 1903.

After relinquishing in 1901 the lectures of a general course in physiology in the medical faculty of Moscow University and having transferred the chair to L. Z. Morokhovets, he gave an unusual (and therefore optional) course of lectures on human work motions which left an indelible impression on his contemporaries by the daring and novelty of the formulated problems. This optional course, as remembered by his contemporaries, attracted a great number of university students who came to "listen to Sechenov."

---

[57] This refers to Professor Zav'yalov.
[58] "An Anthology to Assist the Jews who Suffered from the Drought" Moscow, 1901.

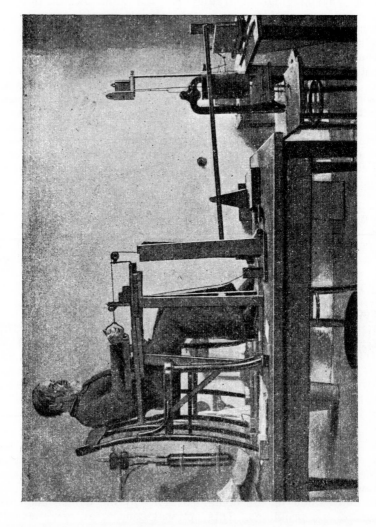

I. M. Sechenov during an experiment in the laboratory of Moscow University in the early 1900's.

The actual content of Sechenov's lecture on the length of the working day is not available. For reasons of censorhsip it could not be published. But the mention of this lecture in the closing pages of the book Essay on the Work Movements of Man clearly reveals the trend of Sechenov's thinking. "First of all it must be recognized that man, irrespective of work, even unemployed, requires an average of 8 hours of sleep, consequently the working and restive time cannot exceed a total of 16 hours a day."[59]

Subsequently, Sechenov approached a solution to the problem as to how long the work portion of the day should be within the limits of the sixteen hours, if such work is not to produce fatigue. As a physiologist he analyzed the work of the heart, an organ consisting of muscle that works the most effectively during the whole lifetime.

Sechenov brings forward a number of very important arguments for the rational organization of work and rest and for an organization of the actual muscular movements of man during physical work such as to cause the least fatigue. He brings forward arguments against the proposition that the hours of rest from work should be the hours of sleep. The eight-hour sleeping time is to assure the rest of the organism. This amount of sleep is required even for a totally "idle" man.

Just as at the dawn of his scientific career Ivan Mikhaylovich Sechenov had chosen a theme for his first scientific investigation the subject of alcoholic poisoning, closely linked to the difficult life of the Russian people poisoned by vodka, so at the twilight of his activity his last theme concerned the causes of onset of fatigue with excessive overwork and the methods of combating fatigue.

The 73-year-old Sechenov again began to experiment on himself. In 1902-1903 he worked in two small rooms on the ground floor of the newly rebuilt physiological institute in the university yard. In one of these he sat at a simple instrument which registered the amount of work performed by his hand (lifting a weight to a definite height). His hand movements followed the monotonous rhythm set by a metronome, "with mechanical regularity (like the metronome) without participation of the will, akin to the leg movements in walking." Sechenov sought the "most efficient tempo for a working hand and the maximum load that is to be elevated to heights that remain constant for several hours." His search was persistent. With such a load he performed a total of 4,800 movements for four hours without fatiguing the hand. He changed to greater loads and determined the signs of fatigue: the height of lifting decreases more and more. He then sought the most effective forms of rest from fatigue, and after numerous tests of various forms of rest he arrived unexpectedly at a very important discovery. He found that "the most effective rest is not the temporary rest of the working hand, but rather a brief period of rest connected with work of the other hand."[60]

---

[59] I. M. Sechenov. An Essay on the Work Movements of Man, p. 135.
[60] I. M. Sechenov. Autobiographical Notes, p. 189.

Having discovered this phenomenon, Sechenov made the assumption that the cause of the rapid elimination of fatigue in the hand following a short spell of work with the other hand lies in the sensory impulses which are generated by the working hand. He verified this assumption with appropriate experiments. After the working hand experiences great fatigue to the extent of inability to move this hand, Sechenov applied a light tetanization (an electrical stimulus) to the other hand, and the fatigue of the working hand was reduced. Thus the impulses that have arisen as a result of stimulation of the sensory elements of the other hand are directed to the central nervous system and facilitate by way of nervous reactions the reduction of fatigue of the fatigued muscles of the working hand. "Thus," — writes Sechenov, — "these facts had to be attributed to the long known work aids: a lively mood, songs, music, etc. But specifically, perhaps the discovered facts have a significance as aids against fatigue during walking and all work in general where the various working organs function alternately."[61]

This was Sechenov's last laboratory investigation. The great experimenter began his scientific research in a new direction, but its completion was to be the task of the new generation of physiologists and, especially, of Soviet physiologists who developed Sechenov's scientific heritage and thus have solved a number of important problems of physiology of the working human organism and have contributed much to the scientific organization of rest and work schedules.

The period of Sechenov's transfer to Moscow was characterized by a great upsurge in physiological research work in Russia. A number of organizational steps were taken that were of great significance for the successful development of physiology and related disciplines. Thus, in 1898, the Society of Friends of the Natural Sciences, Anthropology and Ethnography at Moscow University organized a special physiological society that soon was to publish the first printed physiological journal in our country. This was the journal Le Physiologiste Russe which, although short-lived (1898-1904), played an important role in the history of Russian physiology. Its founder and editor was the professor of physiology at Moscow University, L. Z. Morokhovets. The journal was published in French and in German, which assured complete knowledge abroad as to the achievements of our Russian scientists. This important undertaking was sponsored privately; in particular, great financial assistance was rendered by one of the most outstanding public-spirited women of Moscow at the end of the 19th century, Yu. I. Bazanova. It is for this reason that we find Bazanova's portrait on the title page of every issue of Le Physiologists Russe.

Yu. I. Bazanova also donated funds for the organization of a physiological laboratory at the Ear, Nose and Throat Clinic of the University where the director of the clinic, S. S. Shteyn, conducted his interesting research on the physiology and pathology of the vestibular apparatus. There the subsequently famous physiologist P. P. Lazarev also began his work.

---

[61] Ibid.

At the same time, the Proceedings [Trudy] of the Physiological Institute of Moscow University began to appear, and this reflects the active scientific endeavors of Moscow physiologists at the beginning of the 20th century.

In order to make room for the younger workers, Sechenov in 1901 relinquished administration of the department, reserving for himself just a small laboratory and teaching only a small, as well as optional, course. The direction of the department was transferred to L. Z. Morokhovets. For a short time the teaching of the course was divided between Morokhovets and A. F. Samoylov, but soon (1903) Samoylov was transferred in the capacity of professor to Kazan'. He returned again to Moscow University as professor of physiology on the physico-mathematical faculty only in 1923.

M. N. Shaternikov continued his work in the department of physiology and in 1906 was confirmed as Privatdozent.

During the strained period in the history of Moscow University[62] in 1912, the Minister of Education, Kasso, appointed Statkevich as professor of physiology. However, in 1917, after the February revolution, Statekevich was fired and M. N. Shaternikov, a student of Sechenov's, was elected as professor of physiology, and he directed the department for more than 20 years, up to 1939.

In 1912, upon Pavlov's recommendation, a student of his, N. A. Rozhanskiy, was invited to the department of physiology in Moscow; subsequently, he was to become one of the prominent Soviet physiologists and a professor at Rostov University. In spite of Rozhanskiy's short sojourn at Moscow University (1912-1916), he organized an excellent practical program that provided the first physiological training of the future leaders of Moscow physiology and, among them, the late professor of physiology at the university's biological faculty, I. L. Kan (1892-1942), as well as professor K. Kh. Kekcheyev. [63]

Sechenov's work, which extended over half a century, advanced Russian physiology to one of the leading positions in world science. All cultural Russia listened attentively to Sechenov's voice as the voice of a teacher and considered him the pride of Russia. But the Imperial

---

[62] In 1911, in connection with the reactionary measures of the minister of education, Kasso, and, in particular, as a result of his appointment of professors against university regulations, a number of progressive professors and lecturers, headed by the rector of the university, A. A. Manuylov, resigned.

[63] I sidestepped here somewhat from the direct trend of the presentation in order to point out the various stages in the history of the department of physiology at Moscow University. For details see: Scientific Memoirs Moscow State University, Jubilee edition, Biology, Moscow, 1940; "175 years of the first Moscow State Medical Institute," M., 1940.

Academy of Sciences which, according to Timiryazev's words, had brilliantly distinguished itself by the absence of the most outstanding Russian scientists (Mendeleyev, Mechnikov, Tsenkovskiy), was indifferent to the work and activities of the great physiologist. Thirty-five years had passed from the day of Sechenov's election as a corresponding member of the Academy of Sciences; twice his candidacy was unsuccessfully proposed for active membership in the Academy. But finally the day had come when the Imperial Academy of Sciences "had considered it a special pleasure" to elect I. M. Sechenov as honorary member. This occurred on December 4, 1904, almost a year before Sechenov's death. On the 15th* of November, 1905, Sechenov died in Moscow. Russia lost one of its most remarkable sons, and world physiology lost one of its most outstanding workers. But the beginning laid "by the father of Russian physiology" developed fruitfully through the efforts of his disciples and followers.

In Petersburg, Pavlov, Vartanov, and Vedenskiy; in Kazan', Mislavskiy and Samoylov; in Khar'kov, Danilevskiy; in Kiev, Chagovets; and others continued working successfully on various problems of physiology. Their achievements will be presented in the following chapters.

---

*November 2nd according to old Russian calendar.

CHAPTER XVI

N. Ye. Vedenskiy. His work and its significance for world neurophysiology. The Vedenskiy school; A. A. Ukhtomskiy.

The St. Petersburg period of Sechenov's activities, full of important discoveries and investigations, was especially important in the history of Russian physiology through the creation of a brilliant school of scientists formed by his direct disciples. Among the pleiad of Sechenov's students during that period (the pharmacologist Krakov, the hygienist Khlopin, the physiologist Verigo), the name of his disciple, Nikolay Yevgen'yevich Vedenskiy, shines like a brilliant star. Sechenov, Pavlov, and Vedenskiy represent the pillars of Russian physiology, whose endeavors led it to such an outstanding place in science.

N. Ye. Vedenskiy was born on the 16th of April, 1852. In 1872, upon graduation from a theological seminary, he entered the Petersburg University. In the summer of 1874 he engaged in revolutionary propaganda among the peasants, and on October 5, 1874, he was arrested in Petersburg and spent a year and 8 months in prison in Zhizdra. In 1877 Vedenskiy was tried by a special Senate commission, the indictment accusing him of membership in an unlawful organization and distribution of forbidden printed matter (file 193).[1] Only in January of 1878 was Vedenskiy acquitted (but left under police surveillance) and given the opportunity to return to the University.

From the start Sechenov was particularly attentive to the 26-year-old Vedenskiy, who came to him as a student after four full years of separation from science imposed by the police. He obtained a laboratory assistant-ship in zoology for him with professor N. P. Vagner[2] and drew him to active scientific investigations concerning problems that were of vital interest to Sechenov himself on the physiology of the nervous system. Vedenskiy worked with rapture; he rapidly finished his first two independent investigations ("On the Periodicity of Breathing and the Innervation of Movement in Ranae temporaria" and "On the Influence of Light on the Excitability of Animals"), which Sechenov presented for an award to the first congress of Russian natural scientists and physicians.

---

[1] Personalities in the Russian Revolutionary Movement. Bibliographical dictionary, 1932 (the 1870's).

[2] In a most moving remark Ukhtomskiy mentions the time when Vedenskiy was pasting labels on jars with preparations brought from the White Sea. See Physiological Journal, USSR, vol. XIX, issue 1, 1935, p. 314.

In 1883, in the Bulletin of the Petersburg Academy of Sciences, appeared the first communication of a series of the so-called Vedenskiy telephonic investigations, and the second appeared in the following year.[3] The first communication was read in the Academy of Sciences on the 21st of December, 1882. In these communications Vedenskiy presented the results of his investigations, begun in the laboratory of Du-Bois Reymond, which permitted him to establish the telephonic method of listening to action currents and rhythms of the nerve trunk. In 1884 his classic work on this topic was published under the title Telephonic Investigations on the Electrical Phenomena in the Muscular and Nervous Apparatuses (St. Petersburg). It presented the telephonograms of both muscles and nerves and put the problems of the indefatigability of the nerve conductor on a new basis. In this dissertation the 28-year-old Vedenskiy outlined an entirely new approach to the investigation of complex problems of nervous activity.

The question of awarding Vedenskiy a scientific degree for this work rested with the physico-mathematical faculty of Petersburg University, and Vedenskiy's great teacher, I. M. Sechenov, reviewed it. We quote here Sechenov's report in its entirety from the original, which is preserved in the Leningrad District Archives.[4]

On the 14th of March, 1884, Sechenov wrote to the physico-mathematical faculty of Petersburg University as follows.

The work Telephonic Investigations of Nikolay Vedenskiy represents an experimental exploration of the problem of application of the telephone to the investigation of galvanic phenomena in the muscles and nerves. As to the first topic, although having predecessors, Vedenskiy has achieved significant progress by establishing more definite conditions for obtaining factual data concerning the activity of the muscles of cold-blooded as well as warm-blooded animals and man himself. Due to this he has found a way to apply the telephone for the first time to the study of galvanic phenomena that accompany the natural contraction of the muscle. This special problem represents the principal content of the first chapter of his thesis. In the detailed elaboration we find some substantial gaps; it is also impossible to agree with the principal conclusion from his experiments, but at the same time his investigation presents new facts concerning the natural contraction of muscles which nevertheless represent a step forward. In the application of the telephone to the study of galvanic phenomena in the nerve, Vedenskiy had no predecessors whatever. Here, too, his application was successful since we derive from it the coincidence of telephonic phenomena

---

[3] N. Wedenskii [Vedenskiy]. Die Telephonischen Wirkungen des erregten Nerven. Bull. de l'Acad. de St. Petersbourg, 1883, v. XXVIII, No. 3, p. 290-292; the subsequent communications in the same bulletin, 1884, v. XXIX.
[4] Published for the first time. My thanks to the Archives for sending me the materials concerning I. M. Sechenov.

N. Ye. Vedenskiy (1852–1922).

with various consequences of excitation of the nerve by ascending and descending constant currents. Just as the natural contraction of the muscle represents the most important problem in the first part of the thesis, so in the second chapter, after establishing the general conditions of obtaining telephonic phenomena in the nerve, the author turns predominantly towards the problem of fatigability of the nerve. Here the only essentially new feature lies in a modification of Bernstein's method of temporary isolation of the muscle from the influences of the stimulating nerve; but the modification is substantial because the indefatigability of the nerve emerges from Vedenskiy's experiments more effectively than from those of his predecessor. At the end of the thesis are presented a few telephonic experiments on the central nervous system which permit hope for a successful application of the telephone to this area of phenomena.

In general Mr. Vedenskiy's thesis leaves the impression of a certain scattering and in places a limited completeness that depends in part on the broadness of scope at which the author aims and in part on the unevenness of his presentation. Nevertheless, considering the abundance and significance of the experimental facts presented, the work of Mr. Vedenskiy, in my opinion, entirely merits the scientific degree for the attainment of which he presented this thesis to the faculty."

This brief review has many implications. It bears the seal of the restraint of a strict scientist; it also contains an element of pride in the originality of his disciple and in the fact that the Russian scientist does not follow the beaten paths of science but discovers new phenomena and opens new perspectives for the experimental exploration of nature.

A brilliant completion of Vedenskiy's telephonic investigations is represented in his work On the Relationships between Stimulation and Excitation in Tetanus[5], printed by the Academy of Sciences in 1886. In this work Vedenskiy expounded for the first time his classical theory on the optimum and pessimum of stimulation.

This investigation, as well as the preceding ones, was performed in Sechenov's laboratory under the latter's constant advice and guidance, and it was Vedenskiy's doctoral dissertation. This monograph contains an enormous wealth of factual data. In the preface to the second edition, Ukhtomskiy wrote of it: "This dissertation was written by the author in great haste in order to present it to his teacher, Sechenov. The experimental data and ideas that it had taken years to accumulate were written up in one and a half to two months. Later on the author reminisced that he wrote that monograph in a kind of stupor, standing almost all of the time and hardly leaving the writing desk."[6]

There is a most interesting history linked to Vedenskiy's Telephonic Investigations on the Electrical Phenomena in the Muscular and Nervous

---

[5] Re-edited in 1934. N. Ye. Vedenskiy. Collected Works, v. II. Publ. Leningrad State University.
[6] Ibid., p. 3.

Apparatuses and On the Relationship between Stimulation, Excitation and Tetanus. These two investigations, published in the years 1884-1886, in fact provided the foundation of electrophysiology in Russia in its broadest concept. In these works Vedenskiy formulated and solved a number of important problems with regard to the physiology of muscle and nerve, radically modifying the methods of investigation and making use of data of contemporary physiology. However, this particular series of investigations that created an entire new era in world physiology became the subject of systematic criticism by his contemporaries.

In a historical perspective it is interesting to note Pavlov's attitude toward certain results obtained by Vedenskiy in his telephonic investigations. In 1884 Vedenskiy published the results of his telephonic observation on the dog's heart upon stimulation of the vagus and arrived at the conclusion that there were motor fibers in the composition of this nerve. In a polemic with Vedenskiy, considering his conclusion improbable, Pavlov wrote (1888): "It would seem necessary to concede that such a nerve exists exclusively for experiments of listening to the heart through the telephone. With all this in mind one can hardly doubt that the whole system of Vedenskiy's telephonic facts is but a series of errors of observation."[7]

In a sizeable volume (over 1200 pages) by A. Feoktistov, Electrometric Investigations in the Field of Physiology, which appeared in 1896,[8] Vedenskiy's investigations on this topic were subjected to especially severe criticism. Feoktistov's book, which caused a great deal of excitement at that time, was a compilation of contemporary physical concepts on the nature and methods of investigation of electricity and also contained numerous attacks on physiology and physiologists in connection with the development at that time of electrophysiology. These entirely unfounded attacks emanated from Feoktistov's prejudices and ignorance in numerous aspects of physiology and the physics of electricity.

Feoktistov devoted particular attention to the Vedenskiy investigations, finding in them "horrors," "impossible concepts," "discoveries unheard of up to now," "a horrifying example," "the usual excessive ignorance," "the height of ignorance of the pure physiologist," "a brilliant display of ignorance," etc. Since both Vedenskiy's monographs were published in the Proceedings of the Academy of Sciences and one of them was awarded a prize in the Academy of Sciences, he wrote a special memorandum to the Academy of Sciences with regard to Feoktistov's book. This memorandum is extremely interesting in the history of physiology. We discover here Vedenskiy's exceptional passion in the defense of the new in physiology; he gives a brilliant analysis of Feoktistov's fallacies, proves the perniciousness of his book, and demands that the Academy pronounce its judgment officially concerning this matter, of such importance for Russian science.

---

[7] I. P. Pavlov. Complete Works. Pub. AS USSR, 1940, v. I, pp. 272-273.
[8] Supplement to vol. XXVI of Annals of the Imperial Academy of Sciences.

The Academy of Sciences created a special committee for the purpose of investigating Vedenskiy's memorandum, a committee composed of an array of academicians and, among them, the biologists Ovsyannikov, A. O. Kovalevskiy, Famintsyn, and the physicist Golitsyn.

Vedenskiy was greatly perturbed by all this. He even considered going to court, but sensibly concluded that the court could only deal with a case of personal libel, and not with libel of science. He turned to the Moscow physicists Stoletov and Sokolov, and they sent him a letter full of expressions of sympathy and expressed their sharp criticism of Feoktistov's book from the standpoint of physics. Twice Vedenskiy appeared with papers on this subject before the sections of zoology and physiology of the Society of Natural Scientists (December 20, 1894, at the meeting under the chairmanship of A. O. Kovalevskiy, and the 16th of December, 1895).

Vedenskiy's protest was successful: the Academy of Sciences decided "to retract from sale" Feoktistov's book. Vedenskiy was officially notified of this by a letter dated December 23, 1894, from the permanent secretary of the Academy of Sciences. It must be stated that the Vedensky-Feoktistov controversy did not end here, but further mention would only involve us in certain details of a more general nature.[9]

In 1902-1903, Professor S. I. Chir'yev came up with criticism of the telephonic method. He asserted that the telephonic current described by Vedenskiy "represents a purely physical phenomenon and not a physiological one." The circumstances, contents, and fallacy of Chir'yev's critical remarks are analyzed in detail in Vedenskiy's brilliant polemic article, which contains a wealth of historical material and was published in the Annals of The Academy of Sciences (1904, vol. 15, no. 4) under the title "The Telephone as an Indicator of Nervous Excitation."

Much later, in 1907, A. Yudin in Moscow, in his dissertation "On the Action Currents of Nerves," again cast a doubt on the value of the telephonic method proposed by Vedenskiy. In a special article, Vedenskiy exposed Yudin's errors and defended his new method and the conclusions based on telephonic investigations.[10]

In 1897 and 1901, Vedenskiy reported the results of his telephonic investigations at the Congress of Natural Scientists and Physicians in Odessa, imitating in his own voice the auditory phenomena that he was able to detect upon excitation of his muscles by means of a simple telephone earphone. He also demonstrated his telephonic method to physiologists of various countries at the second and third International Congresses of Physiologists (Liège, 1892, and Berne, 1895). Among those present at

---

[9] Readers interested in this episode of Russian physiological history are referred to Vedenskiy's brilliant polemical article "Concerning a New Phenomenon in the Scientific Literature" (separate reprint from the Proceedings of the St. Petersburg Society of Naturalists, Department of Zoology and Physiology, v. XXV, 1895).
[10] Publications of the physiological laboratory of St. Petersburg University, v. III. 1908, p. 133.

these demonstrations were Tigerstedt, Einthoven, Boruttau, and other prominent specialists in electrophysiology.

Many years later, at the International Physiological Congress in Groningen (1913), the German physiologist Piper demonstrated Vedenskiy's discovery of rhythmic impulses in the muscles, using an apparatus that had been perfected by that time for physiological experimentation—the string galvanometer. Piper did not have to use his vocal cords, since the vibrations of the string galvanometer projected on a screen (or registered photographically) gave a full illustration of the phenomenon discovered by Vedenskiy.

Finally, in 1928, at the celebrations commemorating the 300th anniversary of the publication of W. Harvey's immortal treatise on the causes of the movements of the heart and blood, the Cambridge physiologist Adrian demonstrated to the prominent physiologists of the world the rhythmic action currents of the phrenic nerve of the rabbit, using still more refined techniques. Using a system of amplifiers consisting of three tubes with condensors, he induced the rhythmic currents of this nerve into the apparatus and from it led the output into a capillary electrometer and loudspeaker. In this case it was not Vedenskiy's voice but the loudspeaker that transmitted to the audience the sequence pattern in the form of sounds of the rhythmic waves of excitation in the nerve.

It must be noted that Vedenskiy's closest collaborator, N. P. Rezvyakov, was one of the first to apply the contemporary amplifying technique for the reproduction of Vedenskiy's telephonic investigations.[11]

Developing further the views of his teacher Sechenov on the phenomena of summation, Vedenskiy formulated the theory on the role of the rhythm of excitations and the adoption of this rhythm on the basis of his own numerous experimental investigations concerning the dependence of intensity of excitation on the intensity of the stimuli and the time interval between them.

These experimental data and the very significant conclusions derived from them form the basis for the latest investigations of such outstanding physiologists of our times as Hill (England), who demonstrated the significance of time intervals between successive acts of excitation during tetanus, and Kato (Japan), who determined the conditions under which nonexcitability arises in a series of subliminal stimuli applied at short time intervals.

Of special significance in the history of development of physiological views is Vedenskiy's theory of lability, which he formulated in the early 1890's. This theory was a natural consequence of Vedenskiy's thorough investigation of the significance of rhythms of excitation, i.e., the significance of the time factor in the development of excitatory phenomena

---

[11] A. A. Ukhtomskiy. See Physiological Journal, USSR, v. XIX, 1935, issue 1, p. 328.

N. Ye. Vedenskiy in his laboratory at Leningrad University.

and the response of an excitable system to a nerve stimulus. In 1892 in a work published in the French language,[12] Vedenskiy formulated "the law of relative lability," where for the first time in a most clearcut form he demonstrated the role of speed of elementary reactions that accompany functional activity: "I consider the measure of lability," wrote Vedenskiy, "to be the maximum number of electrical oscillations that a given physiological unit is capable of reproducing per second in full quantitative correlation with the rhythm of maximal excitations."

Thus, Vedenskiy's "law of relative lability" is the expression of the time characteristics of an excitable system.

The contemporary views on the role of the time factor in phenomena of excitation are synthesized in the theory of chronaxie proposed by the French physiologist Lapicque. However, in the paper he read before the plenary session of the XVth International Physiological Congress in 1935, he was compelled to make the following statement. "Finally, I must give credit—and I apologize for not having done so earlier—to Vedenskiy whose concept of lability to some degree was a form of chronaxie. His article presenting his theory of lability and published in a French journal was omitted by me." In his article under the title "Evolution of the Contemporary Theories Pertaining to the Nervous System," also published in 1935, Lapicque, dwelling on his predecessors, wrote: "Among them I must give due credit to Vedenskiy, before whom I am guilty, having forgotten about him when I made my historical review of this problem. The concept of lability established by this author in 1892 clearly implies duration (of conduction) as a property of the tissue under experimentation; in other words, in the final account, the concept of chronaxie."[13]

In 1896, Vedenskiy reported to the Third International Physiological Congress in Munich on his experiments of great significance in the understanding of the processes of nervous regulation in the most complex reflex acts of motor coordination. His experiments demonstrated that, with combined simultaneous stimulation on both hemispheres of the points for the coordination of the anterior extremities, "stimulation of a point of the cortex in one hemisphere expresses itself in an inhibitory influence on the homonymous point in the other and an excitatory influence on the point antagonistic to it" (Vedenskiy).

In 1897, E. Hering[14] and Sherrington, on the basis of their experiments on the hemispheres of monkeys, also came to the conclusion that stimulation of a definite cortical point in one hemisphere will evoke, along with contraction of the corresponding muscles, a relaxation of the antagonistic muscles. Sherrington's broad investigations in this direction led to the

---

[12] N. Vedenskiy [Vedensky]. Des relations entre les processus rythmiques et l'activité fonctionelle de l'appareil neuro-musculaire. Arch. de physiol. norm. et pathol., 5 sér., v. IV, No. 1, 1892.
[13] L. Lapicque. See Physiological Journal, USSR, v. XIX, No. 1, 1935, p. 232.
[14] The famous physiologist Evald Hering.

formulation of one of the most important postulates in neuro-muscular physiology, namely, the concept of reciprocal innervation.

For the sake of historical objectivity, however, it must be noted that the extremely important conclusions reached by the British scientist were founded on the achievements of the Sechenov school.[15] In this connection we quote Vedenskiy: "These investigations [on the antagonistic influences of excitation of various regions of the cerebral cortex—Kh. K.] were reported by me at the Third International Congress of Psychology in Munich in the summer of 1896. Hering was present at the reading of my paper. The following year the latter, in collaboration with Sherrington, developed the same proposition with regard to stimulation of the cerebral cortex of the monkey... Thus now Sherrington, too, finds that cortical excitation is not as indifferent for the attainment of inhibitory effects as he had found in his earlier investigations. And if these two authors fail to mention what I had discovered before them, I think this is some kind of misunderstanding."[16]

After his report to the Congress in 1896, Vedenskiy published his work in the Journal of Social Conservation of Public Health in 1897 (no. 1). This work was extremely important for the further elaboration of the basic problems of physiology of the central nervous system. Although Vedenskiy did not return in subsequent years to the physiology of the central nervous system and devoted all his attention to the physiology of peripheral structures, these problems continued to be explored in his laboratory. In 1911, therefore, his closest disciple and successor, A. A. Ukhtomskiy, published an investigation "On the Dependence of Cortical Motor Effects on Secondary Central Influences," in which he formulated the principle of the dominanta, which greatly influenced the further development of physiology of the central nervous system.

On the classical model of the neuromuscular preparation, Vedenskiy succeeded in discovering hitherto unknown physiological patterns of phenomena of excitation and inhibition, which attained their synthesis in the well-composed Vedenskiy theory of parabiosis.

According to the theory of parabiosis, the processes of excitation and inhibition are stages of one and the same process of excitation of the protoplasm of nervous structures, of both peripheral and central origin. Vedenskiy's classical work expounding these new views in the field of physiology under the title Excitation, Inhibition and Narcosis was published in 1901 in Russian and in 1903 in German and outlined for a long time ahead the subjects of investigations in the physiological laboratories of the whole world, developing numerous aspects of the physiology of nervous activity.

The most important aspect of Vedenskiy's views on the principles of the nature of inhibition in the nervous system is that he considered

---

[15] See my article in the journal Nature, 1943, April.

[16] N. Ye. Vedenskiy. Collected Works, vol. IV, pub. Leningrad State University, 1935, p. 14.

inhibition to have a genetic relationship with phenomena of excitation. From Vedenskiy's standpoint the process of inhibition evolves from the process of excitation through a series of successive phases and during microintervals of time, on the basis of changes within these same time intervals in the physiological state (lability) of the tissues that are being stimulated. The determination "of genesis of the act of inhibition from the act of excitation" (Ukhtomskiy) is particularly distinctive of Vedenskiy and his school.

The term parabiosis itself (introduced into physiology by Vedenskiy before its application to mechanics of development) indicates that we are dealing with some phenomena in the protoplasm at the borderline between life and death. It is precisely such a state of the protoplasm before reaching the limits of reversibility that Vedenskiy designated by the term para- biosis. But protoplasm may revert again to its original state as determined by physiological indices if the factor evoking the parabiosis (the parabiotic factor) is removed.

A detailed analysis of the phenomenon he discovered led Vedenskiy to describe in detail the successive stages of phenomena of nerve conductivity under parabiosis. He discovered and explored the three basic stages of parabiosis of a nervous conductor that nervous tissue undergoes under the influence of parabiotic factors, and whose recurrence in reverse order causes the tissue to emerge from the parabiotic state.

Vedenskiy's evolutionary generalizations are interesting. In his pub- lications of 1903, he points out that in the early stages of development of excitable systems any excitation of the protoplasm that exceeds a certain threshold may lead to the transformation of this protoplasm along the lines of parabiosis, and that the evolution of excitable systems must have proceeded through the development of mechanisms capable of restoring an area of protoplasm that had become parabiotic. In this work Vedenskiy touched upon the most important problem concerning the pathways through which local stable processes of excitation are transformed into a general- ized process of excitation.

From this angle, Vedenskiy's parabiotic theory had and still has a very exceptional significance for contemporary physiology.[17]

The theory of parabiosis and the related Vedenskiy concepts on the nature of the inhibitory phenomena continued to assert themselves by constant analysis and by overcoming objections brought forward by out- standing physiologists, Vedenskiy's contemporaries. From the very beginning of the formulation of the theory of parabiosis, objections

---

[17] See Ye. K. Zhukov's excellent article "The Evolutionary Method in the Vedenskiy-Ukhtomskiy School." Scientific Records of Leningrad State University [Uchen. Zap. Leningradsk. Gos. Univers.] 1944, no. 77, pp. 3-21.

against its basic postulates were raised by such outstanding physiologists as Hoffmann, Boruttau, Frölich, and others.[18]

Although Vedenskiy's classical investigations on parabiosis dealt with the nerve trunk, his conclusions gained a more general significance with regard to nerve tissue. Vedenskiy set forth the most important problems of cellular physiology of the peripheral synapses in the light of his theory. It was Vedenskiy's work that demonstrated that many patterns of nerve cell function may be determined by exploring the physiology of nerve conductors that were more accessible to experimentation with the available experimental techniques.

Indeed, a little over 20 years later, Vedenskiy's views concerning the genetic relationship between excitation and inhibition and the phasic stages of transition from one state to the other, as presented in his theory of parabiosis, were excellently confirmed by the Pavlovian school, which was concerned with investigation of functional patterns of nerve cells of the higher sections of the central nervous system. This is evidenced first of all in two articles by Pavlov referable to 1923-1925[19] summarizing the current investigations by M. K. Petrova, I. P. Razenkov,[20] and others; these investigations produced data revealing a deep relationship between phenomena of excitation and inhibition in cortical cells with successive alternation of phases during the transition from one state to the other. In presenting and generalizing these experiments Pavlov wrote:

"In studying these deviations in the direction of predominance of inhibition, weakening of the stimulating process, we became convinced that one of the discoveries of our outstanding scientist, the late N. Ye. Vedenskiy, was very justified. Vedenskiy accomplished much in neurophysiology, and he was fortunate in discovering some major facts in this area, but for some reason he is not given his due credit in the foreign literature. Among other works, he is the author of the monograph Excitation, Inhibition and Narcosis, in which he establishes the changes in nerve fiber under the influence of strong stimuli and distinguishes several phases in this process. And now we see that these particular phases are reproduced in their entirety in the nerve

---

[18] See the analysis of these criticisms in an article by a Vedenskiy disciple, N. F. Saks, "Concerning the Theory of Paradoxical Conduction in the Nerve." Publications of the Physiological Laboratory of St. Petersburg University, v. III, 1908, pp. 101-119.
[19] "The Latest Advances in the Objective Study of Higher Nervous Activity" (1923), Twenty Years of Experience. . . . , 1935, pp. 349-360; "On the Relationship between Stimulation and Inhibition, Distinction between Excitation and Inhibition and Experimental Neuroses in Dogs" (1925), ibid., pp. 360-372.
[20] I. P. Razenkov, subsequent director of the department of physiology at the First Moscow Medical Institute. Elected to the department upon M. N. Shaternikov's death. (1939).

cells too when a severe stress is inflicted upon the struggle between the stimulating and inhibiting processes. I do not doubt that after such a coincidence Vedenskiy's work will finally receive its due credit."[21]

The entirely new conception of the essence of one of the most enigmatic phenomena in the physiology of the nervous system, the process of inhibition, advanced by Vedenskiy, attracted the attention of many world physiologists. After a many-sided critical evaluation of Vedenskiy's views and a verification of his facts, "Vedenskiy inhibition" as a distinct form of inhibition attained world fame and general recognition.

The problem of inhibition as a whole, after Sechenov's discovery of central inhibition, was developed in Russia with great impetus. In the formulation of views on the nature of phenomena of peripheral inhibition and on the presence of inhibitory influences on the muscular locomotion, a most outstanding role was played by the publication, in 1885, in the German language (in Pflügers Archiv) of Pavlov's classic work "How does the edentate open its folds (experiments and inquiries in general muscle and nerve physiology)."[22]

Analogous investigations by the German physiologist, Biederman, dealing with inhibitory influences on the musculature of the crayfish, were published later on, in 1887.

Thus, through the efforts of Russian scientists, Sechenov, Tsion, Pavlov, and Vedenskiy, the theory concerning the phenomena of inhibition in the nervous system was developed in great detail from the analytical standpoint and, at the same time, was elucidated from a general biological, synthetic standpoint, demonstrating the significance of phenomena of inhibition in a broad range and, what is particularly valuable, the genetic relationship between the phenomena of excitation and inhibition.

A. A. Ukhtomskiy deserves much credit for having analyzed historically the development of Vedenskiy's theory of other aspects of the scientific creativity of his teacher. As Ukhtomskiy has indicated, Vedenskiy's theory of parabiosis developed progressively in the laboratory of Petersburg University as a continuation on the one hand of Sechenov's theory on the inhibitory mechanisms of spinal reflexes and, on the other hand, of Tsion's views on the nature of inhibition as a consequence of interaction of excitations or, as Tsion used to put it, of interference of excitation. Indeed, in the early 1870's Tsion was the first to express the fruitful idea of the organic relationship between the act of inhibition and excitation,[23] and only Vedenskiy, more than 20 years later, again approached this problem and elaborated it with extreme thoroughness,

[21] I. P. Pavlov. Twenty Years of Experience. . . . Pub. 1932, p. 356.
[22] I. P. Pavlov. Collected Works. Pub. AS USSR, 1940, v. I, p. 297.
[23] E. Cyon [I. Tsion]. Zur Hemmungstheorie d. reflectorischen Erregungen. Beiträge zur Anat. u. Physiol. Als Festgabe C. Ludwig, gewidm. v. s. Schülern. I. H., 1875.

creating an entirely new theory, the theory of parabiosis. In the theory of parabiosis the chronological sequence is particularly interesting; in our opinion, Vedenskiy was the first in the history of experimental biology to present a picture of alternation of different manifestations in the functional activity of protoplasm; he emphasized the transitions from one form of function to another within microintervals of time.

Ukhtomskiy also demonstrated that in the development of the theory of parabiosis a definite role was played by the investigations of Vedenskiy's colleague in the department, B. F. Verigo, who, in the early 1880's, proved experimentally his views on the genetic connection of cathodal depression and the circuit-closing catelectrotonus.[24]

These examples are very convincing evidence of the great influence of Vedenskiy's pathbreaking investigations on the development of world physiology, and, what is particularly important, not only the facts discovered by Vedenskiy were new but also the methods he proposed. Thus the search for more sensitive instruments for the undistorted registration of bioelectrical potentials led first to a transition from the string galvanometer to a capillary electrometer combined with a system of amplifying tubes, while in most recent times Matthews and Adrian in Cambridge found it necessary to design a new instrument on the principle of the telephone disk, i.e., a principle used by N. Ye. Vedenskiy in his telephonic investigations.

N. Ye. Vedenskiy died on September 3, 1922, in his home village of Kochkovo, in the Shuyskiy district. His memory, that of a man humble and boundlessly devoted to science, lives on among his disciples.[25] "I have spent my whole life in the company of a neuromuscular preparation," Vedenskiy used to say jokingly of himself.

Vedenskiy was not a brilliant lecturer, but he was indeed a genuine creator and leader of a school of scientists. Under his guidance, one of the best representatives of Russian theoretical physiological thought, and a future academician, A. A. Ukhtomskiy, began his scientific career. The present head of Georgian physiologists, Academician I. S. Beritashvili, also began his investigations in Vedenskiy's laboratory. Professor L. L. Vasil'yev, the present director of the department of physiology at Leningrad University; N. P. Rezvyakov, professor of physiology at Kazan' University; Professor F. Ye. Tur; and such active Soviet physiological investigators as I. A. Vetyukov, M. I. Vinogradov, D. S. Vorontsov, N. V. Golikov, and others became prominent researchers in Vedenskiy's laboratory.

The credit for having summarized and popularized Vedenskiy's theories and works belongs first of all to his most loyal disciple, A. A. Ukhtomskiy.

---

[24] A. A. Ukhtomskiy. See Physiol. Jour., USSR, v. XVI, 1933, p. 57–59, 61–69; the same journal, v. XIX, pp. 315, 317–318.

[25] See the obituary by A. Ukhtomskiy "Nikolay Yevgen'yevich Vedenskiy and his Scientific Work." Russian Physiological Journal, v. VI, 1923, p. 31.

A. A. Ukhtomskiy (1875-1942) began his higher education at the Moscow Theological Academy, where he studied the problems of the theory of knowledge and various historical disciplines. At the Theological Academy work on his candidate's dissertation of a philosophical nature confronted Ukhtomskiy with a series of problems directly linked to the functions of the brain and nervous activity in general. As Ukhtomskiy himself remarks in his autobiography, this served as a motivating factor for his enrollment in the physicomathematical faculty of Petersburg University, which he did in 1899. In 1902 Ukhtomskiy the student first began to work in the physiological laboratory of the University, thus linking his future with his teacher N. Ye. Vedenskiy for a long time. In 1903 he published his first work under the title "On the Changes of Muscular Excitability with Contractures."[26] From the very beginning of his scientific activity Ukhtomskiy was attracted by physiological research on the problem concerning the significance of respiratory exchange for the function of the neuromuscular apparatus. In the same year, 1903, Ukhtomskiy's article on the effect of anemia on the neuromuscular apparatus appeared in Pflügers Archiv. He worked on this problem for the next few years, and in 1907 we see among his publications the remarkable article "On the Problem of the Oxygen Needs of the Nerve."[27]

In 1906, Ukhtomskiy was appointed to the position of laboratory assistant in the physiological laboratory of the University and subsequently as an assistant to the department. In 1909, together with Vedenskiy, he conducted the remarkable experimental research on antagonistic reflexes. At this time he became inspired by his teacher's ideas with regard to cortical motor processes and continued to work in this direction; in 1911 he published his famous dissertation On the Dependence of Cortical Motor Acts on Secondary Central Reactions. In 1923, in the Russian Physiological Journal, he summarizes his work in this direction in "The Dominanta as a Working Principle of the Nerve Centers."[28] Later on, Ukhtomskiy made a brilliant attempt to combine Vedenskiy's theory of parabiosis with his own theory of the dominanta, and, in 1927, he published the monograph Parabiosis and the Dominanta.

In 1922 he took his teacher's place in the department of physiology at the University. In succeeding Vedenskiy, Ukhtomskiy set forth the task of the broad development of Vedenskiy's heritage from the scientific as well as teaching aspects. Extremely deep in their content, Ukhtomskiy's university lectures were published in part in 1927 and aroused much interest.[29] As a result, over a period of almost 20 years Ukhtomskiy and his disciples, "Vedenskiy's grandchildren," discovered new facts concerning a number of basic problems set forth by Vedenskiy and confirmed his basic views.

---

[26] Proceedings of the IX Pirogov Congress, 1903.
[27] Reports of the Physiological Laboratory of St. Petersburg University, v. II, 1907.
[28] See Russian Physiol. Jour., v. VI, 1923.
[29] A. A. Ukhtomskiy. The physiology of the motor apparatus, issue 1, pub., Practical Med., 1927. (Praktich. med.)

Of great significance for the development of the Vedenskiy trend was the creation, in 1932, of the Physiological Institute of Leningrad University, the publications of which appeared regularly beginning in 1934, under Ukhtomskiy's editorship. They undoubtedly represent a great contribution to world physiology during the Soviet period.[30]

The Novo-Peterhof branch of the physiological laboratory, organized during Vedenskiy's lifetime, was a part of the newly organized Institute.

In the Physiological Institute of Leningrad University, exceptional conditions were created for the further development of Vedenskiy's scientific heritage. Along with the central neurophysiological problems of Vedenskiy's theory, special attention was given to the development of problems concerning the nature of muscular contraction.

The problems of the physiology of muscular contraction have always occupied and still continue to occupy a paramount position in the endeavors of Russian physiologists. Vedenskiy and other physiologists before him devoted persistent attention to the physiological aspects of muscular contraction, and it was V. Ya. Danilevskiy who first turned his attention towards the central problem of the physiology of muscular contraction, i.e., the sources of the dynamics of this process. In 1876, Danilevskiy's article "On the origin of muscular strength" appeared; in it he expressed a series of views which were new for his time, which have not lost their significance up to the present times.

The problems of tonic and tetanic nature of muscular activity, the problems of the energetics of muscular contraction in a comparative physiological connection, were revealed in a most enlightening manner in the works of Ukhtomskiy's disciples.

At that time the biochemist V. A. Engelhardt was attracted by the work in the department of physiology at the Physiological Institute of Leningrad University. Working in direct contact with the aggregate of Vedenskiy's and Ukhtomskiy's students, Engelhardt, with his own collaborators, delved more and more deeply into the central problems of chemodynamics of muscular contraction, and in time this led him to the discovery of the enzyme activity of muscular albumin—myosin. V. A. Engelhardt's and M. N. Lyubimova's publication (1939)[31] received an unusually broad response, and, thanks to their investigations, we now have a more accurate insight into the nature of energetic sources of muscular contraction.

---

[30] From 1903 to 1916 Vedenskiy published ten issues of his Laboratory Reports under the title "Proceedings of the Physiological Laboratory of the St. Petersburg University." The publication was renewed in 1930 under the title "Anthology of works from the physiological laboratory of Leningrad University," and this was designated as the 11th issue; the 12th issue appeared under the title "Proceedings of the Peterhof Scientific Institute" and, beginning with the 13th issue, the publication is continued as "Proceedings of the Physiological Scientific Research Institute of Leningrad State University."

[31] Nature, v. 144, 1939, p. 668.

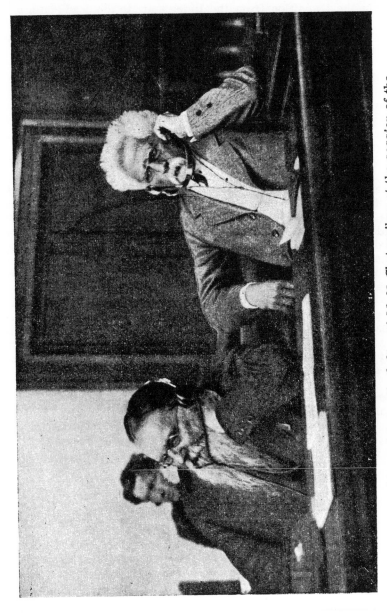

A. A. Ukhtomskiy (on the left) and M. N. Shaternikov at the session of the XVth International Physiological Congress.

As part of the same Institute, a laboratory of cellular physiology was organized under the direction of D. N. Nasonov. Working with histophysiological methods, Nasonov, jointly with Aleksandrov, developed his theory of paranecrosis, demonstrating the transformations of protoplasm in the transition from the living state to the dead state, a theory related to Vedenskiy's theory of parabiosis. Here Nasonov developed his interesting views concerning the origin of bioelectrical potentials and his criticism of the membrane theory.[32]

Within the walls of the University laboratory and of the Physiological Institute a new generation of Soviet physiologists was reared under Ukhtomskiy's guidance, and they have been developing intensively the major problems of neurophysiology set forth by Vedenskiy and Ukhtomskiy. Vedenskiy's views are also being developed beyond the confines of Leningrad laboratory and are reflected in the excellent investigations of many Soviet physiologists (A. N. Magnitskiy and others).

Thanks to Ukhtomskiy's efforts, it was possible to begin the publication of Vedenskiy's collected works, the first volume of this edition having been published in connection with the XVth International Physiological Congress in 1935. Vedenskiy's works in this edition are supplemented by Ukhtomskiy's valuable editorial remarks, indicating that Vedenskiy's conclusions have by far surpassed his own times and in fact contain the nucleus of many of the latest physiological discoveries.

Up to his death, Ukhtomskiy carefully preserved Vedenskiy's heritage. This remarkable man died during the attack on Leningrad; he could not abandon his beloved department. Among the victims of the Leningrad blockade by the German–Fascist barbarians, the death of Ukhtomskiy, one of the most outstanding Soviet naturalists and thinkers, appears one of the greatest losses.

Ukhtomskiy left us a brilliant historical essay on the department of physiology at Leningrad University. This essay is imbued with the life of the department where Sechenov, Vedenskiy, and Ukhtomskiy had been active. I refer the reader directly to this essay, which also covers in detail the activities of other co-workers in the department.[33]

---

[32] D. N. Nasonov and V. Ya. Aleksandrov. The Reactions of Living Tissue to External Influences. Pub. AS USSR, Moscow–Leningrad, 1940.
[33] See Physiological Journ., USSR, v. XIX, issue 1, 1935, p. 307–339; a most valuable bibliography on the history of the department of physiology at Leningrad University is included.

CHAPTER XVII

Development of views concerning the nature of the nerve process. Chagovets, Samoylov, Lazarev. Humoral theory of nervous excitation.

Since their attention was primarily directed towards problems of physiology of the nervous system, the physiologists of our country constantly returned to the important problem of the nature of the nerve process. This problem has a long history. It was the subject of investigation for many outstanding physiologists the world over, beginning with the classic works of Galvani and Volta. As early as 1866, Sechenov formulated the most fruitful postulate that the "function of the nerve, like the function of any organ in the body, is inconceivable without the consumption of matter."[1] Together with his disciples, Sechenov published a series of investigations that demonstrated with exceptional clarity the dependence of nerve function on conditions of respiration and nutrition, i.e., on the process of metabolism in the nerves. While foreign physiologists in their analysis of the nature of the nerve process were primarily concerned with problems of a physical nature, the Sechenov physiological school devoted much attention to chemical and physico-chemical problems.

This new physico-chemical and chemical trend in the exploration of processes occurring in the neuromuscular system has its deep roots in the history of Russian physiology and in the general scientific outlook of the most advanced scientists of the 19th century. Let us remember Filomafitskiy, who in the 1830's and 1840's deemed it necessary to include in his textbook a statement concerning the limitations of a broadly physical, electrical concept of the nature of the nerve process. Let us recall Professor Sokolovskiy of Kazan' University, who described with such logic and conviction the dependence of the electrical phenomena on the normal chemical transformations of nutrition and respiration of the tissues; he was also one of the first (if not actually the first), in the 1850's, to advance the new principles of pharmacotherapy of the nervous system on the basis of his views. In the course of several decades a pleiad of young energetic Russian physiologists were literally absorbed by this problem. We find Russian investigators among the first scientists to investigate the problem of the dependence of speed of distribution of nervous excitation on factors influencing the intensity of chemical transformations (heat and cold). In the 1860's we find Russian physicians and

---

[1] I. M. Sechenov. Physiology of the Nervous System. St. Petersburg, 1866, p. 21.

and physiologists exploring the new field of neuromuscular physiology, the field of application of various chemical stimuli to the nerves (salts, organic agents) to obtain a muscular response (contraction).

Our physiologists were among the first to begin studies of the important questions of the effect of certain poisons that cut off the transmission of nervous excitation. In 1857 Ye. Pelikan published the results of his pharmacological and physiological investigations on the effect of curare in the Bulletin of the Academy of Sciences.

The problem of the dependence of nerve processes, and in particular of an indication such as electrical current, on a normal supply of oxygen and nutritive substances and the elimination of products of metabolism commanded the interest of many outstanding physiologists, and it is subjected to broad experimental verification in the works of a number of Russian physiologists working here as well as in laboratories abroad.

In the laboratory of Professor I. R. Tarkhanov, a disciple of Sechenov, in the early 1890's, the remarkable physiologist V. Yu. Chagovets began his experiments on the effect of various poisons on the electromotor strength of muscular currents in the frog. The results of these experiments made it possible for Chagovets to formulate conclusions of great significance in the development of the contemporary views concerning the nature of the nerve processes.

V. Yu. Chagovets (1873-1939), subsequently a professor at Kiev University (from 1910) and a member of the Ukrainian Academy of Sciences,[2] published his theory of the diffuse origin of electrical activity in living tissues, on which present day physico-mathematical and chemical theories of the nature of nervous excitation are based; in 1896, in the Russian language, in an article "On the Application of Arrhenius' Theory of Dissociation to Electrical Phenomena in Living Tissues" (Journal of the Russian Physico-Chemical Society); and in 1897 he published a report in the German language in Zeitsch. für Physick. Chemie (B. 23). In 1903, Chagovets' monograph Essays on the Electrical Phenomena in Living Tissues from the Standpoint of the Newest Physico-Chemical Theories (issue 1), was published; it represents one of the most significant works in Russian physiological literature. In the introduction to his monograph Chagovets writes in part: "The results I have obtained had aroused some interest only among the chemists, while they had passed almost entirely unnoticed by the physiologists and physicians. Now that I have been able to return to laboratory work after a four year interval, I realize that the problem I worked on seven years ago has already caught the physiologists' attention, and almost every issue of foreign physiological journals contains something new on this subject." In the interesting article published by Oker-Blom in 1901, the latter not only mentions Chagovets but verifies his experimental data.

Chagovets' work between 1896-1903 actually formed the basis for the so-called ion theory of excitation that is usually linked with the names of

---

[2] He served also as professor of pharmacology at Tomsk and Khar'kov Universities.

V. Yu. Chagovets (1873–1939).

J. Loeb and W. Nernst. However, Loeb's first brief communication in which the assumption is made concerning the role of ions in the phenomena of excitation was published in 1898 [3], i.e., two years after Chagovets' first communication, while Nernst's work proposing the theory of electrical stimulation on the basis of the contemporary theory of solutions was published only in 1908. [4] It is interesting to compare these facts with Loeb's statements concerning the history of this important discovery in his book Dynamics of Living Substances: "In 1897 I had already considered the possibility of such views; I elaborated on this problem with more detail in my lectures [Loeb's reference to his article in 1898]. Later on Oker-Blom expressed a similar view concerning the nature of demarcation current; he mentions that the Russian scientist Chagovets had published the same opinion with regard to the origin of this type of current in one of his works in the Russian language" (here Loeb refers to Oker-Blom's article in the Zeitsch. für Physik and Chemie, 1901).

One point remains obscure in the above quotation. A paper on Chagovets' investigation was published in 1897 in German, in the same German journal that carried Oker-Blom's article in 1901. When one considers all these facts, one arrives at the obvious conclusion that Chagovets was an innovator in the exploration of one of the most important problems in the physiology of the nervous system in the first quarter of this century. This has been recognized by a number of authoritative physiologists (Biederman, Boruttau, Cramer) since 1905.

Chagovets' work represents a stage in the development of world physiology and at the same time completes the long road of development of Russian physiology in the direction of the solution of one of the focal physiological problems. If we were to present the essence of Chagovets' theory as briefly as possible, we could limit ourselves to the two basic conclusions from his work: 1) electrical currents observed in living tissues are concentration currents; and 2) the concentration currents depend on unequal accumulation of products of protoplasmic metabolism in two muscular regions to which galvanometer leads have been connected, and in particular on excessive accumulation at the point of excitation (or injury) of a special association of carbonic acid. Thus in this theory the classical theory of electromotor molecules formulated by Du-Bois Reymond is replaced by the theory of concentration currents, and a chemical interpretation (bio-chemical in the contemporary sense) is given to the concept of the sources of electrical currents in living tissues.

Chagovets began this work while still a student at the Military-Medical Academy. The subject that formed the basis of his monumental work was, as we have indicated before, the influence of various poisons on the

---

[3] J. Loeb. Science, v. VII, p. 154, 1898.
[4] W. Nernst. Pflüg. Arch., Bd. 122, S. 275–314. Even if we take into consideration Nernst's earliest investigation, which only poses this question, we should also consider that this article was published in 1899 ("Reports of the Göttingen Scientific Society"), i.e., three years after Chagovets' first communication.

electromotor strength of muscular currents in the frog. This subject was proposed by I. R. Tarkhanov, who, during the course of his long investigations, had already had the opportunity to become convinced of the extreme degree of fluctuation of electrical phenomena in the neuromuscular system under various conditions. The young Chagovets had an excellent guide in the person of the talented physiologist V. I. Vartanov (1853-1919), at that time an assistant in the Military-Medical Academy and later on professor of the Medical Institute for Women. In the preface to this classic work, Chagovets writes that Vartanov "without ever begrudging his time or labor not once during the several years of my work in the laboratory refused his help in advice or action, and without his help it would have been most difficult for me to bring my work to completion." By the time Chagovets arrived at the laboratory as a student to begin his scientific investigations, Vartanov had already completed and published his remarkable dissertation on the subject "Galvanic Phenomena in the Skin of the Frog" (1892), in which he touched upon a number of basic problems concerning the nature of electrical phenomena in living tissues. In this work one is especially impressed by his postulate that, in the first place, the electrical skin phenomena are subject to reflex influences, and, secondly, that in the skin of the tadpole at the early stages of its development it is impossible to detect electrical current. Vartanov emphasized in his work the analogy between electrical skin phenomena and the electrical phenomena discovered by Sechenov in the spinal cord.[5]

"Chagovets was the first to prove quantitatively the possibility of explaining the electromotor forces in the working muscles by the appearance of ionized products," as Chagovets' role was described by the Academician P. P. Lazarev (1878-1943), whose work was very important in the further development of the ion theory of excitation and its application to a series of cases, including the function of the sense organs. Lazarev's first work on the ion theory of excitation was published in 1916 in the Proceedings of the Academy of Sciences, with an introduction by Pavlov.[6] In 1918 he applied the ion theory of excitation to color vision.[7] Lazarev's works in 1921-1922 were published in Germany, and in 1928 in France, and they were a great contribution in the development of physico-chemical concepts with regard to the complex processes of origin and distribution of excitation in living tissues, including the nervous and muscular systems. He expressed his views in a special monograph "The Ion Theory of Excitation (1923), which was of significant influence on the development of investigations in this field. In the later years of his life Lazarev made a number of interesting attempts to relate the facts and conclusions of the

---

[5]An excellent biographical article on V. I. Vartanov was published by L. A. Orbeli. See Russian Physiological Journal, v. II, issue 4-5, p. V-XIII, 1919; this also contains a bibliographical list of basic investigations.

[6]P. Lassareff [Lazarev]. "La théorie ionique de l'excitation et les lois de Pflüger." Reports A. S., series 6, 1916, v. X, No. 12, p. 1063-1068.

[7]P. P. Lazarev. "Investigations Concerning the Ion Theory of Color Vision." Proceedings AS, USSR, series 6, 1918, v. XII, no. 19, pp. 1047-1058.

A. F. Samoylov (1867–1930)

ion theory to the contemporary chemical ("mediator") theory of nervous excitation. Posthumously, in 1945, his book Contemporary Problems in Biophysics, summarizing Lazarev's many-sided investigation in this field, was published. [8]

Discovery of the patterns of function of the nervous and muscular systems was accomplished on a particularly broad scale thanks to the development of perfected electrophysiological methods. The newest techniques for electrophysiological investigations of neuro-muscular activity achieved an especially high level of development in our country, thanks to the endeavors of the brilliant Soviet physiologist A. F. Samoylov (1867-1930). While still a student at Novorossiysk University in the 1880's, Samoylov exhibited a special interest in electrophysiological phenomena. Much later he reminisced about the enormous impression made on him by the microscopic observation of the movements of mercury in Lipmann's capillary electrometer produced by contractions of the heart. "I was conquered forever by electrophysiology," wrote Samoylov.

Samoylov received excellent preparation training in physiology in Russia, and then worked in a number of European laboratories. Suffice it to say that he was a student and an assistant to Pavlov and Sechenov. In the 1890's Samoylov worked in the field of the physiology of digestion in Pavlov's laboratory at the Institute of Experimental Medicine. However, he did not work there for long. Samoylov mastered the surgical methods of studying digestion and did some very valuable research on the process of digestion of albumens in the rods of Mett but he was attracted by another sphere of physiological problems and methods, and he soon transferred to Sechenov's laboratory in Moscow. Pavlov writes about this period most interestingly in an article dedicated to the memory of Samoylov (1930). Pavlov wrote: "I had counted very much on a long collaboration with Aleksandr Filippovich, but to my regret he soon moved to Moscow, to Sechenov's laboratory in the capacity of an assistant. I do not recall whether we had any conversation concerning the motives for his transfer, but I think that the most important reason was his mental make-up. We all strive toward something that appeals to our individual intellect. And different areas of science or else different methods in a science will appeal to different intellects. I was and still am a pure physiologist, i. e., an investigator exploring the functions of individual organs, the conditions of activity of these organs, and the synthesis of the function of separate organs into a common mechanization of some section or other of the organism or of the whole organism, and I have little interest in the ultimate, deep bases of the function of an organ, and of its tissue, for which a chemical or physical analysis is predominantly required. Hence the division of physiologists into pure physiologists, physiological chemists and physiological physicists. For me, vivisection and physiological surgery prevailed periodically or at times exclusively, while Sechenov nearly always worked by chemical methods and physical instrumentation. Apparently Samoylov was attracted towards instrumental, physical physiology. And indeed,

---

[8] See also Collection of Articles on the History of Biophysics in the USSR pub. Moscow Soc. Explor. of Nature. Moscow, 1940.

having attained a professorship, he subsequently concentrated his most important endeavors in electrophysiology, and he accomplished much in this area. The physical, precise nature of his thinking was brilliantly reflected in all of his work. For me, and I think for everybody else, it was particularly pleasant to read his articles. In each of them the aim of the research was clearly and effectively formulated, the most appropriate approach was conceived for the solution of the problem, and naturally an extremely definitive result was always obtained. He arrived at many such solutions in his career. There was every reason to expect the same results in many other important physiological problems." [9]

Although, as one may see from the preceding letter, Pavlov had little interest for problems of physical and chemical analysis, it must be stated here that the great physiologist not only did not dispute the significance of these trends but considered them very important. Thus in one of his articles he wrote: "One could hardly dispute that a genuine theory of all nervous phenomena may be arrived at only by studying the physico-chemical process occurring in nerve tissue and whose phases will supply us with a complete explanation of all external manifestations of nervous activity, their sequence and relationships." [10] It is also well known that Pavlov, in his analysis of the processes of inhibition in the cerebal cortex, admitted the existence of some kind of chemical processes. All this indicates that Pavlov fully shared the ambitions of the Russian physiologists as described at the beginning of this chapter, with respect to this complex problem.

Samoylov's transfer to Moscow in 1896 turned out to be particularly favorable for the development of his investigations in physiological fields related to physics. First of all he found in Sechenov a teacher who deeply sympathized with his ambitions and helped him. At Moscow University Samoylov soon established a close working relationship with the physicists, and first of all with the outstanding physicist N. A. Umov, with whom he conducted and published an investigation of interest to both the physiologist and the physicist. [11] This collaboration turned out to be useful for Samoylov's future career. In the process of perfecting a capillary electrometer so that it could be used for the registration of the finest processes occurring in the nerves and muscles, he conducted a number of excellent, purely physical investigations. [12]

While developing methods for the most effective use of the capillary electrometer, Samoylov on the one hand achieved maximal flexibility and

[9] I. P. Pavlov. In memory of Aleksandr Filippovich Samoylov. Kazan' Med. Journ. no. 4–5, 1931, pp. 331–332.

[10] I. P. Pavlov. Twenty Years of Experience. . . 5th edition, p. 372.

[11] N. A. Umov and A. F. Samoylov. "Electrical Images in the Field of the Hittorf Tube." Transactions Physiolog. Inst. of Mosc. Univ., v. V, 1896, pp. 53–66.

[12] A. Samojloff [Samoylov]. Ueber die Wiedergabe der Inductionsstrome durch Cappillarelectrometer. Le Physiologiste Russe, 1899, v. 1, no. 8–11, p. 1.

sensitivity of this instrument and, on the other hand, paid much attention to a technique for photographing these oscillations. In the latter endeavors he achieved great success due to a considerable extent, to the fact that Professor L. Z. Morokhovets had provided an excellently equipped photographic laboratory in the new premises of the Physiological Institute of the University. As a result Samoylov developed the technique for photographic registration of data from the capillary electrometer to extreme precision, refinement, and elegance. In 1904 Samoylov published an article dedicated to the action currents of muscles upon double stimulation, in which he demonstrated that by means of the capillary electrometer extremely fine processes can be registered.[13]

Samoylov's work on the capillary electrometer is of great significance, not only in the history of Russian physiology but in the development of electrophysiology in general. It must be borne in mind that Samoylov's work was performed at a time when Vedenskiy's telephone investigations had not yet achieved the necessary conditions of objective registration of sounds picked up by the telephone and were still at a level of subjective evaluation of auditory phenomena. The results of telephonic investigations were registered objectively only much later, after the introduction into practice of the string galvanometer and other instruments. Right after graduating from a secondary school in 1884, Samoylov had the opportunity to hear Vedenskiy's report to the Congress of Natural Scientists and Physicians in Odessa, in which he demonstrated auditory telephonic phenomena in connection with muscular and nervous activity with his own voice. From the chronology of these events, it follows that Samoylov's work on the capillary electrometer was very important in the development of objective registration of active neural and muscular processes.

While Samoylov achieved such outstanding success in the application of the capillary electrometer in Moscow, Einthoven, a professor of physiology at Leyden University, used a string galvanometer (1903) for the exploration of the finest electrical phenomena in the cardiac muscle. The Einthoven string galvanometer which was to play an outstanding role in physiology and medicine, was based on the principle of the telephone constructed by the French engineer C. Ader for the reception of transatlantic messages. In view of its great sensitivity the string galvanometer soon gained an important place in the study of electrical phenomena in living tissues and displaced (but not forever) the more sluggish capillary electrometer.

In 1904, at the International Physiological Congress, Samoylov met Einthoven personally, and from that time on a friendship and a professional relationship were established between these two outstanding electrophysiologists of the first quarter of the 20th century, to the great benefit of world physiology and medicine.

---

[13] A. F. Samoylov. Some Electrophysiological Experiments. Archives of Biolog. Sciences, 1904 [Arkhiv Biologicheskikh Nauk].

Samoylov's efforts in connection with the application of the string galvanometer were extremely important in the development of physiology in Russia. After he started using this fine instrument for the exploration of physiological phenomena, at the beginning of the 20th century, Samoylov achieved such perfection in this field that his laboratory at Kazan' University gained the reputation of being one of the best electrophysiological laboratories not only in Russia but in the whole world.

In this field he could be compared only with Einthoven himself, the founder of electrocardiography. "The Russian Einthoven" was what the foreign physiologists called Samoylov, including the ones in Holland, Einthoven's own country. More than once, the author heard this comparison in the physiological laboratories of many Dutch universities (and first of all in Leyden, the location of the famous Einthoven galvanometric installations).

We cite here two letters from the voluminous correspondence between Samoylov and Einthoven that give a vivid illustration of these two remarkable scientists, the founders of contemporary electrophysiology.

A. F. Samoylov's letter to Einthoven dated March 30, 1923:
"To Professor V. Einthoven: I am writing you to ask that you be good enough to transmit this letter to the esteemed galvanometer or at least to read its contents to the esteemed galvanometer because, as it is now known, the latter is capable of writing well and profusely (to be sure, not always distinctly enough and at times to great excess) — nevertheless it cannot read at all.
Most esteemed string galvanometer! Recently while looking through the Pflüger Archiv, I learned that you recorded the first electrocardiogram in 1903. It is customary to celebrate the 25th anniversary, but no one could forbid me to congratulate you on your 20th anniversary. I am sort of in love with you, and if a day passes without writing with you, I feel that something is missing. I am a frank person, and must confess that there have been moments when I, respected string galvanometer, wanted to smash you into a thousand pieces. Consequently. . . look here! Your metallic parts never irritated me, but. . . the string! When one finally gets ready to begin the experiment one discovers that the string refuses to conduct the current or begins to quiver as if somebody had frightened it, or as if it were overcome by an attack of malaria (we even tried quinine, but to no avail). In general the strings are very willful, and just like the strings of musical instruments, they fail to produce what is expected of them. Being a pianist, I know this only too well. An acquaintance of mine, a lady violinist in Leyden (a relative of yours through Professor Einthoven) could possibly also have something to say to you. But it is out of place to talk to a celebrant of an anniversary of anything other than his accomplishments. Much could be said of your great achievements in the field of physics and biology, but I shall refrain from touching upon this theme. On this solemn occasion I shall speak of your achievements in another field, and first of all in the field of linguistics. Here you

have created something marvelous: you have created the fantastic word "electrocardiogram." How beautiful and proud this word sounds and it must be noted it does so in all languages; thus it is international!

A group of children and grandchildren have gathered around this stem, "electrocardiogram," a series of other designations that are almost as beautiful and sonorous. I shall mention only a few: Electrogram, myoelectrogram, vagogram, vagoelectrogram, destrocardiogram, bielectrogram, levocardio-electro-gramo-phono-mono-di-tri. . . There is no need for me to elaborate further, the string speaks for itself. I now turn to your achievements in the field of industry. How many workers must extol your name while manufacturing thousands and thousands of meters of paper for you, etc.

My dear friend and colleague Einthoven! Kindly forgive me for this joke. If you and yours laugh over it, I shall be very pleased, for this was my intention. Life is serious and at times grave, and one should not lose his sense of humor, since it makes life easier.

Please give my regards to your wife and family. With cordial greetings, yours, A. Samoylov.

Einthoven's reply to A. F. Samoylov dated April 10, 1923:

My dear friend and colleague!

We all greatly enjoyed your letter of the 30th of last month. The whole family laughed heartily when reading it, and by chance my brother-in-law was here too—we had not seen him for several months. Everybody asked me to give you their regards and best wishes, and I was justly reproached for not answering you sooner.

The string galvanometer was delighted at your words of praise. He did not realize he was the reason for so much work by people. He told me that the difficulties concerning the strings may be obviated if you order them from the United States, where a mechanic manufactures them excellently. But while I was reading the galvanometer suddenly fell into a rage: "Me, not able to read? This is an intolerable and terrible libel. Do I not read the most hidden secrets of the human heart? And did I not succeed in reading distinctly and precisely a telegram for you from India? I soon calmed him down and asked him to be of even greater usefulness than he had been thus far.

My best wishes to you and your wife as well as to your dear friend Mislavskiy.[14] Devotedly yours, W. Einthoven.[15]

---

[14] N. A. Mislavskiy, professor on the medical faculty of Kazan' University, worked in Einthoven's laboratory and together with Samoylov contributed much to the development of electrocardiography in Russia.

[15] These letters are published in a translation by A. A. Samoylova who gave us the opportunity to acquaint ourselves with the texts in their entirety. Excerpts had been published by A. F. Samoylov in his article dedicated to W. Einthoven.

Samoylov, as did Einthoven, made a most successful use of the string galvanometer in the study of electrical phenomena in the healthy and in the sick heart. He was the first to introduce electrocardiography in Russia as a method of physiological and clinical investigation. He created in Kazan', and later in Moscow, an entire school of specialists in the field of electrocardiography.

Samoylov's merit is that he was one of the first in world physiology to apply the string galvanometer for the investigation of functions of the skeletal musculature of nerves and complex reflex acts. Here we must mention the great significance of Beritashvili's [Beritov's]electromyographic research, the results of which were first published in 1913 and contributed much new material for the understanding of the nature of the processes of excitation and inhibition of the spinal reflexes.[16] It is important to remember that Beritashvili had worked in Samoylov's Kazan' laboratory.

In the summer of 1930, Samoylov presented a paper at the All-Union Congress of Physiologists, Biochemists and Pharmacologists on "Electrophysiological Methods in the Theory of Reflexes." This report was one of the most outstanding summaries in the field of electrophysiology.[17]

Samoylov followed closely all the newest achievements in electrophysiological techniques and consistently maintained electrophysiological experimentation in his famous Kazan' laboratory on a high technical level.

Soon the string galvanometer was replaced by new instruments—oscillographs based on the use of systems of amplifying vacuum tubes that can amplify the bioelectrical currents hundreds, thousands, tens and hundreds of thousands of times and can lead them into a telephone, a loudspeaker, and capillary electrometer and also make photography possible. It was the capillary electrometer and not the string galvanometer into which the nerve current, amplified by a system of amplifier tubes, was directed in the apparatus of the English physiologist Adrian. In this regard we quote here from Samoylov's report to the All-Union Physiological Congress in 1930. "In general it seems to me that the use of cathode ray tubes for amplification of bioelectric reactions will push the string galvanometer to the background... The idea of replacing the string galvanometer with the capillary electrometer, which at one time had appeared to be a thing of the past, must be considered most fortunate. The amplified animal current may of course be fed into a telephone and a loudspeaker."[18]

These lines reflect the vivid history of physiological research. At the same time they revive a remarkable page in the history of electrophysiology

---

[16] J. Beritoff [Beritov (Beritashvili)]. Z. Biol. v. 62, 1913; ib. v. 64, 1914, ib. v. 80, 1924.
[17] A. F. Samoylov. See Achievements of Contemporary Biology v. I, issue 5-6, 1932, p. 178-201.
[18] Ibid., p. 198.

First row from l. to r. A. F. Samoylov and I. P. Pavlov.
In London during the Harvey celebrations after the reception by the king.

relating to the use of the capillary electrometer in which Samoylov had displayed a relentless interest for almost a half century; they demonstrate the complex and cyclical paths in the development of techniques for scientific research.

The impetus give by A. F. Samoylov showed many results in the development of Russian electrophysiology. Contingents of new electrophysiologists were created in Samoylov's laboratory (Kiselev, Yun'yev), as well as in the laboratories of Petersburg, Moscow, and Kiev Universities, and the Military-Medical Academy. The Russian physiologists established contact with outstanding electrophysiologists of other countries. N. A. Rozhanskiy worked in the laboratory of Lucas in England in 1914. During the Soviet period one of the most outstanding Soviet electrophysiologists, I. L. Kan, worked in Hill's laboratory, as did P. S. Kupalov. N. I. Grashchenko worked in Adrian's laboratory. Lazarev and his students' biophysical research broadened the theoretical problems of electrophysiology. Chagovets was the first to install precise electrophysiological instruments in Russia. Pravdich-Neminskiy was the first to use the galvanometer for the registration of bio-currents from the brain.

In recent years big centers for electrophysiological research have been founded, such as the one at the Brain Institute (Livanov), at the Institute imeni Pavlov at the Academy of Sceinces, USSR, in a number of physiological laboratories of VIEM (now the Academy of Medical Sciences); and in the Physiological Institute of Tbilisi University (Academician I. S. Beritashvili).

Samoylov's work on the crucial problem of nervous physiology, on the nature of processes of transmission of excitation from one kind of structures to others, is particularly outstanding.

In a brilliant article published in 1925 under the title "On the Passage of Excitation from the Motor Nerve to the Muscle,"[19] Samoylov expresses the proposition that "at the border between two cells, one of them secretes some unknown substance and this substance serves as a stimulating agent for the other cell." The article was preceded by a long and very precise study of the question of the temperature co-efficient of processes occurring at the point of transmission of excitation from the nerve endings to the muscles, on the basis of which Samoylov arrived at the conclusion with regard to the chemical nature of these processes.

Samoylov conducted these investigations at a time when physiological thought was occupied with a newly published theory (1921) of humoral transmission of the nervous excitation formulated by Otto Loewi. But Loewi's theory was based on experiments on the heart muscle and the autonomic nervous system. Samoylov was the first one in world literature to formulate the question of the chemical nature of transmission of excitation from the somatic nerve to the skeletal musculature, and almost 15 years after Samoylov's investigations this was confirmed by the

---

[19] Anthology in Honor of I. P. Pavlov's 75th Birthday, 1925.

experiments of the British physiologist Dale and by Feldberg.

Of still greater significance were Samoylov's investigations on the humoral nature of central inhibition. In the above-mentioned 1925 paper, Samoylov was the first to express the idea that in the synapses of the central nervous system "occurs a secretion of a special substance that elicits the effect of central inhibition." A year later, and independently of Samoylov, Sherrington[20] arrived at the same conclusion with regard to the humoral nature of central inhibition, as did other outstanding physiologists (Fulton, Liddell).

During the years 1925-1927, jointly with his disciple, the brilliant experimenter M. A. Kiselv,[21] Samoylov obtained decisive experimental data confirming his views with regard to the humoral nature of central inhibition.[22]

It is noteworthy that the outstanding English physiologist Adrian, whose views were the opposite of Samoylov's also accepted the humoral theory of intracentral processes of inhibition after the publication of Samoylov's work.

Thus, Samoylov shed a new light on a phenomenon that had concerned the Russian physiological school ever since Sechenov's discovery of central inhibition.

Because of his irreproachable special investigations, which were marked by astounding beauty and precision of experimental techniques, his brilliant and profound reports to international congresses, and his lectures for the students and physicians of Europe and America, Samoylov gained a tremendous authority among the best representatives of world physiology and electrocardiography.

In a letter to the Narkompros [ministry of education], the director of the electrocardiographic department of the central hospital in Boston (where Samoylov had read a series of lectures for physicians), Professor Weiss, wrote about Samoylov: "he is one of the greatest scientists of our times and we would be happy to see him among us again, should the

---

[20] C. Sherrington. Proc. Roy. Soc., v. 97, pp. 509-549.
[21] M. A. Kiselev was one of the most loyal of Samoylov's assistants. His unusual skill contributed greatly to science. M. A. Kiselev was a co-worker in the department of physiology at Kazan' and Moscow Universities, and for a short time he was also a professor at the Kazan' University. His untimely death did not give him the opportunity to materialize his creative ideas in the wonderful Kazan' physiological laboratory that he helped Samoylov to create.
[22] A. F. Samoylov and M. A. Kiselev. "Concerning the Characteristics of Central Processes of Inhibition." Journ. Exp. Biol. and Med. no. 15, 1927, pp. 35-49. Pflüg. Archiv, bd. 215, 1927.

opportunity present itself."[23]

During the last years of his life Samoylov combined his work at Kazan' University with duties at Moscow University, where he was elected chairman of the department of physiology on the physico-mathematical faculty. In 1930 he was to move to Moscow, but he died suddenly in July of the same year.[24]

In the medical faculty of Kazan' University, the department of physiology was headed by Samoylov's friend, a student and successor of N. O. Kovalevskiy, N. A. Mislavskiy (1854-1929).

Mislavskiy conducted his first significant investigations under the guidance of the famous neurologist and clinician V. M. Bekhterev (1857-1927).

In Kazan', where Bekhterev was confirmed as professor of psychiatry in 1886, he developed extensive experimental investigations, to which he attracted N. Mislavskiy. Jointly with Mislavskiy, Bekhterev published during the years 1886-1890[25] a whole series of investigations which demonstrated comprehensively the influence of the cerebral cortex on heart action and circulation, on salivation, and on the movements of the urinary bladder, as well as some articles on the central innervation of the intestines.

In 1898, Bekhterev proved the existence of a tear secretion center. In 1898, one of Bekhterev's students, V. P. Osipov, published his work on the presence of centers in the cerebral cortex related to the activity of the large intestine.[26] Bekhterev's work gained world recognition which to some extent found expression in his election to foreign academies and scientific societies. His classic works The Pathways of the Spinal Cord and the Brain and The Functions of the Brain have elevated to an unprecedented height the research concerning the physiology and morphology of the central nervous system.

Bekhterev's great merit and, before him, that of V. Ya. Danilevskiy (1852-1934), a professor at Khar'kov University, is that they established the existence of cortical brain centers having a direct relationship with regulation of the vegetative organs and processes. Danilevskiy was the first to demonstrate, in 1857,[27] the presence of a center in the frontal lobe of the cortex related to cardiac activity. Bekhterev, who devoted his first investigation to the problem of impaired thermoregulation in the

---

[23]The original of this letter is in the hands of A. A. Samoylova.
[24]See the special issue of the Journal of the Kazan' Medical Society dedicated to Samoylov's memory, 1931, nos. 4-5.
[25]W. Bechterew and N. Mislawski [V. Bekhterev and N. Mislavskiy]. Neurol. Zbl. 1886, 5, 193-195; ibid. -1890, v. 8, pp. 173-174; ibid. -1890, v. 9, pp. 195-199; Arch. Anat. Physiol. Leipzig (Physiol. Abt), pp. 380-393.
[26]Psychiatric Review, 1898, v. 3, pp. 193-200.
[27]W. Danilewsky [Danilevskiy]. Experimentelle Beiträge zur Physiologie des Gehirns. Pflüg. Arch. ges. Physiol., 1875, v. 11, pp. 128-158.

mentally ill (1879), published a physiological investigation in 1881 concerning the influence of the cerebral cortex on the body temperature,[28] and, later on, he published the investigations conducted jointly with Mislavskiy and Osipov.

The work begun by Danilevskiy's research also continued its development in Khar'kov. Here, in 1892, appeared the interesting monograph by Cherevkov specifically devoted to the new problem of cortical regulation of cardiovascular activity.

Thus, these Russian investigators were the first to pay attention to a most important brain function that is now being investigated with such persistence, particularly by the American physiologists, who are giving high priority to the question of cortical regulation of the so-called autonomic processes. Fulton's latest summary on the physiology of the nervous system, as well as current articles published in the American Journal of Neurophysiology, contain constant references to and recognition of the pathbreaking investigations of Russian physiologists, as well as mere repetitions of work that they had done long ago.

N. A. Mislavskiy devoted considerable attention to the problem of nervous regulation of the glands of internal secretion. Mislavskiy's discovery of the secretory nerve for the suprarenal glands and the secretory significance of the superior laryngeal nerve for the function of the thyroid gland are among the most significant achievements of Russian physiology.

In 1924, in Mislavskiy's laboratory, K. M. Bykov, a contemporary outstanding Soviet physiologist, together with Pavlova, developed a method of perfusion of the upper cervical sympathetic ganglion.[29] This method was of great importance in the study of the role of humoral factors in the transmission of impulses in the central nervous system. In 1933, the young Kazan' physiologist A. V. Kibyakov, using this method, "found that a nutrient solution obtained through the blood vessels of the superior cervical ganglion during stimulation of the cervical sympathetic nerves elicits a contraction of the nictitating membrane similar to that elicited by the stimulation itself when it is introduced into the carotid artery."[30]

For the first time in world literature this proved the chemical transmission of excitation from one neuron to the other.[31] Kibyakov's work fully reflects the influence of Samoylov, who was the first to pose the question of the chemical nature of transmission of stimulation from

---

[28] V. M. Bekhterev. "On temperature changes in the mentally ill." Herald of Med., 1879. Also: Der Einfluss der Hirnrinde auf die Körpertemperatur. St.-Pet. Med. Wochenschr. No. 25, 1881.

[29] Anthology Dedicated to I. P. Pavlov's 75th Birthday, pp. 413–426.

[30] W. Cannon. Some Conclusions from the Fact of Chemical Transmission of Nerve Impulses. Biomedgiz, 1935.

[31] A. V. Kibyakov - see Kazan' Med. Journ.: No. 5-6, 1936, p. 457; also: Pflüg. Arch., v. 232, 1933, p. 432.

one cell to the other.

On the whole, we had the opportunity to convince ourselves that the ideas concerning the chemical and physico-chemical nature of nerve excitation which dominate the minds of contemporary physiologists were to a great extent first suggested and substantiated by the physiologists of our country, and that the Kazan' physiological school has made a large contribution towards the development of this question.

The chemical theory of nervous excitation is being intensively developed at present in the laboratories of Orbeli, Bykov, Razenkov, Lena Stern, Beritov, and others.

The problems of neuro-humoral regulation and neuro-humoral connections began to occupy the center of attention in these laboratories. This trend of investigation of the principles of regulation of the activity of digestive glands has been particularly developed in the work of I. P. Razenkov and his collaborators.[32] L. S. Stern and her collaborators have also explored the problem of neurohumoral regulations on a broad general physiological basis in the specially organized Physiological Institute (1929) in Moscow. The investigations of this institute have led to conclusions of scientific and practical significance concerning the possibility of direct influence on the nervous centers.[33]

In recent years a more general evolutionary significance of the chemical theory of nervous excitation is reflected in a series of investigations by Soviet physiologists.

The problem of neurohumoral regulation is closely related to problems of physiology of glands of internal secretion. In this field the Russian scientists have made a great contribution to world science. We have already mentioned Mislavskiy's work on the innervation of the glands of internal secretion. Great significance is attributed in our times to the investigations of M. M. Zavadovskiy and B. M. Zavadovskiy in the field of physiology of glands of internal secretion. However, this area of physiology required special scrutiny and is not within the scope of these Essays. The bibliography appended to this volume supplies a number of sources dealing with this question.

---

[32] See for instance the volumes that were edited by I. P. Razenkov: On the Neurohumoral Regulation of Gastric Secretion pub. VIEM, 1936; On the Mechanism of Neurohumoral Connections MEDGIZ, 1940.

[33] See "Anthology of works" and Transactions of the Institute of Physiology, Narkompros, for the years 1934-1938.

CHAPTER XVIII

The classical work of I. P. Pavlov and his school in the field of physiology and digestion. Further development of investigations in this direction.

The minutes of the meeting of the zoological division of the Petersburg Society of Natural Scientists, dated February 28, 1876, carry the brief and dry entry: "3. Pavlov and Afanas'yev spoke of their investigation on the pancreas.[1]

The same minutes cover in detail the discussions of other reports from F.V. Ovsyannikov's physiological laboratory, where Pavlov and Afanas'yev had performed their investigations on the pancreas.

This was a great beginning: the 26-year old Pavlov had entered the very field of physiology that he was to transform later on. Like any beginning of something great and new, Pavlov's presentation passed with little notice by his contemporaries.

As a student of natural sciences at Petersburg University, Pavlov began to work in the physiological laboratory of this University, where intensive work in the various fields of physiology and histology was being performed under the direction of Professor F.V. Ovsyannikov. In the same laboratory, investigations concerning the digestive glands were also being conducted. It is interesting to note that in 1867 (when Pavlov was doing experimental work on the neural regulation of pancreatic activity), the student Lebedev completed his own work on the innervation of the pancreas. Lebedev's work has been completely forgotten by now: no references to it may be found even in Babkin's comprehensive summary of works on the physiology of the digestive glands. Yet, Lebedev was the first to prove that the sympathetic nerve acts as a secretory nerve for the pancreas.[2] Lebedev worked in collaboration with V.N. Velikiy. This minor historical detail indicates that Pavlov's work in the University laboratory did not start from scratch. The minutes indicate that Pavlov had attended the meeting of the zoological division of the Petersburg Society of Natural Scientists when Lebedev presented his report.

---

[1] Transact. St. Petersburg Soc. Natural Scientists, v. VII, 1876, p. XCV, proceedings of the session of January 22, 1876.

[2] Transact. St. Petersburg Soc. Natural Scientists, v. VII, 1876, p. XCVI.

At the meetings of this Society, the future great physiologist had the opportunity to acquaint himself with all trends in the work of Russian physiologists. Here the physiologists of the two basic physiological institutions of the 1870's, from Petersburg University and the Medical-Surgical Academy, used to meet and report on their work. Here they assembled once a month for evening meetings that at times lasted up to 3:00 a.m. and even later. Tarkhanov and Ovsyannikov, Voroshilov and Velikiy, Afanas'yev and Pavlov, Istomin and Fortunatov, as well as the disciples of Sechenov, Ovsyannikov, and Tarkhanov participated in the sharp discussions. Here also the students of the University and the Medico-Surgical Academy presented reports on their work.

At the end of 1875 (the beginning of I.P. Pavlov's scientific career), the scientific work of Russian physiologists in Petersburg was so intensive that on December 18, 1875, Professor I.R. Tarkhanov proposed that a special physiological section be formed in the zoological department of the St. Petersburg Society of Natural Scientists. Tarkhanov's proposal was considered by the council of the Society, which found it possible to form such a section. This decision was adopted on February 28, 1876, a day that should be considered as the beginning of the activities of the first physiological society in Russia.

In his early investigations, mostly in collaboration with Afanas'yev, Pavlov (like Lebedev before him) devoted himself not only to the problem of secretory influence of the nerves (sympathetic and vagus) on the pancreas but to the questions of reflex regulation of pancreatic secretion as well.[3]

The experiments with the pancreas, as well as the earlier experiments (with Velikiy) on the innervation of circulation (1874), convinced Pavlov of the limitations in the significance of results obtained in acute experiments and of the necessity of developing new methods of physiological research whereby an animal having experienced the effect of a surgical operation could recover from the surgery and only afterwards become the subject of investigations - in a healthy and lively condition.

Thus, Pavlov, in the third quarter of the past century, embarking on investigation of the digestive processes of animals, set for himself the task of creating new paths for investigation of this problem, deeply aware of the fact that new methods of investigation are the key to the attainment of new theoretical conclusions. Pavlov expressed himself on this subject as follows. "It has been said frequently, and justly so, that science moves in spurts, depending on the methodological achievements. With every forward step in methodology, we, so to speak, climb a rung higher from which a broader horizon reveals itself to us filled with hereto unseen objects. It is for this reason that the development of the new method was our first task."[4]

---

[3] M. Afanassieff und I. Pawlow [Afanas'ev and Pavlov]. Beiträge zur Physiologie der Bauchspeicheldrüse. Pflug. Arch., 1878, v. 16, p. 123.

[4] I.P. Pavlov. Lectures on the Function of the Main Digestive Glands, 3rd edition, 1924, p. 196.

Pavlov proceeded with exceptional energy to materialize his conceived plans experimentally, first of all with regard to new methods of study of the pancreas. In 1879 Pavlov published the results of his work on making a permanent fistula in the pancreas.[5] He was the first in the history of physiology to succeed in making a permanent fistula in a digestive gland as distinct from the temporary "permanent" fistulae that were made by his predecessors. Herein lies the difference between Pavlov's method and the method suggested before him by the German physiologists Weimann and Bernstein, and his technique became the basis for all future suggestions in this direction. As Babkin states, the method proposed by Heidenhain in 1886 for making a permanent fistula of the pancreas was identical in idea with the Pavlov method.

Continuing to work on pancreas, in 1890 Pavlov published the results of work done in collaboration with Shumova-Simanovskaya concerning the classic experiments with sham feeding. In these experiments pavlov succeeded for the first time in the history of physiology in obtaining pure gastric juice from an entirely healthy animal.[6] In the early 1890's Pavlov began his operations on the stomach and in 1894 published a method for isolating the "small stomach" while preserving its connection with the nervous system. We mention only Pavlov's important operations performed prior to the summary of his works in his classical Lectures on the Function of the Main Digestive Glands, 1897. But these principal and basic operations unveiled entirely new possibilities for the exploration of digestive processes in the normal organism.[7]

His oldest disciple, the late Soviet scientist A. F. Samoylov, spoke vividly of the manner in which Pavlov so thoroughly fulfilled his conceived plan of revising physiological investigations in the complex field of research on the digestive glands. In an address dedicated to Pavlov's 75th birthday, Samoylov stated: "I witnessed the development of the operation of the so-called small stomach. I remember my enchantment with Pavlov's daring and faith in the correctness of his surgical plan. At first the operation was unsuccessful, about 30 large dogs were sacrificed, much effort and time, almost 6 months, were expended without results, and the faint-hearted were already losing their courage. I remember that some professors in related disciplines asserted that this operation cannot and will not be successful because the location of the blood vessels of the stomach contradicts the idea of such an operation. Ivan Petrovich just roared with laughter at such statements the way only Pavlov can laugh; a few more efforts and the operation was a success."[8]

---

[5] I.P. Pavlov. "New methods for making a pancreatic fistula." Transact. St. Petersburg Soc. Natural Scientists, v. II, 1879, p. 51.

[6] I.P. Pavlov and Ye. O. Shumova-Simanovskaya. "Innervation of the Gastric Glands of the Dogs." Medic, 1890, No. 41.

[7] The essential details of these significant dates in the history of Russian physiology were repeatedly illuminated in our press. See B. Babkin. External Secretion of the Digestive Glands. OGIZ, 1922.

[8] A.F. Samoylov. "A General Description of I.P. Pavlov's Research Personality." Journ. Experim. Biol., series B., v. I, issue 1-2, 1925, p. 10.

The successful isolation through surgery of the small stomach, with preservation of nerve connections, was a major step in the history of the physiology of digestion. Pavlov succeeded where Heidenhain failed; the latter's method did not assure preservation of the innervation of the small stomach. In this difficult task Pavlov had the invaluable assistance of his disciple P.P. Khizhin, whose dissertation gave a description of the entire surgical technique for isolating the small stomach. This description alone covers four pages of small type; separately, the laborious task of "cutting" and "sewing up" is described. The work required much energy, concentration, and patience. On the average, such an operation took about four hours. Up to 200 stiches were taken. Khizhin reminisces that "the concentration and patience of the participants in the surgery were subjected to a severe test."

Pavlov's classical curves presenting the gastric secretions elicited by meat, bread, and milk were first obtained on the dog Druzhok[Little Friend]—one of the first to survive the Pavlov-Khizhin operation.

As a result of these searches for new procedures in physiological research, the Pavlov surgical method in physiology, a major achievement in the natural sciences at the end of the 19th century, was born. In order to understand the enormous significance of this trend, it suffices to point out that, during the period of Pavlov's work towards perfecting the surgical method, the so-called vivisection method was prevalent, whereby the functions of individual isolated organs were studied; and it was precisely against this vivisection method, which disturbed the integrity of the organism, that Pavlov's work was directed to find a surgical method that would permit observation of physiological phenomena in the whole organism.

It must be emphasized here that the results attained by Pavlov in the development of methods for the study of digestive processes now commonly used in physiological laboratories are important precisely as an affirmation of the great significance of the study of the animal organism as a whole. Herein lies Pavlov's great advantage over his predecessors (Basov, Blondlot, Claude Bernard, the school of Ludwig, and Heidenhain), who also worked on the so-called fistular metholodogy. We know that research in the field of fistular methodology did not begin in the 19th century but considerably earlier, in the 17th century (Graaf); and the significance of Pavlov's achievements does not stem from the fact that he hereby perfected already existing procedures in fistular methodology, but rather that he saw in it the basis for an integrated study of physiological processes. This extremely important biological trend of studying the whole organism characterizes not only the period of Pavlov's work on the digestive glands but the whole approach of the Pavlovian school to the most complex problem of conditioned reflexes.

For us it is of special importance that the surgical method of research developed by Pavlov was, in his words an expression of "physiological thinking." And it is thanks to this "physiological thinking" that Pavlov became one of the few representatives of integrated study of physiological processes at the end of the 19th and beginning of the 20th century, the golden age of analytical physiology. And therefore it was not just by accident that he related the development of this method of physiological research to the development of synthetic physiology. The well-known physiologist A.F. Samoylov tells in his memoirs of these subjective experiences of Pavlov the scientist in a period of struggle for investigation of the physiology of the animal with preservation of the integrity of the system.

"Once, soon after I began working in this laboratory, I was reading some article in the library of the Institute. Ivan Petrovich came in. He began to look through the new journals rapidly. I observed that something had irked him. Holding a journal in his hands, he read the titles of the articles and remarked irritably: 'Sure, if one works on such problems and such material he shall not get very far!' He threw the magazine on the table and added, as he was leaving: 'My eyes should not have seen all this!'

I was greatly puzzled. Instantly I took the irritating issue and began to examine its content. There were reports on investigations on separate cells, on muscles, on nerves, and discussions on the nature of excitability and conductivity. To me all this appeared highly interesting and valuable. I confess that now, 30 years later, I view it in the same manner as then. The general physiology of excitable tissues justifies its existence and does not require any special defense. But I think I understand the reasons for Pavlov's disapproval and even hostility toward this approach to physiological research.

All these investigations, which dealt with isolated parts of the body, appeared to him much too remote from the animal mechanism as a whole, to him they seemed too abstract, outdated, and devoid in his view of any urgency. His talent steered him in an entirely different direction and it is most fortunate for the development of science that Pavlov was able to and dared to reject some aspects of the physiological trends that were in his way. He thus was able to devote himself all the more to that aspect which attracted him most. The field of phenomena wherein he felt most at ease embraces the animal organism as a whole, in its relationship to the environment surrounding and affecting it, and this represents the strong biological tendency of the Pavlov genius. He placed the highest value on experimentation on the whole, non-anesthetized animal, an animal with its normal reactions to stimulation, an animal that is alert and in good spirits." [9]

It must be noted that Pavlov was the first in the history of physiology to succeed in proving beyond a doubt the presence of special secretory fibers in the vagus and sympathetic nerves. The history of the research into the mechanism of excitation of the pancreas is of particular interest; the presence of secretory pancreatic fibers was described by Pavlov as early as 1888. With the discovery of the humoral mechanism of pancreatic excitation by the British physiologists Bayliss and Starling (the discovery of secretin in 1902), the latter questioned Pavlov's experiments, which

---

[9] Ibid., pp. 7-8.

they were inclined to attribute to the penetration of hydrochloric acid from the stomach into the duodenum upon stimulation of the nerve and consequently to pancreatic excitation by secretin formed under the influence of hydrochloric acid. However, the English investigators failed to take into account that in the Pavlovian laboratory since 1896 all experiments dealing with the effect of nerve stimulation on the secretory function of the pancreas were performed under conditions including separation of the pylorus from the duodenum in order to prevent the passage of gastric acids into the duodenum. Subsequently, however, Anrep, a disciple of Pavlov's, was able to demonstrate to the English physiologists the presence of secretory fibers leading to the pancreas in the composition of the vagus, which was then definitely accepted.

Meanwhile, Pavlov appointed V.V. Savich to verify Bayliss' and Starling's findings concerning the purely humoral excitation of the pancreas without participation of the nervous system and had to accept the findings of the British investigators.

In this connection, in his preface to the second edition of his Lectures on the Function of the Main Digestive Glands (1917), Pavlov wrote: "The next item that must be amended is the concept dealing with the mechanism of the effect of acid as the principal stimulant of the pancreas. Years ago, on the basis of reliable facts, we decided that we were dealing here with reflex stimulation of the gland by acid from the mucous membrane of the upper portion of the small intestine. A chance experiment by the British physiologists (Bayliss and Starling) led them to the discovery of an entirely new and entirely unexpected mechanism. They discovered that the acid absorbed through the mucous membrane of the upper portion of the small intestine extracts from it a special substance (secretin) that collects there and that is carried by the blood to the pancreatic cells; this substance directly stimulates the secretory activity of these cells. As a result there was a very significant broadening of the concept of the excitatory mechanism of the digestive glands: in addition to the indisputable nervous mechanism linking the gland with its elementary stimulants, there emerged a purely chemical mechanism that operates through the general body fluids, blood and lymph,—what is now called humoral mechanism."

As a result of nearly 25 years of work on the physiology of digestion, Pavlov published two major works that were of exceptional significance in the development of world physiology. These are first of all the book Lectures on the Function of the Main Digestive Glands (1897) and the long article, in German, "Physiological Surgery of the Digestive Tract" (1902).[10] These works created not only a new trend in the physiology of digestion but also a new "surgical trend" in experimental biology as a whole. This is the evaluation given to Pavlov's work by one of the most outstanding experimental surgeons of the 20th Century, the American surgeon Carrel.[11]

---

[10] I. Pawlow [Pavlov]. Erg. der Physiologie, 1902, v. I.

[11] It is interesting that not all contemporaries were able to appreciate fully the enormous significance of Pavlov's monograph Lectures on the Work of the Main Digestive Glands. Thus the famous anatomist P.F. Lesgaft, in his review of this work, was very critical of Pavlov's basic

During the 22-year-period between Pavlov's first modest experiments in the field of physiology of digestion (1875) and the publication of his classical work Lectures on the Function of the Main Digestive Glands (1897), Pavlov and his disciples described a number of facts in the field of physiology of the digestive glands that shed a light on the chaos that prevailed in this field of Pavlov's investigations. It is known that these investigations became the foundation for contemporary views on neural and chemical regulation of the digestive process. They supplied a clear understanding of the sequence of digestive processes in the various sections of the gastrointestinal tract. They also provided data and new discoveries in the field of the actual fermenting processes that occur in the intestinal tract (discovery of enterokinase). These investigations clearly demonstrated the dependence of the nature of secretion of various glands on the kind of food stimulus (Pavlov's classical curves of secretion); they laid the foundation for profound biological investigations concerning the adaptation of the glands of the digestive tract to qualitatively different prolonged feeding.

The classical Pavlovian curves of secretion in response to various nutrient stimuli, astounding in their consistency in tens of thousands of experiments, have become an inalienable component of exact natural science of our times.[1,2] The scope of Pavlov's work astounded his contemporaries. Little wonder that I. Munk, the famous German physiologist, wrote in a review on Pavlov's Lectures on the Function of the Main Digestive Glands: "Since Heidenhain's time there had not been another investigator who made in a few years so many discoveries in physiology as are described in Pavlov's book."[13]

The astounding scope and pace of the work done by Pavlov and his students is to be attributed to the creative teamwork characteristic of the Pavlovian school.

Let us listen to the testimony of the disciples themselves. Here we have, for instance, one of the Pavlovian disciples Zavriyev. He completed his dissertation in 1901 and in the concluding paragraph made a statement that is characteristic of the sentiment of all his coworkers. "Only one who has worked in Pavlov's physiological laboratory at the Institute of Experimental Medicine can understand the significance of the favorable

---

postulates and facts. See Rep. St. Petersburg Biol. Lab., v. II, issue 2, 1897, pp. 57-69.

[1,2]We find it necessary to present here a roster of 22 Pavlovian coworkers whose investigations formed the basis for Pavlov's classical "Lectures." Here are these names: N.M. Bekker, A.A. Val'ter, V.N. Vasilyev, D.L. Glinskiy, N.I. Damaskin, I.L. Dolinskiy, N. Ya. Ketcher, P.N. Konovalov, P.D. Kuvshinskiy, V.V. Kudrevestskiy, I.O. Lobasov, S.G. Mett, L.B. Popel'skiy, N.V. Ryazantsev, A.F. Samoylov, A.S. Sanotskiy, V.G. Ushakov, P.P. Khizhin, I.O. Shirokikh, Ye. O. Shumova-Simanovskaya, N.P. Yurgens, Yu. M. Yablonskiy.

[13]Quoted from A.F. Samoylov. See Journ. Experimental Biol. series B, v. I, issue 1-2, 1925, p. 10.

atmosphere that every coworker enters. Only he understands what sort of guide-innovator he finds in the person of the director of the laboratory, Professor Pavlov. Only he knows that in moments of disappointment, unavoidable in scientific work, he will always find the friendly support of the laboratory assistant, Ye. A. Ganike, as well as of all other coworkers in the laboratory. This relieves at times difficult chores of the investigator and fills his heart with gratitude to all the laboratory personnel, not excluding the maintenance men.''

In those times, physicians, after a certain period of practical experience, were assigned to clinics and laboratories to prepare their dissertation for the academic degree of doctor in medical sciences. It was considered a special honor to write a dissertation under Professor Ivan Petrovich Pavlov, whose fame as a teacher and scientist was growing to greater and greater dimensions. Usually at least two or three physicians were assigned to the Pavlovian laboratory annually. They worked together harmoniously, often working through the night, and shared with their teacher the hardships and joys of the work. The names of nearly all the student-aspirants who worked with Pavlov at that time in the field of physiology of digestion are to be forever inscribed in the annals of physiological science. Together with these disciples, whose number grew constantly, Pavlov created the theory of the physiology of digestion. As we have seen, quite a few major discoveries are credited, of course, to Pavlov as a teacher of genius and to the one student who directly obtained these facts through his own experimentation, and to the whole team of workers headed by Pavlov, since no laboratory problem was worked out behind closed doors by any one person, isolated from the others. No, indeed, on the contrary, what was done by one belonged to everyone in the laboratory and became the object of untiring concern for the master and his coworkers. It was of this very atmosphere of team work that Pavlov wrote much later: ''We are all engaged in a common task and everyone progresses to the extent of his strength and ability. Here we frequently are unable to distinguish between what is 'mine' and what is 'thine' but this only enhances our common task.''

The investigations of Pavlov and his disciples of the chemism of digestive processes were also rewarded with remarkable results. Suffice it to mention the discovery of enterokinase by Pavlov and Shepoval'nikov. The discovery of enterokinase was a new milestone in physiological chemistry, since it led to the discovery of a hitherto unknown class of phenomena, i.e., the activation of ferment action. Although at the present time enterokinase is not considered a coferment, the discovery of enterokinase was the beginning of work in this field.

It is difficult to overestimate Pavlov's significance in the development of the physiological chemistry of digestion. It can be stated without exaggeration that all of the latest achievements in this field became possible only after the achievements of Pavlov and his school. The Pavlovian Lectures on the Function of the Main Digestive Glands were translated into many foreign languages. B. P. Babkin's book External Secretion of the Digestive Glands has been published in a number of editions and various foreign languages (in Europe and America in the last 30 years, guiding all research in this important field of digestion along Pavlovian principles.

During the period of his investigations in the field of physiology of digestion, Pavlov's views on the relationship between physiology and medicine were formed and gained great scientific and practical significance. Together with his coworkers he observed for hours on end the work of digestive glands, and Pavlov as a natural scientist derived profound satisfaction in discovering the truly remarkable pattern of their function. He wrote: "Indeed, by now secretion under identical conditions has taken on a truly stereotyped character. The strong impression of such an almost physical precision in a complex process is one of the pleasant distractions during the many hours of observation of the functioning glands." In a speech dedicated to S.P. Botkin's memory in 1899, again emphasizing "the astounding beauty" that reveals itself before the investigator while observing the normal course of the digestive process, Pavlov keenly posed the question: "Should we, as experimenters, be satisfied with this? I do not think so. Is it not natural when observing the deviations from the normal and having thoroughly studied their mechanism that one should desire to reverse them to normal? This alone is the last test of the fullness of your physiological knowledge and a measure of your command of the subject."

And, as if concentrating his thoughts on the necessity of a very close relationship between theory and practice, and on the fact that the final confirmation of a physiological theory lies in its test by medicine, he declared in the same address: "When a mechanic completes his study of some machine, he submits to a test consisting of assembling the dismantled machine. The same should apply to the physiologist. Only he who was able to restore an impaired life process back to normal has the right to affirm that he has mastered the knowledge about life.[14]

This clear purposefulness of Pavlov the experimenter, in the study of the mechanism in order to control it, to restore to normal a process disturbed by a pathological agent, created the scientific basis of experimental therapy. Experimental therapy in Pavlov's words "is in substance a verification of physiological findings."

Convinced of the enormous significance of the experiment in the study of processes in the normal organism, Pavlov became an ardent proponent of the experimental method in the field of medicine. "Only through the fire of experimentation, can medicine become what it should be, namely intelligent and consequently always acting purposefully... Therefore I have the audacity to predict that the progress of medicine in any country, in any scientific or teaching medical institution will be measured by the attention and interest it devotes to experimental medicine." Thus it is not by chance that we find Pavlov among the founders of the Institute of Experimental Medicine.

Indeed, Pavlov's immense work in the field of physiology of digestion was crowned, in 1904, with the highest worldwide reward for a scientist—

---

[14] I.P. Pavlov. Lectures on the Functions of the Main Digestive Glands, 3rd edition, p. 34.

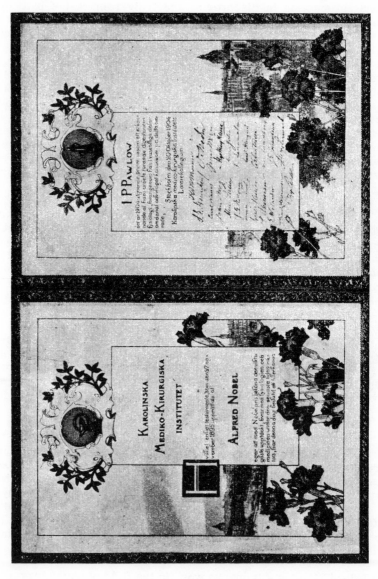

I. P. Pavlov's Nobel Prize Diploma.

the Nobel Prize. The second natural scientist who was awarded the Nobel Prize in 1904 was the outstanding physicist of our times, W. Ramsey.

At that time Pavlov was the only Nobel Laureate among Russian scientists. Later on the same award was given to only one other Russian, Mechnikov (1908). Pavlov's Nobel Prize diploma was the first one to include a text in the Russian language. It read:

"The Caroline Medico-Surgical Institute, according to the will executed 15/27 November 1895 by

Alfred Nobel,

having the right to award the Nobel Prize for important discoveries that in recent times have enriched physiology and medicine, has resolved on this date to award a prize, in this year 1904, to

Ivan Petrovich Pavlov

in recognition of his works on the physiology of digestion with which works he transformed and broadened substantially the knowledge in this field.

Stockholm
7/20 October, 1904
The Professorial Council of the
Caroline Medico-Surgical Institute.

The whole world acclaimed Pavlov as a great physiologist. The students of Cambridge University, who once presented Charles Darwin with a toy monkey, presented Pavlov with a toy dog trimmed with fistular tubes when he received an honorary doctorate from Cambridge University.

Here is what the participants of this event have to say. I quote here from a personal letter* written to me by the famous British physiologist, Professor Archibald Hill, who was one of the participants in the dog presentation and supplied me with some detailed data of this event. He wrote:

---

*Upon writing to Professor Hill for a copy of the original letter in English written by him to Dr. Koshtoyants, I received the following reply: "University College London, Gower Street WC1, Physiology Department, 12th October, 1961. Dear Dr. Boder, I am sure I have no copy of the letter I wrote to Koshtoyants. But the essentials of the story can be found on p. 161 of my book "The Ethical Dilemma of Science" published last year by the Rockefeller Institute Press, New York. It was reprinted there from the British Medical Journal 7 March 1936, p. 508-9. Yours sincerely, A.V. Hill." Instead of giving an indirect translation from the Russian we reproduce here Dr. Hill's English text from "The Ethical Dilemma of Science," p. 161. DPB.

"Here is a story about him which is not generally known. About 1912 Pavlov came to Cambridge to get an honorary degree - I forget the exact occasion. The students of physiology at that time knew his name very well in connection with his work on digestion. They thought they would have to do something to improve the occasion of the degree-giving. They went to a toyshop and bought a large and life-like dog, which they proceeded to decorate with rubber stoppers, glass tubes, pieces of rubber tubing, and any other physical, chemical, or physiological appliance that they could think of. They took it to the Senate House and suspended it from gallery to gallery by a long string. As Pavlov walked away, having received his degree, they let it down to him on the string. He was highly delighted, took the dog from the string, and carried it away under his arm. Later on that day I was talking to him at a party (I think it was in the Hall of Christ's College), and he repeatedly said how delighted he was at what he thought was the greatest honor that had ever been done him! 'Why, even the students know of my work!' That he continued to feel the greatness of the honor is shown by the fact that for many years he kept that dog in his study in Leningrad, as I was told by one of his colleagues more than ten years later." [The Koshtoyants version contains one additional sentence attributed to Dr. Hill: "Of all this I have retained only a rather general impression but I hope that the details I have cited are correct."]

During the ceremony and the awarding of the degree of honorary doctor of Cambridge University to Pavlov the speaker delivered a short greeting in Latin which we present here in translation. The speaker said:

"At the beginning of our solemn gathering, seeing here so many famous guests of our Royal Society who have come here to Cambridge after the celebration of the hundredth anniversary of the Royal Society we greet them in the name of our entire Academy. Thus each and every one of you is being welcomed by our University, this world of Bacon, Newton and other past and present famous men in the realm of natural history. At the sight of so many famous workers in science, so different one from another, who have come from so many countries of the globe to our shores and even to the groves of our Academy, there emerges before us again the truth of the words of the prophet who said: 'Many men will pass before us and many-sided shall knowledge be.' Our Senate has decided to confer our high scientific degree, as part of our celebration, which honor will be glorified by the presence of all of you and as we hope confirmed by the benevolent consent of all of you, to certain delegates from among those famous guests of ours who have come from different peoples, who represent such different sciences.

"Honorable chancellor, chairman of the Senate and the whole Academy!

"From the vast country of the Russians who are so far from us and at the same time so near through our common endeavors, there has arrived the Petersburg professor of physiology who has investigated the general

288

laws of the digestive processes; for this work he has created a very special institution and founded a most brilliant school of men working in the field of physiology. Not to mention the fact that he has excellently demonstrated that the juices for the digestion of food require not only circulation and changes under psychic influences but are even adapted to every kind of food, resist noxious elements and cause an opposing effect. We have seen how Prudentius narrates in a certain heroic poem about the struggle of the soul; but the struggle of the body, the inner partnership of the psychic and physical have been glorified, as we all heard, by this man [Pavlov]. On the basis of the work of such scientists we may accept with much greater conviction the directions of the famous Cornelius Celsus, who says: 'First of all let each know the nature of his body.' I present to you the outstanding professor of physiology, Ivan Petrovich Pavlov.'' [15]

At the turn of our century Pavlov devoted himself entirely to the elaboration of the important problems related to the theory of conditioned reflexes. At the beginning of chapter XIV we dwelt in detail on the historical link between Pavlov's investigations in the field of physiology of digestion and the theory of conditioned reflexes.

The newly discovered field of phenomena took a progressively greater hold over Pavlov's thinking. He saw the broad possibilities of revealing the secrets of brain function. The conditioned reflexes of the digestive glands which he had discovered served as the foundation on which he began to erect the gradiose structure of physiology.

Having once become aware of the new possibilities of scientific development, having discovered this new and unknown field and the difficulty of investigation in this field, Pavlov irrevocably decided to devote himself solely to it. Everything else was to be abandoned by him and by his coworkers.

In 1905, at the climax of elaboration of the basic principles of conditioned reflexes, Pavlov categorically prohibited the continuation of any work on digestion. He stopped operating himself and forbade others to perform surgery connected with the study of digestive processes.

He no longer accepted new students desirous of studying the physiology of digestion. And there were many such applicants, since Pavlov's work in this direction was extremely fascinating. A few of Pavlov's collaborators could not drop work they had begun, even though Pavlov demanded it. Then those who were particularly inspired by their teacher in the field of the physiology of digestion began to conduct their experiments in secret, in remote rooms of the laboratory. This is understandable. It was impossible to stop the current created in science by Pavlov which held the promise of so many new discoveries. The Pavlovian trend in the field of physiology of digestion continued to develop further without him through the work of his disciples and followers.

---

[15] The original text of this address in Latin was first published in my book ''A Story from the Life of Academician Pavlov,'' 1937.

An indication of the development of the physiology of digestion in the Pavlovian direction was the consistently growing roster of authors in successive editions of Lectures on the Function of the Main Digestive Glands after 1897. It includes the names of L.A. Orbeli and V.V. Savich, who made a valuable contribution for the further understanding of the digestive mechanism. Later on G.V. Fol'bort described the new pathways of neural regulation of gastric secretion from the sympathetic nervous system. I.P. Razenkov and his collaborators contributed much towards the understanding of the humoral regulation of the secretion of the gastric and pancreatic glands. S.I. Chechulin restated the question of secretion of gastric glands in response to mechanical stimulation.

The investigations of V.N. Boldyrev, who worked first in Kazan' and then in I.P. Pavlov's laboratory, were of great significance in the development of an important chapter in the physiology of the gastrointestinal tract, specifically the periodic nature of its activity. His work has received worldwide recognition.

While Pavlov and his numerous coworkers, using the fistular method, had given a comprehensive picture of the mechanism of function of the gastrointestinal tract, E.S. London (1868-1940) and his collaborators, using the same method, obtained very valuable data on the chemism of digestibility and ways of absorption of various nutrient substances. Later on, London developed the worldwide recognized method of making "fistulae" on vessels, so-called angiostomy or vasostomy. This method made it possible, for the first time, to observe the dynamics of penetration into the blood of the products of digestion from the intestine, as well as to study the dynamics of chemical transformation of individual organs by way of angiostomy of the vessels of these organs. The angiostomy method developed by London and his disciples was and still is widely used in the laboratories of Europe and U.S.A. and has given very valuable results.

In the Soviet period, great strides have been made in the development of research in the field of physiology of digestion of farm animals. I.S. Tsitovich first applied the fistular method to studies of digestion of birds in Pavlov's laboratory. In recent years the fistular method has given very valuable results in the study of the physiology of digestion in many farm animals (horses, cattle, pigs, etc.).

Great progress has also been made by Soviet physiologists in research on the physiology of digestion in the lower vertebrates (fish, amphibia [A.I. Smirnov], reptiles), using the Pavlovian methods and based on the theoretical achievements of the Pavlovian school.

CHAPTER XIX

Problems of physiology of circulation. Discovery of the Tsion brothers, and Ludwig. Theory of reflex regulation of blood circulation. Pavlov's investigation. The Kazan' school of physiologists and histologists.

In the broadly explored physiological field of circulation of the blood, Russian physiologists conducted investigations that were of exceptional significance. This work was performed during the second half of the 19th century in close connection with the laboratory of the originator of the most outstanding physiological school of the 19th century, Professor Karl Ludwig, who, after Harvey, can be considered the most outstanding investigator in the field of the physiology of circulation. The Russian scientists, and first of all I.F. Tsion and I.P. Pavlov, both disciples of Ludwig, actually laid the basis for the contemporary concept of reflex regulation of the cardiovascular system.

In 1866, the Tsion brothers, together with Ludwig, discovered the "cardio-sensory" nerve, or the depressor nerve, the stimulation of the central end of which elicits reflex reaction as expressed by a sharp drop in blood pressure and dilatation of the blood vessels.[1] The work of I.F. Tsion that first described a new type of relationships between the heart and the blood vessels, i.e., the reflex type from the sensory nerves of the heart to the motor nerves of the blood vessels, was awarded the first Montyon prize of the Paris Academy of Sciences. This was an investigation which in fact disclosed a new page in the history of physiology. And up to present times questions of reflex regulation of circulation have occupied the center of attention of world physiology.

The experiments of Ludwig and Pavlov were performed on rabbits, and it is in these animals that they discovered the existence of a special nerve trunk, the stimulation of the central end of which produces the above-mentioned depressor effect. The discovery of the depressor nerve and of the new form of reflex relationships aroused, as was to be expected, much interest among the physiologists of many countries who, of course, first of all proceeded to verify the existence of this depressor nerve and its physiological significance in various other animals. Such comparative data in the early 1880's gave rise to a number of contradictions that were overcome, thanks to a number of experimental investigations by V.I. Vartanov jointly with N.O. Tsybul'skiy; their results

---

[1] E. Cyon [I. Tsion] u. C. Ludwig. Die Reflexe eines der sensibilen Nerven des Herzens auf die motorische der Blutgefässe. Ber. Sächs. Gesell. d. Wiss., v. 18, p. 307, 1866.

were presented in a report under the title "On the Relationship Between the Depressor and Vagus Nerves" at a session of the Society of Naturalists (December 4, 1882). Having completed an extensive anatomo-physiological investigation, Vartanov and Tsybul'skiy came to the conclusion that the variation in results of stimulation of the central end of the depressor nerve depends on the distribution of fibers having various physiological effects on the cardiovascular system in the common trunk of the vagus into which the depressor nerve enters.

As has already been noted by Academician L. Orbeli in his introductory article to the first volume of Pavlov's works, the latter had discovered much earlier than many contemporary foreign scientists, in his experimental investigations on the regulation of circulation conducted during the 1880's, the then unknown aspects of reflex regulation of circulation.

In joint investigations with V.N. Velikiy (1851-1904), reported in such articles as "On the Influence of the Laryngeal Nerve on Circulation" and "On the Centripetal Accelerators of Heart Beat" (both articles were published in 1874),[2] Pavlov first brought up the possibility of reflex increase in activity of the cardiovascular system, i.e., of a pressor action. This broadened and enhanced the significance of the Tsion brothers' and Ludwig's discovery of this important physiological phenomenon.

As early as 1877, Pavlov published in Pflügers Archiv an article under the meaningful title "Experimental Data Concerning the Mechanism of Accommodation of Blood Vessels," in which he brought forward the extremely important idea of reflex adaptation of the activity of the heart and blood vessels. Pavlov conducted this research, as well as a number of other works of that period, in the physiological laboratory of Professor A.O. Ustimovich, one of the first Russian physiological research laboratories. It is interesting to note that in his book on the history of physiology the Mexican physiologist, Izquierdo, mentions Ustimovich along with Pavlov as the organizer of physiological research in Russia.

Analyzing the significance of Pavlov's works in this field, L.A. Orbeli writes: "This work is imbued with one basic idea, the idea of self-regulation of the apparatus of circulation; an idea that has become most fashionable and never fails to appear on the pages of physiological journals since the 1920's after Hering's discovery of the sinus nerve. Meanwhile in Pavlov's and Velikiy's work we already find the established facts of the existence of centripetal nerves that reflexively accelerate heart action just as the depressor nerves of Ludwig and Tsion elicit a reflex slowing of the heart and dilation of the cardiac channel."[3]

---

[2] Trans. of the St. Petersburg Society of Natural Scientists, v. V, 1874, p. LXVI. See also: I.P. Pavlov. Complete Works, v. I, Pub. AS, USSR, 1940, p. 35.

[3] I.P. Pavlov. Complete Works, v. I, p. 13, (introduction by L.A. Orbeli).

N. O. Kovalevskiy (1840–1891).

V.N. Velikiy (like Pavlov) studied in the natural science faculty of Petersburg University and, together with Pavlov, started his work in physiology under the guidance of F.V. Ovsyannikov. During his student years Velikiy was Ovsyannikov's assistant and later on worked with him in the physiological laboratory of the Academy of Sciences. Velikiy's independent works include some interesting research on the physiology and anatomy of lymph hearts and lymph transformation and, in particular, investigations demonstrating the influence of the accelerator and depressor nerves on lymph circulation.

The innovatory role of Russian physiologists in the formulation of the most important contemporary physiological problem, the reflex regulation of the cardiovascular system, is witnessed by I.M. Sechenov's works and those of the Kazan' professor I.M. Dogiel (1830-1916) in the 1860's. In his research on the depressing reflex action resulting from stimulation of the center he discovered, Sechenov proved that stimulation of the center leads to depression not only of reflex activity of the body muscles but also of cardiac activity. He demonstrated the latter on the blood heart of the frog, while his student P.V. Suslova established the same on the lymph hearts of the same animals.

Just how important Sechenov considered these investigations may be seen in a letter that he wrote on October 31, 1867 to his wife, M.A. Sechenova-Bokova. The letter begins with the following statements:

"Congratulate me... this morning the whole structure of the lymph hearts and the inhibiting mechanisms was crowned with brilliant success. Upon stimulation of the transverse section of the optic thalamus (the same place from which according to my previous experiments inhibition of reflexes is produced) of four frogs, I obtained a diastolic stoppage of all four lymph hearts, a similar stoppage of the blood heart and together with it occurs a depression of the cerebrospinal reflexes. I nearly choked from joy because these experiments, as you must understand, finally solve the whole question concerning the existence of inhibitory centers in the brain."

In 1873, the journal Centralblatt f. d. wissensch. Med. (No. 11 and 19) published two excellent communications on the subject of the inhibitory cardiac nerves, signed by Sechenov and Mechnikov.

These joint experimental investigations by Sechenov and Mechnikov refer to the period of their meeting in Graz. Mechnikov was astounded by "the experiment of the white lady," while Sechenov, for the purpose of clarification of the relationships between the various sectors of the central nervous system in the phenomena of depression of spinal reflexes, stubbornly pursued the search for general characteristics in the relationships between the central and peripheral nervous apparatus participating in the depression of cardiac activity. Hence the attempt to analyze experimentally the nature of the depressor effect of the vagus nerve on the heart.

During the same period (1866), I.M. Dogiel's important article was published in the Reicherts Archive, under the title "On the Influence of Chloroform on the Animal Organism as a Whole and Especially on the Movement of the Eyeballs,"[4] in which it was demonstrated for the first time that in the rabbit a reflex stoppage of heart action can be obtained by stimulation (in experiments with chloroform) of the sensory endings of the nasal mucosa. A. Schweitzer,[5] in a very recent summary on the autonomic reflexes, recognizes that the work mentioned by Dogiel paved the way for the study of reflex regulation of cardiac activity, as did the classical experiment by Goltz, who obtained a heart stoppage by mechanical stimulation of the abdominal organs.

For several decades, an array of outstanding physiologists worked on the analysis of ways and means of realization of the cardiac reflex discovered by I.M. Dogiel. Having dedicated himself to the study of physiology and pharmacology of heart action, much later, in 1894, I.M. Dogiel published his comparative-physiological investigations demonstrating that reflex influences on the heart also exist in invertebrates, and that the reflex depression of heart action may be elicited in such animals (the crayfish type in Dogiel's experiments), even upon stimulation of any part of their body.[6]

I.M. Dogiel, an offspring of the Medical-Surgical Academy, defended his doctoral dissertation at Moscow University and became one of the most outstanding representatives of experimental physiology and pharmacology at Kazan' University. His work exercised an enormous influence on the development of contemporary physiology (general and comparative) and especially of pharmacology.

In 1879-1880, V.K. Anrep's interesting investigations on the formation of the depressor action of nerves on cardiac activity appeared in print. In his experiments, Anrep, for the first time, presented a comprehensive description of the remarkable phenomenon of absence of influence of the vagus nerves on the animal heart during the first few days of post-natal life, and this was demonstrated by experiments with stimulation of the vagus with induction currents, as well as transection of these nerves or atropinization of the animals. Although Anrep was in the department of forensic medicine, first at the Khar'kov University and subsequently at the Clinical Institute in Petersburg, much of his work pertains to physiology and pharmacology.

At Kazan' University, extensive research in the field of regulation of circulation was developed by F.V. Ovsyannikov's successor, the remarkable Russian physiologist N.O. Kovalevskiy (1840-1891), son of a professor at the same university, O.N. Kovalevskiy, the first Russian scholar on Mongolia. N.O. Kovalevskiy, together with Ovsyannikov, must be considered the founder of the Kazan' physiological school that produced later

---

[4] Reicherts Arch. 1866, p. 231 and 415.

[5] A. Schweitzer. Die Irradiation autonomer Reflexe. Basel, 1937, p. 182.

[6] Arch. Mikroskop. Anat., v. 43, p. 223, 1894.

on a pleiad of excellent Russian physiologists. His undergraduate research, published under the title "Anatomico-Physiological Investigations
of the Spleen" in 1860, has not lost its scientific significance up to this
day. To a large extent under Kovalevskiy's guidance, the classical dissertation of one of the best Russian opthalmologists, Dr. Ye. V. Adamyuk,
on the subject of intraocular pressure (published in 1865), was completed
at the Kazan' Physiological Laboratory. In 1865 the young Kovalevskiy
was appointed extraordinary professor and three years later ordinary
professor of physiology at Kazan' University. Up to his death he was most
active in university affairs, and at the beginning of the 1880's he was appointed rector.

In 1868 Kovalevskiy published his paper in the field of reflex regulation of circulation. This paper was dedicated to the Tsion-Ludwig nerve.
In this period of formulation of the theory of reflex regulation of the
cardiovascular system, Kovalevskiy was the first to approach comprehensively the problem of relationships between the condition of the
cardiovascular system and pulmonary activity. As an example, we can
cite his work, executed jointly with Navalikhin, on the subject 'The Influence of Changes in Gas Metabolism in the Lungs on the Pressure in
the /blood/ Vessels (1869) and the article published in Pflügers Archiv
in 1870 on the subject of variations in circulation under conditions of
breath-holding, and, finally, his large work Data on the Influence of
Respiration on Circulation that appeared in the transactions of the Kazan'
Society of Natural Scientists in 1877. In the light of contemporary concepts concerning the reflex connections between the respiratory and
cardiovascular systems, the Kovalevskiy investigations cited referable
to the 1870's acquire great significance. There is no doubt that the work of
Russian physiologists and histologists that made a valuable contribution to
the field of neuroreflectory regulation of the cardiovascular system is
distinctly influenced to this day by F.V. Ovsyannikov, I.M. Dogiel, and
N.O. Kovalevskiy.

The discovery by physiologists of the special centripetal cardiac and
vascular nerves and of the reflex regulation of the cardiovascular system
were a prerequisite for the search of the corresponding morphological
nervous structures in the heart and in the vessels. Of great significance
in the development of this physiologically and histologically important
problem were the investigations of Russian histologists and, first of all,
the representatives of the Kazan' histological school, the founder of which
was K.A. Arnshteyn. Working in close contact with the physiological
laboratory of professor N.A. Mislavskiy, this group of investigators
achieved exceptional results. In 1895-1900 the histological investigations
of A. Ye. Smirnov indicating the presence of sensory elements in the
cardiovascular system were published.[7]

In 1897, in Petersburg, an alumnus of Kazan' University and famous
histologist A.S. Dogiel (1852-1922) presented a paper to the Society of
Russian Physicians under the title "The Endings of Sensory Nerves in the
Heart and Blood Vessels of Mammals."

---

[7] A. Ye. Smirnov. Anat. Anz., Bd. X, 1895; Bd. XXXV, 1900.

In a discussion of this paper I.P. Pavlov stated in part: "It is with understandable gratification that the physiologists hear of the discovery of sensory nerve endings in the heart because such a discovery has vividly demonstrated the substance of their reasoning and assumptions. What the physiologists could only imagine has now become visible: the results of physiological investigations were in perfect agreement with the histological data since the discovery of the sensory nerves in the heart is explained by the existence of cardiac reflexes. But in this respect physiology goes much further than histology; it classifies the cardiac reflexes by their properties. Now it has been recognized that four reflex phenomena may emanate from the heart: slowing and acceleration of contractions, drop and rise of blood pressure. This probably is not the whole picture; possibly there are cardiac reflexes with yet different properties, but in this respect physiological thinking is already uncertain. For this reason I as a physiologist should like to know whether there is any indication of such heterogenous origins of these reflexes in the anatomical structure of the discovered nerve endings."[8]

This excerpt from Pavlov's commentary on Dogiel's paper is of utmost significance, since it proves that Pavlov, even at the end of the past century, had clearly delineated the morpho-physiological problems that arise in connection with the discovery of sensory elements in the reflexogenic zones of the heart and vessels.

The latest investigations of a number of foreign authors, on the one hand, are developing the histological discoveries of the Kazan' histological school and, on the other hand, thoroughly confirm Pavlov's physiological findings concerning the fine morphologo-physiological differences in the sensory elements lying at the basis of reflex influences on the cardiovascular system.

Great strides have been made recently in this direction in the histological research of B.I. Lavrent'yev (1892-1943), in the morphological investigations of G.P. Ivanov, and in the physiological experiments of K.M. Bykov, V.V. Parin, and their collaborators.

No less significant was the research done by Russian histologists and physiologists on the histo-physiology of the centripetal cardiac nerves. In 1944, one of the best contemporary histophysiologists, B.I. Lavrent'yev, wrote, and with good reason: "One may note with great satisfaction that the most important facts concerning the neural apparatuses of the heart and the vessels were discovered by Russian science. All that is available on this question in the foreign literature is, without any exaggeration, either a repetition of what has been done by Russian scientists or a minor addition. I have in mind the investigations of the Russian schools founded by Arnshteyn, Dogiel, Mislavskiy and others."

As to the principle problems of histophysiology of the centripetal cardiac nerves, this refers first of all to the interrelationships between

---

[8] I.P. Pavlov. Complete Works, v. I, 1940, p. 279.

extracardial and intracardial nervous elements. V.V. Nikolayev, working in the Kazan' University laboratory, was the first (1893) to demonstrate, by means of transection of the vagi and subsequent observation of the phenomena of regeneration of nervous elements, that fibers of the vagus terminate on the nerve cells within the cardiac ganglia and that the intracardiac nervous apparatus undergoes regeneration after transection of the vagus nerve.[9] To this same problem was devoted the monograph of the Kazan' physiologist, D.V. Polumordvinov, that appeared in 1909 under the title "On the Transfer of Excitation from the Auricles to the Ventricle of the Frog's Heart" (Kazan'), and another by his disciple I.P. Razenkov, who demonstrated the same phenomena in the heart of warm-blooded animals.[10] The fine and complex question of the interrelationships between the sympathetic nervous system and the heart was recently explored in great detail by B.I. Lavrent'yev and his disciples and was reported in B.I. Lavrent'yev's excellent monograph Morphology of the Autonomic Nervous System (1940).

A important place in the research of Russian physiologists was given to problems of vascular innervation. In 1842, a few years before the classic works of Claude Bernard, a student of N.I. Pirogov, subsequently a professor of Kiev University, A.P. Val'ter, published his investigation "On the Significance of Sympathetic Nerve Fibers Included in the Frog's Sciatic Nerve," where for the first time the relationship of the sympathetic nerves to the blood vessels was demonstrated. In Claude Bernard's laboratory a number of Russian physicians and physiologists participated in the experimental investigations of this great French physiologist, to whom belongs the honor of discovering and defining the role of the sympathetic nervous system in the regulation of the functions of vessels and its vasoconstricting effect. These investigations of Claude Bernard were first published in 1853.

For a long time the question of the nature of nervous influences leading to vasodilatation remained obscure. Only at the end of the 19th century did facts begin to appear, indicating the presence of fibers within the posterior roots that have a vasodilating effect. Thus was formulated the theory of antidromic action of the posterior roots. One of the first works concerning this phenomenon is credited to N.M. Verzilov, who, in 1896, published his investigation in the Zentralblatt für Physiologie under the title "The Problem of the Vasomotor Function of the Posterior Roots." It is known that the classical work of the English physiologist W.M. Bayliss on the vasomotor action of the posterior roots that led him to the formulation of the theory of antidromic function appeared at the beginning of the 20th century. In his first communication, published in 1901,[11] Bayliss refers to Verzilov's experiments of 1896.

---

[9] V.V. Nikolayev. On the Problem of Innervation of the Frog Heart. Herald of Neurophysiology, 1894, No. 16; the same article was reprinted in Arch. f. Anat. u. Physiol. Physiol. Abt. 1893, Supplementband.

[10] I.P. Razenkov. On the Physiology of the Intracardiac Nervous Apparatus. Separate reprint, 1922.

[11] W.M. Bayliss. On the Origin from the Spinal Cord of the Vasodilator Fibers of the Hind-limb...J. Physiol., 1901, v. 26, p. 173.

In 1871 F. Ovsyannikov's work appeared in the German language under the title "On the Tonic and Reflex Centers of the Vascular Nerves," [12] in which, for the first time with the necessary experimental proof, he demonstrated the presence of nerve centers regulating blood pressure in the vessels, i.e., the presence of vasomotor centers. In 1876, A. Ostroumov published his experimental investigation "Experiments on the Inhibitory Vascular Nerves," [13] which, along with Ovsyannikov's research, represent the beginning of a series of investigations in this important branch of the physiology of circulatory regulation, in Russia as well as abroad. As we have stated before, it was precisely in that period, in 1875, that V. Ya. Danilevskiy's work was published; it, along with Schiff's investigation, first raises the question concerning the presence of centers in the cerebral cortex regulating heart action, and somewhat later there appeared the work of Bekhterev and his collaborators in the same direction.

Of great significance are the investigations of Russian scientists in the field of cardiac physiology. We have already mentioned A.F. Samoylov and his disciples in connection with this topic. The outstanding research on the physiology of the isolated heart in warm-blooded animals is particularly noteworthy. Attempts were undertaken in this direction in K. Ludwig's laboratory, but the results were so unsuccessful that the famous physiologist categorically declared that the heart of mammals was absolutely unsuitable for experiments with artificial circulation.

However, this declaration did not stop the courageous physiologists, among them Dr. Stol'nikov, who developed in Ludwig's laboratory a number of new methods for the study of circulation, and Pavlov. On the basis of the method that Stol'nikov[14] used for the determination of the speed of blood flow in the aorta, Pavlov developed and published, in 1888, a new method for the physiological isolation of the heart. This consisted essentially of replacing the greater circulation by an artificial device in such a manner that normal defibrinated blood circulated in the closed vascular channel, and the gas content of this blood was restored by its passage through the lungs by means of artificial respiration. Thus, many years before the British physiologist Starling, Pavlov developed a method of physiological isolation of the heart which is now called the Starling cardiopulmonary preparation. The details of this method were described in a dissertation by the Pavlovian student N. Ya. Chistovich.[15]

The academician L.A. Orbeli, in his introductory chapter to the first edition of Pavlov's works, called attention to this important historical

---

[12] Die tonichen und reflectorisch. Centra der Gefässnerven. Ber. d. sächs. Ges. d. Wiss. Math.-Physik. Abth., Mai, 1871.

[13] A. Ostroumoff. Versuche über Hemmungsnerven. Arch. f. d. ges. Physiol., v. XI, 1876, p. 252.

[14] Stolnikow. Die Eilung des Blutstromes in der Aorta des Hundes. Arch. für Anat. und Physiol., 1886.

[15] Chistovich, N. Ya. Dissertation. SPb., 1888. (pp. 78-79 and 103-104).

fact, and he also mentioned that Pavlov, much before Howell, pointed out the feasibility of forming anticoagulant substances in pulmonary tissue.

A special place is occupied by the investigations of one of Ovsyannikov's collaborators, the outstanding physiologist A.A. Kulyabko (1866-1930), professor of physiology at Kazan' and Tomsk universities. Soon after Locke's remarkable demonstrations, at the Fifth International Congress of Physiology in September 1901, of experiments with the survival of the rabbit's heart in a salt solution (for as long as 12 hours), Kulyabko started his own experiments with the isolated animal heart in October 1901.

In a series of carefully executed experimental investigations with the isolated hearts of various animals (fish, birds, mammals), Kulyabko solved a number of physiological and pharmacological problems concerning the activity of the isolated heart, the results of which were presented in a detailed form in 1904 in a work under the title "Pharmacological and Toxicological Investigations on an Excised Heart" (Annals of the Academy of Sciences, v. XVI, no. 7).

In 1902, in the Proceedings of the Academy of Sciences, v. XVII, appeared a remarkable communication by Kulyabko under the title "Further Experiments on the Resuscitation of the Heart. Resuscitation of the Human Heart," in which, for the first time, exact experimental data were presented concerning this problem of such concern to medicine as well as physiology. The first experiments on the excised human heart were performed on the hearts of stillborn premature infants in the seventh-eighth month, which were given to Kulyabko by Professor I.N. Grammatikati. Although the possibility of maintaining life in the isolated heart of warm-blooded animals had already been raised before Kulyabko, and although Gley had published his observations on a human heart from a man shortly after he had been guillotined shortly before Kulyabko's experiments, still, Kulyabko's experiments, by the daring formulation of the problem and by his precise observations, made a tremendous impression and became the basis for numerous subsequent attempts to resuscitate human hearts, as well as other organs, and even whole animals. The very promising experiments of Soviet and foreign investigators in the field of resuscitation of animals and humans will make use of all the rich experience in the physiology of the central nervous system, the physiology of neuro-reflex regulation of cardiovascular systems, in the accumulation of which Russian scientists are among the leaders.[16]

An important role in the development of the experimental trend in research of the physiology (as well as pathophysiology) of the cardiovascular

---

[16] The first to pose the question of exploration of the physiological properties of the surviving nervous system was V. Ya. Danilevskiy. In his article "Experiments on Postmortem Excitability of the Nervous Apparatuses of the Mammal Heart" (1904), he demonstrated the preservation of excitability of the vagus of the rabbit heart for 24 hours after death.

system (and lymph circulation) was played by the Moscow laboratory of the famous pathologist, A.B. Focht (1848-1930). The dissertations and monographs published under his guidance are of great interest to this day from the standpoint of their conclusions as well as of methodology.

Problems referring to the physiology of nervous regulation of cardiac function have been developed in recent times through the work of A.I. Smirnov and his collaborators, while the methodology of cardiac microscopy developed by the Leningrad physiologist Gramenitskiy has opened new horizons in the study of the physiology of cardiac activity.

CHAPTER XX

Development of views on the trophic influences of the nervous system. Basic sources and contemporary achievements.

I.P. Pavlov's investigations in the field of physiology of cardiac innervation are of great significance for the general theory of physiology of the nervous system, and he presented some very important theoretical conclusions in his classical work The Centrifugal Nerves of the Heart (1883),[1] which was his doctoral dissertation. While investigating in detail the effect on the heart of intensifying (sympathetic) and depressing (parasympathetic) nerves Pavlov became convinced that, along with nervous influences on the heart resulting in acceleration or slowing of the rhythm of the sections of the heart, there are other neural influences affecting the functional activity of both the cardiac muscle and of its conductive system. The latter type of neural influence manifests itself in that, as a consequence of stimulation, for instance, of the sympathetic nerve, there is not only acceleration and intensification of cardiac activity but also an increase of speed of pervasion of excitation over the various sections of the heart.

At the beginning of the 1880's, Pavlov demonstrated his experiments to the most outstanding Russian physiologists: Sechenov, Tarkhanov, and Ovsyannikov, as well as to the famous clinician Botkin. These experiments permitted him to draw the conclusion, entirely new in physiology, that "the work of the heart is governed by four centrifugal nerves with the respective functions of slowing, accelerating, weakening and intensifying." "The manuscript of this work," wrote Pavlov at the beginning of his article On the Centrifugal Nerves of the Heart in the journal Arch. für Anatomie u. Physiologie for 1887, "was ready for publication in 1881." In September of 1882, The Weekly Clinical Gazette published a special investigation by Pavlov on the pharmacology of the heart, in which he presents his views on the special form of nervous influence (special nerve fibers in the composition of the sympathetic and vagus nerves) on the heart. In October of the same year, Pavlov demonstrated to the zoological section of the Society of Naturalists at Petersburg University his curves dealing with experiments of stimulation of various branches of the cardiac nerves. The first preliminary communication on the subject was made by Pavlov in the German language in Zentralblatt für die med. Wissensch, in 1883. Pavlov made a comprehensive presentation of all the conclusions

---

[1] I.P. Pavlov. Complete Works, vol. I, 1940. Pub. AS USSR, pp.57, 142.

and extensive experimental data in his classical work The Centrifugal Nerves of the Heart, published in the form of a dissertation for the degree of doctor of medicine in 1883. Pavlov performed his experiments on warm-blooded animals and terminated them in 1881. In 1882 (the year of publication of Pavlov's communication in the Weekly Clinical Gazette), a preliminary communication appeared in print in the English Physiological Journal by the English physiologist Gaskell, who on the basis of his own experiments on the effect of nerve stimulation on the turtle's heart came to the same conclusions as Pavlov. On the basis of these facts, there can be no doubt as to Pavlov's priority or the originality of his investigations. This was pointed out by Pavlov himself in a note to the concluding chapter of his dissertation, in which he cites the dates and emphasizes that he read Gaskell's article published in the August issue of the English Physiological Journal for 1882 only at the beginning of 1883. Almost 40 years later, in December of 1920, in his address "On Trophic Innervation,"[3] Pavlov, on the basis of cited experiments on cardiac innervation, as well as on the basis of his vast experience accumulated during many years of observation on the consequences of operations on the internal organs, and, finally, on the basis of numerous observations on the changes in the chemical composition of saliva under the influence of the secretory nerves, amplified and raised to a high theoretical level the concept of trophic influence of the nervous system. This theory exercised a great influence on the development of normal and pathological physiology of the nervous system and pathology in general in our country.

The experimental substantiation of trophic influence on the nervous system was first supplied by Magendie's experiments; he demonstrated significant changes in the condition of the cornea after intracranial transection of the trigeminal nerve. Magendie himself explained his disturbance in the condition of the cornea by the fact that denervation of the organ leads to marked disturbances in its nutrition. Claude Bernard continued his teacher's investigations, observing for long periods the consequences of trigeminal transection, and described in detail a series of disturbances in the mucosa of the mouth, the lips, etc., demonstrating trophic influence.

These remarkable experiments and the conclusions drawn from them concerning the special influence of the nervous system on tissues and organs attracted the attention of progressive physicians and influenced the formulation by the clinicists of special theoretical views concerning the role of the nervous system and, in particular, of the trophic nerves in the development of pathological states.

It is particularly interesting that these views were developed in the 1850's by outstanding Russian physicians and, among them, the professor of surgery at Moscow University F.I. Inozemtsev. This is confirmed by

---

[2] Ibid., p. 179.

[3] Ibid., p. 402; paper read on the 31st of December, 1920 in Petrograd at the meeting in honor of the 50th year of Professor A.A. Nechayev's scientific activity.

statements in Sechenov's Autobiographical Notes referring to Inozemtsev: "At his clinical lectures we heard that at certain times a definite genius morborum always reigns, constituting the basic characteristic of all illnesses in general. Thus in Broussais' times (1772-1838) in his own words there was a reign of the inflammatory type, while at present we observe predominantly poor nutrition of the body with catarrh of the mucous tissues which indicates that in nearly all people the ganglionic system governing nutrition is involved. Inozemtsev apparently acquired the latter idea during his student years; but just how he linked catarrh with sympathetic nerve involvement I do not know... Although at the time F.I. labelled ganglionic system involvement as the genius morborum the idea of sympathetic nerve influence on the nutrition of the body was questioned rather than proved by physiological investigations, it was pardonable for him, as a surgeon and old practitioner not to know this; consequently, the theory he formulated was no worse than other medical theories and at any rate characterized F.I. as a thinking physician given to the consideration of serious problems."[4] These reminiscences refer to the years 1853-1854. In the genesis of Pavlov's ideas as to the trophic influence of the nervous system, it seems important to note that in those years Inozemtsev's lectures were attended by the famous therapeutist S.P. Botkin, whose views concerning the role of the nervous system in the development of pathological processes played an important role in the formation of Pavlov's views.

From a historical standpoint, Pavlov's closing lines in his classical work Centrifugal Nerves of the Heart are particularly significant. He wrote: "The idea of this investigation and its fulfillment is mine alone. But I was surrounded by Professor Botkin's clinical ideas and with sincere gratitude I recognize the fruitful influence on this work as well as on my physiological views in general of one whose profound and broad views on nervism preceding the experimental data and in my opinion it is a most important service that Sergey Petrovich [Botkin] has rendered to physiology." In a footnote Pavlov adds: "By nervism I mean the trend in physiology which tends to extend the influence of the nervous system over the largest possible number of organic functions."

As early as 1859, Einbrodt, a classmate of Sechenov's in Moscow University and subsequently a professor of physiology at the same University, published his investigation demonstrating the presence of fibers within the vagus which have a trophic influence on the heart muscle.[5]

The first most comprehensive summary of facts concerning the trophic influence of the nervous system and the theoretical conclusions on the role of this trophic influence in normal and pathological organic processes in animals and man was given in Samuel's book in 1860.[6] This work instigated intensive elaboration of the theory of trophic influence of the nervous system.

[4] I.M. Sechenov. Autobiographical Notes, pub. AS USSR, 1945, pp.61-62.
[5] Einbrodt. Arch. f. Anat. u. Physiol. 1859, p. 439.
[6] Samual. Die trophischen Nerven. Ein Beitrag zur Physiologie und Pathologie. Liepzig, 1860.

The participation of Russian physicians and physiologists in the research dealing with this first important milestone in the formulation of physiological concepts of trophic influence of the nervous system was of great significance. Six years after the publication of Samuel's work, one of the first experimental investigations was conducted in this direction by the Russian physiologist-physicist, S.I. Lamanskiy (the translator of Focht's Physiological Letters), who was the first to succeed, in experiments on a dog, in removing the abdominal sympathetic ganglia and in observing the animal for many months after surgery. Lamanskiy's work was published in 1866;[7] in it he reports some very interesting observations on the changes in the condition of the operated animal, and on the basis of these observations he offers a broad physiological concept on the role of the sympathetic ganglia in maintaining normal nutrition of the animal's tissues.

In the following year, N.P. Obolenskiy (subsequently the famous founder of the therapeutic school at Khar'kov University) published an article describing his experiments on dogs and rabbits in which he transected the nerves of one of the testes; two to three weeks later, he found very pronounced atrophic processes on the side corresponding to the transection. Obolenskiy also describes a clinical case of one-sided atrophy of the testes in man as a consequence of degenerative phenomena in the nerve on the corresponding side.[8]

In the early 1870's the question of trophic influence of the nervous system came to the attention of F.V. Ovsyannikov's laboratory, where I.P. Pavlov had just begun his scientific research. Upon Ovsyannikov's suggestion and under his direct guidance, Ya. M. Chistoserdov executed in the University's physiological laboratory an extensive experimental investigation for the purpose of clarifying the causes of changes occurring in the eye after transection of the trigeminal nerve. Analyzing this classical example of trophic influence on the nervous system which had been first described by Magendie, Chistoserdov arrived at an important conclusion on the role of the lacrimal gland in the process of these disturbances. Chistoserdov presented his rich store of factual data and theoretical conclusions at the first meeting of the newly organized physiological section of the St. Petersburg Society of Natural Scientists on January 22, 1876.[9] Pavlov was also present at this meeting; as may be seen from the minutes, he participated in the discussion of I. R. Tarkhanov's paper on the influence of compressed air, oxygen, and carbonic acid on the nervous excitability.

In the same year, 1876, Ya. M. Chistoserdov was appointed, together with V.N. Velikiy, as laboratory assistant in the department of physiology at Petersburg University and became one of Sechenov's first assistants, the latter just having begun his lectures at the University. The problem

---

[7] Lamansky, Ztschr. f. rat. Med., 1866, v. XXXIII (3), p. 59.

[8] Obolensky, Centralbl. f. d. med. Wiss. 1867, p. 497.

[9] Transactions of the St. Petersburg Society of Natural Scientists, v. VII, 1876, pp. 97-101.

Opening of the XVth International Physiological Congress (Leningrad, 1935). At the table of the presiding officers: Lapicque, Pavlov, Hill; at the lectern reading his paper, L. A. Orbeli.

306

first posed by Chistoserdov on the possible role of functional disturbances in the lacrimal gland (as a result of denervation) in the development of trophic corneal disorders acquires a particular interest in connection with new data on the therapeutic properties of tears as a source of lysozyme.

In 1878 Kassovich published an investigation in which he demonstrates noticeable changes in the bones of the extremities after transection of the sciatic nerve.[10]

Now we approach directly the period when I.P. Pavlov worked on the problems that led him to comprehend the complex essence of trophic influence of the nervous system. This occurred during 1879-1881. We see that in 1881 Pavlov's manuscript presenting his ideas on the complexity and versatility of cardiac nerve function was already ready for publication.

Thus the Russian physiologists and physicians who preceded Pavlov prepared the ground for the development of the theory of trophic influence of the nervous system. Moreover, we saw that in the laboratory where Pavlov began his scientific researches, Ovsyannikov and Chistoserdov performed experiments on the mechanism of trophic influence of the nervous system. Consequently, Ovsyannikov's role as Pavlov's teacher was of much greater significance then is usually considered.

Botkin transmitted to Pavlov views that the former had acquired from Inozemtsev with regard to the role of the nervous system in the genesis of disturbances in organic functions, while Pavlov, under Ovsyannikov's influence, became interested in the experimental exploration of this problem. The rest of Pavlov's discoveries and the most substantial among them were achieved by Pavlov thanks to his own intensive efforts. In his work the theory of the trophic influence of the nervous system reached an exceptional depth and was extremely fruitful for physiology as well as for medicine.

Since 1923, Pavlov's closest disciple, L.A. Orbeli (born 1882), with his own numerous disciples, in our times produced the most convincing experimental proofs of the influence of stimulation of the sympathetic nerve on the basic functional processes in the tissue (especially in the skeletal muscles). L.A. Orbeli's Sympathetic Innervation of the Skeletal Muscles published in 1923[11] (on the basis of experiments performed jointly with A. G. Ginetsinskiy), has initiated a new trend in the physiological research on the nervous system. The most striking of the numerous series of experiments conducted in Orbeli's laboratory is the experiment of eliminating fatigue (incurred as a consequence of reported contractions) from a skeletal muscle by additional stimulation of the sympathetic fibers. This experiment obtained international recognition as "the Orbeli-Ginetsinskiy phenomenon." L.A. Orbeli published the results of his investigations on the physiology of the nervous system in 1933 in the book Lectures on the

---

[10] Kassowitz. Centralbl. f. d. med. Wiss. 1878, p. 790.
[11] L.A. Orbeli "Reports from the Lesgaft Scientific Institute," v. VI, 1923, p. 1.

Physiology of the Nervous System, which was subsequently published in a number of editions and has played a great role in the development of contemporary investigations of the physiology of the vegetative nervous system.

As to the trends of development of the problem of trophic influence of the nervous system, only recently L.A. Orbeli reported on them in a paper from which we present an excerpt.

"In the Orbeli school the problem of the trophic role of the nervous system was developed in four different directions. First, a series of projects (Ginetsinskiy, Strel'tsov, Gershuni, Khudorozheva) proved that the sympathetic fibers exercise influences, analogous to those known for the cardiac muscle, on the skeletal musculature causing changes in the thresholds of excitability, reducing the chronaxie and increasing the developing tension, extending the work period, restoring efficiency in fatigue, etc., in other words, influencing the basic functional properties of the muscular tissues. Further on it was revealed that the 'adaptive,' in Orbeli's terminology, influence also takes place with regard to the peripheral nerves, the receptors and the entire central nervous system from the spinal cord to the cortex of the cerebral hemispheres, and this constitutes the basic and universal function of the sympathetic system (Tonkikh, Kunstman, Savich, Krestovnikov, Speranskaya-Stepanova, Gershuni, Vorob'yev and others). Second, in a series of investigations it was established that at the basis of these changes in functional properties ("adaptive" influences) lies the influence of the sympathetic system on the physico-chemical properties—electroconductivity (Lebedinskiy, Aleksanyan, Mikhaleva), elastic-viscous properties (Lebedinskiy and N.I. Mikhel'son) and metabolism (Orbeli, Yushchenko, Tonkikh, Kunstman, Kreps and collaborators), i.e., the trophic influence.

"Thirdly, the analogous effects of the cerebellum have been demonstrated and the facts of interaction of the sympathetic system and the cerebellum have been determined, and a clarification of the role of the cerebellum as a universal regulator and stabilizer not only of motor functions but of functions of all sensory and vegetative activities has been obtained (Voronin, Zimkina, Saprokhin, Tetyayeva and Yankovskaya).

"Fourth, the peculiar antidromic trophic function of fibers within the posterior root (sensory) fibers was clarified (Sonin, Saprokhin), and the relative role of individual types of fibers in the maintenance of normal trophicity in the development of dystrophic processes was determined (Bekauri, Lebedinskiy and collaborators). The application of the evolutionary principle and the parallel utilization of ontogenic data (Klaas, Khudorozheva), phylogeny and experimental surgical methods (Ginetsinskiy, N.I. Mikhel'son, Itina, Chenykayeva, Sharmarina, R. Leybson, Voskresenskaya)—all these made it possible for Orbeli to create a definite conception of the evolution of the neuromuscular apparatus...

"Petrova, after many years (10 to 15) of systematic observation on the same dogs, demonstrated that conditioned reflex work which is strenuous and difficult for the dogs, in addition to certain functional disturbances of the nervous system, leads to the appearance of a number of trophic disturbances such as loss of hair, itches and eczematic phenomena on the skin, cutaneous papillomas, lipomas, spasms of the sphincters and abnormal segmentation of the digestive tract, ulceration of the mucosa and further on to significant acceleration of appearance of pre-cancerous processes and cancer-like neoplasms in the skin under the influence of cancerogenic agents. The Tomsk school of Popov and Bayandurov, by means of partial extirpation of cortical and subcortical ganglia in the cerebrum determined the extremely powerful trophic role of the striate region with regard to its influence on metabolism and on the process of development of birds and mammals in the early postnatal period."[12]

The problem of the trophic influence of the nervous system became the center of experimental investigations of another Pavlovian disciple, the Academician A.D. Speranskiy, and his numerous coworkers. In 1930, Speranskiy, in his work The Nervous System in Pathology, for the first time advanced a broad plan for a new approach to the understanding of the pathogenesis of various illnesses and therapeutic methods based on the theory of the trophic influence of the nervous system. Speranskiy summarized his views in 1935 in his book Elements of Construction of a Theory of Medicine, which covers the broad scope of his experimental work and that of his disciples.[13]

Thanks to Orbeli's and Speranskiy's investigations, the theory of trophic influence of the nervous system was deeply and usefully rooted into the theory and practice of Soviet physicians.

Thus, Magendie's daring experiment in the early 1800's, of intracranial transection of the trigeminal nerve, and his subsequent observations on the state of the cornea; the theoretical foresight of the Russian clinician Inozemtsev in the 1850's; Lamanskiy's and Obolenskiy's experiments in the 1860's; the extremely interesting experiments of the student Chistoserdov in Ovsyannikov's laboratory dealing with the analysis of the Magendie phenomena; Pavlov's constant communication with the clinician Botkin (a disciple of Inozemtsev)—all this laid the foundation for the contemporary theory of trophic influence of the nervous system. In the development of this theory a special place belongs to Soviet physiology.

The significance and application of the theory of trophic influence of the nervous system not exhausted by far. While it has penetrated firmly into the field of experimental medicine, the field of experimental biology has not yet experienced to a full measure the influence of this theory. Meanwhile, a number of major questions on the role of the nervous system in the processes of a formative nature, i.e., processes concerning the

---

[12] L.A. Orbeli. The Academician Ivan Petrovich Pavlov and the Russian physiological school. Address at the jubilee session of AS USSR, Moscow-Leningrad, 1945, pub. AS USSR, pp. 10-11.
[13] In 1935 this book was published in the English language by VIEM on the occasion of the XVth International Physiological Congress.

development of organisms, may gain new insight in the light of the theory of trophic influence of the nervous system. But I have discussed this problem in a special article dedicated to the memory of the great teacher, I.P. Pavlov, and I refer to it the reader interested in this aspect of the development of the theory of trophic influence of the nervous system.[14]

[14]Kh. S. Koshtoyants. "The trophic influence of the nervous system in the ontogenesis of animals." Physiolog. Jour., USSR, v. XXIV, issue 1-2, p. 222, 1938.

CHAPTER XXI

The basic milestones in the development of evolutionary physiology.

During the first half of the 19th century, physiology was confronted with specific problems: in studying the pattern of function, physiology was struggling for materialism, for the understanding of the physics and chemistry of life processes. However, although it was historically necessary as a progressive step in the development of physiology, this period also harbored the germ of an obstacle for the subsequent development of physiology. This manifested itself in particular in the flourishing development of mechanistic trends in physiology, as well as in the divergence of the paths of physiology and morphology, physiology and evolutionary science, which to some extent has not been overcome to this day.

The appearance of Darwin's works made a deep impression on all fields of biology, including physiology. A number of outstanding physiologists of the 19th century attempted to approach the analysis of the most complex physiological phenomena from the standpoint of the Darwinian evolutionary theory. Let us mention Engleman in connection with the evolution of properties of various contractile tissues (1875), the work of the Jena physiologist V. Preyer, who laid the foundation for the study of problems of appearance and development of functions in the embryonic development of animals. In a number of his investigations, Preyer insistently fostered the idea that "functions may be understood only by studying their history." For Preyer this historical investigation of functions was of great significance, since "such a biochemical and physiological embryological history is indispensable for the understanding of function of mature animals and man" (Preyer, 1885). Indeed, at the beginning of the 20th century an important role in the development of comparative and embryonic physiology was played by Babaka's research (from 1902 on), as well as by the English physiologist Keith Lucas (1908), who emphasized with great foresight the enormous significance of the evolutionary theory for physiology. At the end of the 19th and the beginning of the 20th century, there was an accumulation of a considerable amount of factual data on the scattered research dealing with the physiological peculiarities of a great variety of animals as well as animal foetuses at different ages. Still, the most outstanding biologist of the 20th century, M. Verworn, had to admit that, "while the history of development of organized forms under the influence of the strong impetus generated by the Darwinian theory elaborated mainly by Haeckel and his school had achieved a flourishing status, physiology still had not assimilated the idea of development. The evolution of life processes, the origin

311

and development of functions of various parts of the organism still remain in darkness." In spite of the outstanding achievements of the newest representatives of comparative physiology, such as Loeb, Verworn, Biderman, Pütter, Jordan, and others, Verworn's statement still remains valid to a considerable extent. Even in 1931 one of the most outstanding evolutionists, the Academician A. N. Severtsov, emphasized that in physiology, as is the case in the mechanics of development, "there is total absence of the historical aspect in the formulation of problems."

The Russian biological school made no small contribution to the general development of comparative and evolutionary physiology. Of great significance in the formulation of comparative, evolutional physiology were the investigations of I. I. Mechnikov, especially in the field of intracellular physiology of digestion, and of A. O. Kovalevskiy, in the field of physiology of the secretory processes. These investigations remain until the present time classical models of the evolutionary approach to physiological processes.

In the 1880's the problems of comparative physiology attracted the attention of the famous Russian zoologist-embryologist Aleksandr Kovalevskiy (1840-1901). In a series of investigations on the histophysiology of the secretory organs of invertebrates, mostly arthropoda, published in the Records of the Novorossiysk Society of Natural Scientists ("On the Secretory Organs of the Invertebrates," "On the Secretory Organs of Certain Insects," "On the Secretory Organs of the Arthropoda," etc.) as well as in a number of foreign journals, A. Kovalevskiy developed an entirely new view on the physiological significance of various elements of the excretory organs, the nephrons. His method of excretion by the kidneys of dyes with various reactive properties (indigo-carmine, ammonium carmine) have not lost their significance to this day. A special characteristic of Kovalevskiy's experiments, conclusions, and theory is their broad evolutionary nature. On the basis of numerous experiments, Kovalevskiy comes to the conclusion that the enormous morphological variety in the excretory organs that we observe in the invertebrates as a rule includes elements that are functionally analogous to the renal glomerulus of vertebrates. Subsequent investigations in comparative physiology have, of course, contributed a great deal of important and new data in the field of comparative physiology of the excretory organs. However, Kovalevskiy's idea concerning the presence of functionally (biochemically) analogous units in morphologically totally different structures continues to be a fruitful hypothesis for further investigations.

No less significant in the development of comparative physiology in Russia was the classical work on intracellular digestion by the great Russian biologist I. I. Mechnikov (1845-1916). In 1878 appeared Mechnikov's article, first in a series of investigations on the physiology of intracellular digestion devoted to the digestive processes of the sweet water turbellariae. Subsequently (1878-1884), Mechnikov published a series of investigations concerning the intracellular digestion of the coelenterata and other invertebrates. These investigations are a model of genuine evolutionary research on physiological processes, since the

312

facts obtained in the study of intracellular digestion of various inverte- brates formed the basis of Mechnikov's original ideas on the phylogeny of animals (e. g. , his famous polemics with Haeckel). In his remarkable articles devoted to the problems of Darwinism, Mechnikov emphasized the special significance of physiological signs in the evolution of organisms.

The significance of Mechnikov's investigations in comparative physiol- ogy lies in the convincing form with which he integrated these works and the practical conclusions which he drew from them. The logical chain linking comparative physiology of intracellular digestion with the general problems of the theory of phagocytes and immunity, the development of which was of enormous usefulness to medicine, is a matter of common knowledge.

Mechnikov's work determined the evolutionary approach to the study of comparative physiology and pathology in relation to medical practice, while the investigations of another outstanding Russian scientist, K. A. Timiryazev, posed the important problem of historical exploration of physiological problems from a Darwinian standpoint for the purpose of combatting the idealistic trend in physiology. We refer here to Timiry- azev's classical monograph The Historical Method in Biology, the second chapter of which is devoted to physiology and outlines a broad program of reconstruction of physiology in the direction of historical exploration of physiological problems: ". . . with the significant progress of analytical physiology," wrote Timiryazev, "we do not have a synthetic physiology. In making his synthesis (experimental or only logical), the physiologist, even more than the chemist, cannot be satisfied merely with an analysis of life phenomena; he must also know the history of the organisms. . ."[1] Stressing the significance of the historical method for physiology, Timiryazev linked it with the strictly scientific antivitalistic exploration of the most difficult physiological problems. Thus, he wrote that ". . . physiological perfection, incomprehensible as a direct acquisition during the period of individual development, becomes understandable when con- sidered as the heritage of innumerable centuries of historical develop- ment."

In the shaping of the evolutionary physiology, the investigations of another Russian naturalist, the Soviet Academician A. N. Severtsov, are of major significance. With his strict and concrete investigations of the most difficult problems of evolution of organisms, Severtsov en- riched the evolutionary theory, obtained a number of new facts in the field of evolutionary morphology, and, at the same time, formulated a number of very important problems of evolutionary physiology proper. Severtsov pointed out the paths for genuinely evolutionary research in physiology by methods of evolutionary science itself; by further developing Dorn's theory concerning the principle of functional change; by his special work in the field of phylogenetic reduction of organs; and by his thorough

---

[1] K. A. Timiryazev. The Historical Method in Biology. Pub. AS USSR, 1943, pp. 36-37.

research in a most important physiological field concerning the relationships (correlation) between functions, the relationships between form and function and numerous other investigations, working exclusively on morphological data.

In enumerating the research problems in the field of evolutionary science, Academician Severtsov pointed out the following. "Finally, the third basic task is the evolutionary history of physiological and biological characteristics of organisms, and this possibly represents the most difficult aspect of phylogenetic research. The latter, thus understood in its end result, must supply us with the history of life on earth, as complete and as many-sided as possible."

Finally, we must mention the important investigations of the Soviet geochemist Ya. V. Samoylov (for the years 1917-1926), who is the author of the first work in world literature on an entirely new field of science, paleophysiology. This Soviet scientist, and after him the German paleontologist Wilser (1931), formulated the question of the possibility and necessity of studying functions in fossil organisms for the purpose of reconstructing the history of functions. Samoylov's research deals mostly with the evolution of the skeletal components of animals.

The investigations of Mechnikov, Timiryazev, Severtsov, and Ya. V. Samoylov constitute the foundation of Soviet evolutionary physiology. Some of these investigations, for instance those of Samoylov as well as the later works by Severtsov, represent major achievements of Soviet science.

As to special comparative-physiological and embryo-physiological research, it was conducted in a very unsystematic manner. One must note the important work in this direction by the zoologist N. N. Beletskiy (1851-1882), who, in the middle of the past century, published a number of important investigations on the comparative physiology of various animals.

During his very short lifetime and in only nine years of scientific activity, Beletskiy published a series of outstanding works on the comparative morphophysiology of respiratory organs of birds, fish, and mollusks, as well as on the general physiology of the processes of contraction, which have not lost their scientific significance up to this day.

In the laboratory of the Khar'kov physiologist I. P. Shchelkov (1833-1909), I. I. Mechnikov also carried out his comparative-physiological work on the subject of contractile elements of the vorticella, formulating the question of the evolution of the function of contraction. It was apparently here that the interest of the great biologist was shaped toward problems of physiology; this interest never left him during the course of his scientific activity.

In the physiological laboratory at Khar'kov University, the comparative physiological trend was cultivated later on by Belousov and is being continued at present by A. V. Nagornyy.

In the development of investigations in comparative physiology, it is important to mention the inauguration of the Sevastopol' Biological Station (1871-1872). One of the first works in comparative physiology executed at that station was the investigation of a Sechenov alumnus, N. P. Kravkov, dedicated to the physiology of digestion of the invertebrates.[2] In this work, performed with the cooperation of the director of this station, the zoologist M. P. Pereyaslavtseva, Kravkov accumulated a rich store of data on the physiology of digestion in invertebrates. Together with the data on the intracellular digestion of invertebrates (1883) published five years earlier by Mechnikov, this research is a major contribution to comparative physiology. Of particular value in Kravkov's work is his attempt to approach the subject on the basis of the physico-chemical investigations of Sechenov and Mikhailov on the state of albumen in various media, to gain understanding of the peculiarities in albumen transformation in the process of digestion in vertebrates and invertebrates.

In 1894, D. N. Pryanishnikov published his investigations proving the parallelism of the synthesis of asparagine in plants and of urea in animals and thus laid the foundation for the exploration of problems of evolutionary significance as to the common aspects of albumen metabolism in plants and animals.

Sporadic investigations have been performed (but very rarely) at Russian biological stations, as well as in laboratories and at Soviet agricultural schools. The latter have produced a number of investigations in the field of comparative physiology of farm animals. We shall mention here the work of A. V. Leontovich, who also is credited with one of the early Russian investigations in comparative physiology dealing with the blood circulation of insects (Ranatra). Much later, Vetokhin, in a study of intracellular digestion of the jellyfish, used the method suggested by Leontovich for the investigation of the circulation in the Ranatra of injecting defibrinated blood into the body cavity.

At the end of the past century, I. P. Pavlov turned his attention to comparative physiology. He performed the remarkable work on the inhibitory phenomena in the obturator muscle of the edentata that served as the starting point for new investigations in comparative physiology by Soviet scientists (I. L. Kan and collaborators).

The Pavlovian school, being entirely dedicated to the fulfillment of a grandiose plan of experimental physiological investigations, stood apart from investigations in comparative physiology. But it is important to emphasize that the Pavlovian theory is a deeply biological one, and, although it does not deal with such problems directly, it does bring them up. It was not by chance that Pavlov, at the onset of his investigations on conditioned reflexes, re-evaluated the subjective idealistic views on behavior, being motivated in a large measure by considerations of comparative physiology. Pavlov himself wrote the following on this subject.

_____

[2] Trans. St. Petersburg Soc. of Naturalists, v. XIX, 1888. Minutes of the session of November 12, 1888.

"When Tolochinov and I began our investigations I only knew that with the extension of physiological investigations (in the form of comparative physiology) over the whole animal kingdom, beyond the favorite laboratory specimens of that period (dogs, cats, rabbits and frogs) there was no choice but to discard the subjective viewpoint and attempt to introduce objective investigative procedures and terminology (Loeb's theory of trophism and the proposed objective terminology of Baer, Bethe and Uexküll. Indeed, it would have been difficult and unnatural to think and speak of thoughts and desires of some amoeba or infusoria."[3] His experimental work in the study of the mechanisms of formation of conditioned connections in the cerebral hemispheres, meticulous and grandiose in its significance, demanded more than 20 years and detracted Pavlov's attention from problems of comparative physiology. And only in the years following the Great October Socialist Revolution did the Pavlovian school produce a number of investigators dedicated to the study of the comparative physiology of conditioned reflexes.

Pavlov himself later on established at the biological station in Koltushi a basis for investigations closely related to general problems of evolutionary physiology.

That Pavlov attributed much importance to problems of comparative physiology may be seen, not only from the quoted excerpt from his introduction to Twenty Years of Experience. . . and his persistent attention to these problems during the later years of his life and the activities at the Koltushi biological station but also from the preserved documents of a scientific organizational nature. We present here the full text of one of Pavlov's letters to the physico-mathematical department of the Academy of Sciences, in which he illuminates this aspect of the problem. In that difficult Petrograd period, on November 16, 1920, I. P. Pavlov wrote:

"To the physico-mathematical department of the Academy of Sciences
[from] Acad. I. Pavlov

Memorandum

I have the honor to state the following.

The physiology of animals is now distinctly divided into the chemical aspect and other. The chemical aspect of physiology demands at present such a knowledge of chemistry that a physiological chemist is more chemist than physiologist. Correspondingly, everywhere in our country and abroad there exists a department of physiological chemistry, separately from that of physiology.

It is therefore natural that in our Academy of Sciences we are in need of a special representative of this most important theoretical, as well as practical, specialty.

---

[3] I. P. Pavlov. Twenty Years of Experience. . . 1932, p. 12.

On the other hand, what has been called heretofore the physiology of man and animals was a collection of data on animal processes, representing the four or five animal species usually used for the physiological laboratory experiment. But during recent decades physiological research is gradually extending over the entire animal kingdom; the study of functions in lower animals has progressed especially. Physiology is indeed becoming general or comparative. It would therefore be desirable that the Academy of Sciences in addition to a representative of the former physiology add a special representative of this broadened physiology, especially that of lower animals.

Acad. Iv. Pavlov" [4]

The second part of this extremely important letter refers, as the reader may see, entirely to comparative physiology and reflects Pavlov's attitude toward this section of physiology.

As we have already indicated, in the early 1920's Pavlov directed a request to the director of the Murmansk Biological Station concerning the organization of comparative physiological investigations in marine animals.

It was precisely at this period that the Pavlovian school produced a number of workers who dedicated themselves to the special problems of comparative physiology. This is when Pavlov's assistant, Yu. P. Frolov, undertook his valuable work on the comparative investigation of conditioned reflexes in lower vertebrates, particularly in fish. At the same time, Ye. M. Kreps began his systematic investigations in comparative physiology, working mainly at the Murmansk biological station. The latter has become a training center for new contingents of comparative physiologists. Dozens of young physiologists, students at Moscow and Leningrad Universities, have spent the summer months at the Murmansk biological station, where they could acquaint themselves with the subjects and methods of research in comparative physiology in exceptionally interesting natural surroundings.

The Pavlovian theory on conditioned reflexes as a whole also served as the foundation of the evolutionary concepts of his disciple, L. A. Orbeli. Correlating the data obtained by Sherrington that revealed the extreme complexity and fine synchronization of inborn coordinatory mechanisms with Pavlov's theory on temporary associations in the central nervous system that are established ontogenetically, Orbeli arrived at theoretical conclusions to be the effect that "the study of conditioned reflexes reveals to us the paths of functional evolution of the nervous system; the existing coordinating associations with which we are born were formed over a period of thousands of years according to the same basic laws that govern the formation of new conditioned coordinating associations in the course of weeks and at times days and hours in our individual life" (1923). The development of Orbeli's ideas, as well as of other evolutionary investigations of his school in the field of physiology, belong entirely to the period of Soviet physiology.

---

[4] Archives of the AS USSR, file 1, item 2, 1940, no. 25.

The Great October Revolution gave a powerful impetus towards the development of comparative physiology in the U.S.S.R. Indeed, it can be stated that comparative physiology in its special form as an evolutionary science emerged within Soviet physiology as a trend only after the revolution.

The historical scope of the patterns of nature and of the study of nature in order to conquer it in the interest of the socialist structure constituted the two powerful stimuli for the reconstruction of natural sciences and was directly instrumental in the development of investigations in comparative physiology in the U.S.S.R. The specificity of Soviet comparative physiology is expressed in the following two aspects: 1) exploration of physiological problems in relation to the general problems of animal evolution and 2) exploration of problems of comparative physiology in connection with the special problems of the comparative physiology of utilitarian animals and the physiology of man. Such was the development over the course of the last quarter century of the following physiological trends: evolutionary physiology, ontogenic physiology, zootechnical physiology, and physiology of man.

The term evolutionary physiology itself was suggested, as far as I know, by Academician A. N. Severtsov in 1914; it is not widely used in the foreign literature and characterizes the methodology and subjects of investigations by Soviet physiologists. Research in the direction of evolutional physiology was conducted by Soviet phytophysiologists considerably earlier than by physiologists. We have already pointed out the investigations of K. A. Timiryazev, who in a large measure proceeded from botanical data.

Here we must mention the phytophysiologists N. N. Ivanov and A. V. Blagoveshchenskiy, who also made a major contribution to the general problems of evolutionary physiology. N. Ivanov's work, begun in 1914 and directed to the evolution of the chemical components of plants in relation to their metabolism, attained particular development in the last twenty years and produced many valuable data and conclusions on the question of physiological, biochemical characteristics of organisms and their evolution. The works of N. N. Ivanov deal mostly with oil-forming processes. A. V. Blagoveshchenskiy, beginning in 1925, published a number of articles in the same direction dealing with the formation of cyclical combinations and their role in the evolution of plant organisms.

A number of investigations and papers on general problems of physiology in relation to the theory of evolution are from the years 1932-1934. Thus, in 1932, I published an article under the title "Physiology and the Theory of Evolution," in which I indicated the necessity for exploration of physiological gaps in the light of the history of the development of organisms, the theory of the problem, and some results of my own experimental investigations in this direction. In 1933 there appeared an article by Academician L. Orbeli on the subject "The Evolutionary Trend in Physiology," in which the author formulated a number of special questions of investigation of the evolution of the central nervous system and the skeletal muscles. In the same year (1933), the late Academician

V. S. Gulevich, in a short note in connection with the general problems of organization and development of biochemical investigations, emphasized the importance and necessity of an evolutionary approach in the investigation of problems of biochemistry. The indicated period coincides with the organization of corresponding laboratories in the VIEM system (All-Union Institute of Experimental Medicine) and within the system of the Academy of Sciences. Subsequently, the number of laboratories and workers in this field progressively increased.

In the laboratories of A. V. Palladin, P. K. Anokhin, I. A. Arshavskiy, A. G. Ginetsinskiy, N. V. Yermakov, I. L. Kan, A. V. Nagornyy, and others, intensive inquiries have begun into the development of animal ontogenesis. The problems of comparative pathology have been broadly developed in the investigations of Academician A. A. Bogomolets.

In most recent times the Koltushi Biological Station (village of Pavlovo) has become the center of research in comparative physiology by the Orbeli school. During the last decade great attention was devoted by the Soviet government toward organizing this biological station as a base for further research on the problems of genetics of the higher nervous activity as formulated by Pavlov. The actual genetical work was begun during Pavlov's life but had not yet produced any results. Meanwhile, if the great Pavlovian design is fulfilled, physiology may be closer to the understanding of phenomena of the heredity of physiological traits. At the same Koltushi station Pavlov conducted observations of higher nervous activity in anthropoid apes — observations with a bearing on comparative physiology.

Substantial further development was attained by researchers in comparative physiology in the direction of conditioned reflexes, of special importance from a theoretical standpoint, after the organization of the scientific activities at the ape station in Sukhumi. Here many valuable data were obtained on the peculiarities of conditioned reflex activity in lower level monkeys and anthropoid apes. At the Sukhumi station, data dealing with heat regulation in apes, of significance for comparative physiology,[5] were also clarified.

Inasmuch as the problems of origin and development of processes in time are the core of evolutionary physiology, the attention of the Leningrad physiological school was directed toward them. One of the creators of this school, N. Ye. Vedenskiy, was one of those outstanding physiologists who first raised the question of the role of time factors in the development of physiological processes. At the beginning of the 20th century, Vedenskiy, in his classical work on parabiosis, posed a series of theoretically important problems of the understanding of the patterns of development of functions.[6] A number of profound ideas in the same direction were expressed by A. A. Ukhtomskiy.[7]

---

[5] The results of these investigations are presented in the interesting articles by A. D. Slonim and his collaborators.

[6] See the most interesting article by Ye. K. Zhukov, quoted above.

[7] A. A. Ukhtomskiy. Nature no. 10, 1935.

Work in the field of evolutionary physiology was broadly developed in the Soviet Union in the last quarter of a century.[8] Through their efforts to unveil the great secret of origin, development, and organization of functions, through their efforts to learn the historical patterns of physiological processes for the formulation of strictly materialistic concept of development of organic nature, the U.S.S.R. physiologists, disciples of Sechenov, Pavlov and Vedenskiy, will attain the same decisive achievements as were attained by the great founders of the Russian physiological school in the most difficult areas of physiology.

---

[8] See a detailed review of achievements in comparative physiology in the U.S.S.R. for 25 years in Ye. M. Kreps' article in the volume Twenty-five years of Soviet Biology pub. AS USSR, 1945.

APPENDIX

Kostoyants provides at the end of the book a total of 22 pages of bibliographical material dealing with sources not directly referred to in the text or the footnotes accompanying each chapter. The majority of the listed items were published in Russian journals and collective works, some of them dating back more than 100 years. Interesting as they may be for the historian-specialist, we consider that a translation of these 22 pages would represent a nonjustifiable expenditure of time and resources.

Koshtoyants also gives an index of names. No index has been prepared for the English edition.